20th Century Ut

MW00606014

Homesteading "The Basin"

Uintah Valley Indian Reservation 1906 – 1922

Keri De Vest-Vergari

wanderingkeri

Keri De Vest-Vergari
All rights reserved

ISBN 978-1-7342348-0-0

Copyright 2019 TXu 2-152-456

Library of Congress Control Number: 2019917890

The Nicol Family

Hyrum Chase (H. C.) Nicol

Isabella Crawford Murdoch (Tressa) Nicol

Thomas Murdoch Nicol

Hyrum Chase Nicol, Jr.

Kenneth Crawford Nicol

John Murray Nicol

Alva Moroni Nicol

Alma Victor Nicol

Brigham Rue Nicol

I. Donnavieve Nicol

Behold, I will send you Elijah the prophet before the coming of the great and dreadful day of the LORD:

And he shall turn the heart of the fathers to the children, and the heart of the children to their fathers, lest I come and smite the earth with a curse.

Malachi 4:5-6

Author's Introduction

In 2017 I had several impressions that encouraged me to learn more about the "Indian Ranch", the homestead my great-grandparents Hyrum and Isabella Nicol filed for in 1906. I wrote about those impressions in my blog wanderingkeri.com in July of that year. In my research I found that there were three ranches, not one. The last one was named the 'Indian Ranch', the first was in Midview, and the second was in Sowers Canyon.

Researching land records and transactions between parties, banks, private loans, or trades during this period of time caused confusion. I have chosen to avoid getting entangled in the specifics of the homesteads and their patents, and subsequent sales, purchases and mortgages and focus only on the particulars of the acquisition and disposition of the three different ranches operated by Hyrum and Isabella Nicol.

I have also retained the different spellings found in the source documents for family names.

Chills, a Nudge, and Footsteps

Five years ago I was in Duchesne (pronounced Do-Shane) Utah over the 4th of July on a fire assignment ... before in-briefing I spent a couple of hours in the county records office researching the homestead in Sowers Canyon my great grandparents had near there. I was able to get a copy of the ledger page showing the final patent they received and the sale of the homestead.

Just before we left for another assignment, a few friends and I drove up Sowers Canyon and found the old place, which is now inside the Uintah-Ouray Reservation. We took pictures, Dick made a video and at home I found a photo of my great-grandparents and their first three sons outside the door of what I thought was that cabin. It gave me the chills.

Well, lately the "Indian Ranch" has come to mind more than a few times; I don't know why, but I have learned that when something comes to mind without a reason it's something I should pay attention to. The attention I've been paying to the nudge has lead me to old newspapers, searching for my great-grandfather's name. Eureka! There were more than a few articles and advertisements found; one or two with my great-grandmother's name. So I'm on a hunt. For what, I'm not sure, but I'm certain in time it will be revealed.

I also realize I live under the same sun, watch the same moon and stars each night, and by walking (figuratively or not) their trails and holy places, I follow their footsteps. I'm grateful for the realization and knowledge that I am part of an eternal chain of life; mother and father to child, as far back as life itself. Now it is I who is a great-grandmother (I know, shocking isn't it) and I ask myself, what story will I leave behind? Where are my footsteps leading?

***

Those chills, nudges, and footsteps led me on a two year journey into the lives and the history of the men, women, and children who homesteaded in the dry, barren landscapes of Eastern Utah at the turn into the 20th century.

I have taken author's license filling in gaps left from lack of documentation or family stories. Most of the family stories were expanded from those written by their children found in the James and Mary Murray Murdoch Family History: The James and Mary Murray Murdoch Family Organization. As well as from newspaper clippings, letters, and other historical books with mention of them.

I've attempted to ensure sources are referenced to provide a starting point for readers who may be intrigued and desire to know more.

Isabella and Hyrum Nicol 1903

1 Isabella Crawford Murdoch about 1903

2Hyrum Chase Nicol late 1890's

Prolog

Hyrum and Isabella Nicol were children of Utah Pioneers. They were raised by parents who by faith in the restored gospel of Jesus Christ were baptized members of the Church of Jesus Christ of Latter-day Saints. Their parents accepted the call to gather to Zion no matter the sacrifice. They were children of parents who braved months' long ocean voyages, who overcame heart wrenching loss and grief, and passed through many heartbreaking horrors to tackle the American Great Plains with wagons or handcarts.

They were the product of families who for 40 years wrenched and hacked from the barren sagebrush deserts of the Utah Territory homes, gardens, pastures, and orchards, and built businesses that supported their communities. It was their parent's hard work which brought forth the fulfillment of the prophecies of Isaiah that the '*The wilderness and the solitary places shall be glad for them; and the desert shall rejoice, and blossom as the rose* '[i]

With the opening of the Uintah Valley Indian Reservation in Eastern Utah to white settlement[ii], an unofficial call went out from local ecclesiastic leaders in Heber City encouraging young men and families to move to the reservation and build homes and lives to offset the influx of gentiles who won the land lottery in the fall of 1905.

In the spring of 1906, Hyrum and Isabella Nicol loaded two young sons, and their belongings into a wagon and 'moved east' in answer to that call.[iii] They brought with them faith, determination and a willingness to sacrifice their good lives for the promise of a better one yet to come. Together they battled nature, financial peril, and man-made disasters bound together by love for one another, humor, and their faith in God.

1906

3 Home of John Murray Murdoch, Anne Steele, Isabella Crawford Heber Utah

A sunset of brilliant rose-gold light glinted off the white-washed trim of the red brick two story house while cool shade from the trees planted along its side offered an oasis from the summer heat. Hyrum watched Tressa gather the flotsam required when taking a toddler and newborn visiting. He turned to his in-law's John and Isabella Murdoch[iv], as well as Muz[v], her father's first wife and thanked them for raising such a wonderful daughter.

Isabella, or most often called Tressa for her long dark hair had grown-up in this beautiful home. A home built with hard work and sacrifice, and her parent's unwavering faith in God and his protecting guidance.

4Hyrum C Nicol - Taken on his mission in Auckland New Zealand

Their faith in Jesus Christ was forged deep and indelibly by the trials they endured as converts to the restored Church of Jesus Christ of Latter-day Saints. Their testimonies of that truth were forged into steel by the innumerable persecutions they suffered for their testimonies and faith in Jesus Christ's restored gospel. And by the struggles and privation they bore as immigrants to America; coming by ship, wagon, and handcart to pioneer a new life.

Thinking of Tressa he knew he was blessed. She hadn't lived in the tents and cabins as her parent's and older siblings had, but their stories were rooted deep in her heart. She was the youngest of the combined 22 children of her now prosperous parents, and she had reaped the benefits of their hard work; but she wasn't pampered. She worked hard, learning to care for house and home and family from these industrious women. They had taught her well.

She learned compassion and patience, she also learned to cook on coal or wood fire stoves, mend and sew, and knit. Growing a garden and killing a chicken were also part of her life's skills. Tressa learned to fill her cupboards and the cold cellar of their snug little home with jars of fruit, and vegetables that were put up against their winter needs. She made quilts, and clothes, she learned to make soap, and trim lantern wicks.

She sang like an angel and played the piano to the delight of all who heard. Hyrum could listen to her sing and play the piano for hours, and it was especially sweet when they sang together.

Most importantly to him Hyrum thought was her firm desire to build their own family upon the firm foundation and testimony of Jesus, and his restored church.

How he loved her; they had been sweethearts many years before they were married almost three years ago. He had stood on these very steps when he left for New Zealand to fulfill his three-year mission call when he bid his sweetheart farewell. He hadn't asked Tressa to wait for him, but he had hoped.

The letters he wrote her were filled with his faith, trials, joy, and always his witness of his own deep testimony of the restored gospel of Jesus Christ. When he arrived home, he stood atop these very steps palms sweating and a heart pounding anticipating the smile on Isabella's face. Hoping against hope that she had waited for him.

Three months after he arrived home they were married for time and all eternity in the Great Salt Lake City temple. They were both 27 years old. When they walked out of the large bronzed doors of the temple he thought that on that date, 23rd of September 1903, he couldn't be happier. It was the culmination of all of his dreams.

Or so he'd thought until he held their first son, Thomas Murdoch in his arms that early August morning just shy of one year from the day they married. They had named him Thomas for Hyrum's father and Murdoch, of course, for Isabella's father. Then 19 months later, now three month old Hyrum Chase Jr. had arrived and his love grew again.

But he had another dream, to have a ranch of their own. Tomorrow they were leaving this familiar mountain valley to take advantage of the opportunities available 80 miles east of Heber City on the Uintah Valley Indian Reservation which had opened the previous fall to homesteading.

It was there they were pinning their hopes and dreams of a prosperous tomorrow. Someday they would build a home like this one, to replace the log cabin they knew they would live in these next years.

They would build a legacy for their children. They prayed it would be a legacy as strong as the ones their parents had built for them. Tomorrow the first step of that dream would begin. Anxiety washed through his mind and heart so strongly that he almost felt sick; his knees almost gave way, his heart was pounding, and he felt his hands shake. His mind returned to the question he had been asking himself for months as they made their plans to uproot and move onto the frontier. "Was he ready?"

***

June 1906 *Heading East*

The early summer sunlight dappled the bare floors and walls filtering through the naked windows of their empty house. Tressa sat in the only chair left in the kitchen, feeding baby Chase holding lightly to his tiny fingers as she watched Tom wander around the room on sturdy toddler legs trying to catch sun dust floating through the early morning air.

Glancing out the window she could see Hyrum tying the crate of chickens to the back of the wagon, tightening rope, inventorying again all their belongings a final time.

Then they would join seven other eager homesteaders and their families at the mouth of Daniel's Canyon and they would move east together.

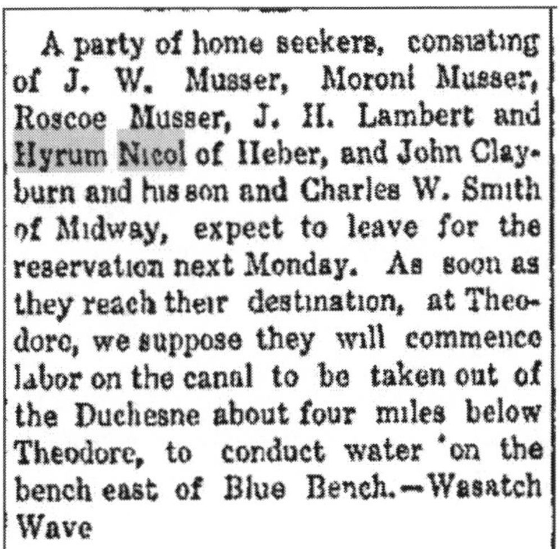
A party of home seekers, consisting of J. W. Musser, Moroni Musser, Roscoe Musser, J. H. Lambert and Hyrum Nicol of Heber, and John Clayburn and his son and Charles W. Smith of Midway, expect to leave for the reservation next Monday. As soon as they reach their destination, at Theodore, we suppose they will commence labor on the canal to be taken out of the Duchesne about four miles below Theodore, to conduct water 'on the bench east of Blue Bench.—Wasatch Wave

5 Wasatch Wave June 2, 1906 A Party of Home seekers

For more than forty years there had been talk of changing the borders of the eastern reservation and to open the land to white settlement. Hyrum had followed with anticipation each step of the government process to finally determine when and how the opened land would be allocated.

She also had read of the initial settlement reports sent to the prophet Brigham Young when he first sent scouts out to determine new areas for colonization. The reports weren't favorable; they gave an unappealing description of the land they were moving onto; "the area was good for nothing but nomad purposes, hunting grounds for Indians and 'to hold the world together'".[vi]

Yet once the government decided to open the land to homesteading, the newspapers began to tout fertile agricultural lands, describing the minerals and precious metals just waiting to be mined creating an unrealistic view of the arid desert.

Before the land lottery the Wasatch Stake Presidency of the Church of Jesus Christ of Latter-day Saints in Heber City created much controversy sending a letter out to encourage young men and families to relocate to the Uintah Basin.[vii] Now the lottery was over and although it wasn't an official mission call to move and settle as Brigham Young had once sent new immigrants throughout the Deseret Territories; Hyrum and Isabella had prayed for guidance, determined to follow the direction and encouragement of their ecclesiastical leadership to move and settle the new area. They were looking to homestead the best of the 'left-overs', or so they hoped.

Looking around her now empty house Isabella couldn't help comparing this snug home near their families with the tiny cut log house built on a town site lot which they would live in while they began to build on the 'right place' homestead. She wondered if she was strong enough to live the pioneer life her parents had lived for more than 40 years.

All of these thoughts flitted through Isabella's mind as she finished wrapping Chase, called Tom to follow and went to find Hyrum. "We're ready Hyrum," she said, walking toward the wagon. We're ready, "she said again, "and remember my chair."

They had one last stop to make before turning the horses toward Daniel's Canyon; a final farewell to Hyrum's parents. In the quiet of their own thoughts the wagon slowed to a stop, leather creaked and metal rattled as the harnesses slid side to side and forward onto the horses' necks when they bent their heads to drink from the trough in front of the gate. The air was damp, the early morning dew had not yet felt the warmth of the sun.

Taking a deep breath the scent of blossoming flowers and herbs in the garden surrounding Hyrum's parent's home filling her nose, but also brought a twinge of pain to Isabella's heart. She was going to miss this valley with its broad pastures, busy streets, and their large families nearby.

Hyrum wrapped the reins around the wagon brake before he jumped nimbly from the wagon seat. He reached up to take Chase before helping her down to the ground. Handing her the bundled up baby, she suppressed a sigh and wrapping her arms a little more tightly around baby Chase, Isabella walked through Hanne's gate and taking another deep breath of the succulent air climbed the steps.

Laughing, Tom toddled up next to her running across the pine board porch. He had learned quickly that something good was behind those doors. His grandmother Hanne was quick to hug, and just as quick to scold if necessary, but she always had a jar filled with fresh-baked cookies for the children who would visit. Grandfather Thomas reached out to tussle his hair but his namesake ran past him toward the kitchen.

Hyrum's mother was the valley mid-wife and had delivered both of Isabella's sons and that experience drew the two women together more closely than marriage. Oh! A jolt washed over her! What would she do the next time her babies came, when they were living days away from this wonderful woman?

Isabella couldn't remember when she hadn't known Hyrum's family. Her father and Thomas Nicol were some of the first settlers in the Heber valley, once known as the Upper Provo Valley. Each had a part defending settlements from Indian raids in the Black Hawk war, and Thomas had gone to Echo canyon with Lot Smith to harass and slow the advance of Johnson's Army. The army had been sent by President James Buchanan to put down a non-existent 'Mormon' rebellion against the United States.

When the army entered the Salt Lake valley her parents became refugees moving south to Provo until danger passed. At the same time Hyrum's family moved to Moroni an area called the San Pete south of the Spanish Fork River. At the time in that area there had been much contention between the Indians and settlers. Murder and massacre[viii] were the culmination of the confrontations. Hyrum's father was a veteran of the Walker and Blackhawk wars. Of course that was long before either one of them was born.

She and Hyrum had much in common, and a smile broke on her face as she thought of the story that they had shared a carriage as babies. But this last stop in their round of good-bye visits was tearing her heart. Just thinking of the move from their families and friends to take up a homestead in the heart of Indian country, pioneering the way in a new area, as their parent's did was daunting.

She was a city girl and for that matter Hyrum was a city boy. They hadn't lived in cabins, or out of a wagon box. But Hyrum had taken to heart the call for the young men of the valley to move onto the reservation. Today they were leaving.

She wasn't surprised that Hyrum had been anxious to take up a homestead, for most of their lives there had been talk of Indian lands going to waste, and there was always an opinion article, or letter to the editor in the Wasatch Wave and other territorial newspapers encouraging changes to the large swaths of land given to the Indians to separate them from the white settlers and discourage confrontations and war. The territorial legislature had taken up the cause long before the territory, named Deseret by the immigrant Saints, became the State of Utah. There was one bright spot in their move east, Hyrum's oldest sister Josephine, nicknamed Phennie, and her husband Alva Moroni Murdock[ix] were already in the town site of Dora. Alva wasn't related to Isabella, his father was Joseph Stacy Murdock[x] and Alva Moroni was born in Nevada when his father was called to the "Muddy Mission" there.

They were Murdock, with a 'k', she thought, not an 'h'. 'A.M.' or 'Al' as he was often called, had run cattle on reservation lands in the Strawberry Valley area on the reservation for 30 years. Once the land was opened to white settlement, A. M., a former Indian Agent at Whiterocks, received government permission to move onto the reservation prior to the lottery settlers. He built a small log home, and immediately put up a huge, white circus style tent to serve as the first store.

After hugging his mother a last time Hyrum helped Isabella up onto the wagon seat then handed her the children one at a time. Behind the seat Chase's small cradle was within easy reach. Tom, when he could sit still would ride between them, but tucked into the wagon seat box at their feet was another quilt where Tom could rest. Sitting down beside Tressa on the wagon seat Hyrum snapped the reins, "hi-ya'd" at the horses and with a smile and wave at his parents turned his face east to their future.

***

"Ruts and rocks are all that holds this road together," Isabella's thought. She hoped that thought would stay off of her tongue. "My bones are rattling and we've been stopped for half an hour. I should be used to traveling this road," she told herself, "but we have never taken it with the children before." She could tell the boys were ragged around the edges. They were very tired, and fussy. Shaking her head she moaned to herself, "I'm not looking forward to climbing back onto that wagon seat any time soon."

They were less than a day on the road and already she was tired. "Time to get moving if we are to reach camp before dark," Hyrum said, picking up an almost 2 year old Tom and swinging him back into the front of the wagon box. "Here Tressa, let me help you back up on the wagon's bench." Then Hyrum handed her baby Chase. "I suppose he's riding well enough in his cradle tucked in behind the seat's back, he seems to like the movement of the road."

Isabella braced her feet against the wagon's box front, took hold of the seat's edge and anticipate the shock when Hyrum "hi-ya'd" the team, flicked the reins, and the wagon jolted forward. Ruts and rocks behind, rocks and ruts ahead.

***

"I rode out to Midview just to look at the place again," Hyrum said. "The sagebrush is thick on part of it which should mean it has potential to grow good crops. I have a good feeling about the future." "What a future we will have Hyrum," exclaimed Isabella. "How lucky we are that we have this small cabin in Theodore to live in while we build our cabin. With Chase only 3 months old I can't see us living in a tent on the flat. I would if we had to, but I'm very glad we don't have to," she said, and smiled again.

6 Midview homestead, circa 1909 Tom, Isabella, Chase, Hyrum, & Kenneth

"Hello son." Hyrum said as he swept Tom up in his arms and kissed the top of Isabella's head. He gave Tom a short hug and tickle before setting him back down on the floor. "Hyrum, will it be ok if I don't unpack all of our belongings, I want most things to stay in their boxes until our cabin is ready. I think of this place as only a stop on the way to our future," said Isabella as she set dinner[xi] plates on the table and she remembered the night Hyrum came home with their homestead claim.

She had heard the door slam as he walked into the kitchen holding an envelope out to her with a huge smile on his face. "It's ours, or it will be in three years,"" he said. Once we've built a cabin and improved the land." She took the paper from his hand and read,

> Hyrum C. Nicol, of Myton, Utah, on May 7 1906 made homestead entry no. 1396, U.I.S. Serial No. 01374, for the N 1/2 SW1/4, Sec. 36; SE1/2 of the NE 1/2. NE1/2, SE1/4, Section 35. Township 3 S., range 3 W., Uinta Special Meridian.[xii]

They held one another for a long time when Hyrum whispered, "we are on our way Tressa, we are on our way."

Shaking her head free from her reverie she said, "Tom's been watching for you all day. Whenever a horse or wagon rumbles past he stands tip-toe on the bench to see from the window. Dinner will be ready soon if you want to wash up." "Come with me Tom, let's put my horse away and feed him before we cleanup for dinner," Hyrum said as he took Tom by the hand. Isabella flashed a grateful smile at him as they went out the door.

While they ate Hyrum told her about the meeting he had attended with the men homesteading around Myton. Without water the land was worthless so they met together to form a corporation which would own and control some water rights of the Duchesne River.

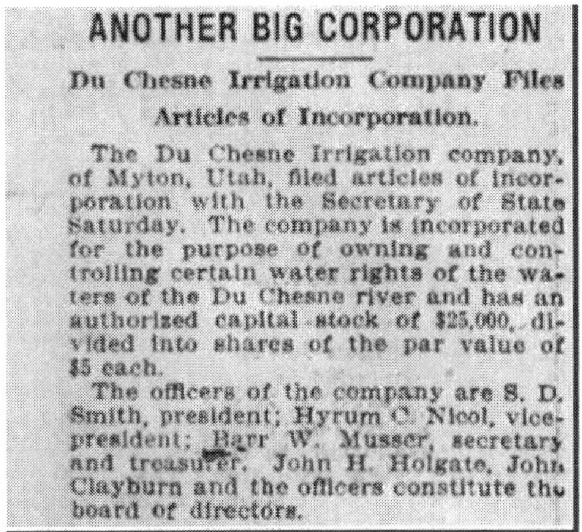

ANOTHER BIG CORPORATION

Du Chesne Irrigation Company Files Articles of Incorporation.

The Du Chesne Irrigation company, of Myton, Utah, filed articles of incorporation with the Secretary of State Saturday. The company is incorporated for the purpose of owning and controlling certain water rights of the waters of the Du Chesne river and has an authorized capital stock of $25,000, divided into shares of the par value of $5 each.

The officers of the company are S. D. Smith, president; Hyrum C. Nicol, vice-president; Barr W. Musser, secretary and treasurer. John H. Holgate, John Clayburn and the officers constitute the board of directors.

7 Salt Lake Tribune July 8, 1906 Duchesne Irrigation Co. Incorporation

"The overall plan is that we will connect a large canal across the Blue Bench toward what is being called Holgate Flats where most of our lands are located. Then we ranchers will run ditches from the canal onto our lands for irrigation."

"It will be a big, and long undertaking. Then he said ducking his head, "I've been voted vice-president of the new Duchesne Irrigation Company. Brother Smith is the president."

We will work in teams and expect to have water to at least 2500 acres of land before winter. Next spring we will clear some acres and start planting.

***

MIDVIEW
"Holgate Flat"

The first families here were John Holgate, Frank Hale, Junior Clayborn, Thornton Richardson, Frank Clayborn, John Clayborn, Dave Clayborn, Hiram Nicols, Alma Burgener, John Cellers, Cal Duke, C. W. Smith, Harold Carter, Edgar Carter, Fred Musser, Bar Musser, John Smith, the Seltzers.

The first school was held at the Dave Clayborn place and a Mr. Reece was the first teacher. Later Fred Musser took this position.

A Ward was organized in 1907 at the home of John Holgate. Fred Musser was the first bishop. Alma Burgener was the next bishop.

In 1910 the Relief Society was organized and Mattie Musser was put in President.

8 MIDVIEW, "Holgate Flats"

***

August 1906 *Wind and Water*

“Will this wind never stop?” Isabella whispered to herself as she watched through their one window as the wind whipped dust devils across the open sagebrush flats. She gazed at the wavy heat mirages floating through the air, just out there on the horizon. She thought if she reached out she might touch them.

“The extra chinking didn’t stop the dirt from filtering through the logs and seeping in around the window and door frame,” she groused to herself as she wiped the table free of dust again before she turned the flour, salt, water, and sourdough starter into dough for bread. With the dough covered and set aside to rest she gathered the laundry and carried it out in the yard. Windy or not the wash had to be done.

Last year when she and Hyrum had made their trips to the reservation searching for homestead land Isabella didn’t recall the constant wind, and she thought, it is also definitely hotter than Heber City.

***

They were excited to find that this piece of ground east of Theodore hadn’t been claimed by any of the land lottery winners. It was well situated, placed as it was between the Lake Fork and Duchesne Rivers at the south end off of the edge of Blue Bench. Isabella was quick to be grateful that the Duchesne River was close, less than a mile west off the edge of the bench where they placed their cabin.

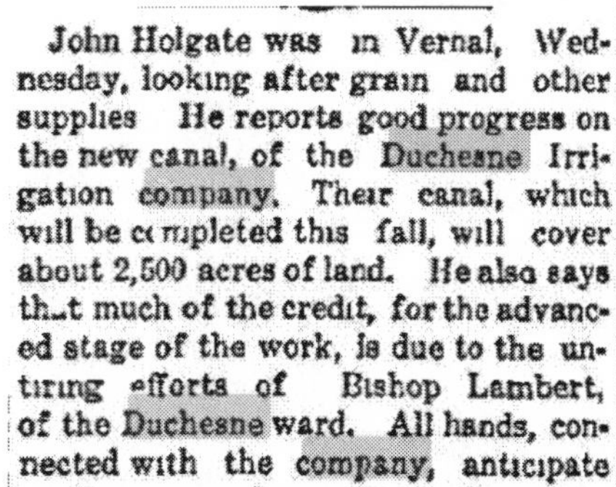
John Holgate was in Vernal, Wednesday, looking after grain and other supplies He reports good progress on the new canal, of the Duchesne Irrigation company. Their canal, which will be completed this fall, will cover about 2,500 acres of land. He also says that much of the credit, for the advanced stage of the work, is due to the untiring efforts of Bishop Lambert, of the Duchesne ward. All hands, connected with the company, anticipate producing good crops, on their new farms next season.

9 Duchesne Vernal Express 1906 Nov 24 Canal projections

“No time to doddle,” she said to Tom so she wasn’t always talking to herself. “The bread is rising and I want to finish the laundry, use the warm water to bathe you and Chase before I need to start dinner.”

The bread baked, and the laundry almost finished, Tressa sat in the leeward shade of the cabin as she finished feeding Chase. She laid him down in the basket covered to keep dust from drifting over him and waited for the water to heat to finish the last of the wash.

Later she would need to bring more water up to the cabin; she has used quite a bit doing the laundry. Water was so precious, and every drop was brought with tedious effort from the river a barrel at a time. She hauled water daily; it was an exhausting and time-consuming chore. Thankfully Hyrum tied empty barrels into the wagon bed so she could fill them bucket by bucket at the river then drive the wagon back to the cabin and repeat the process, transferring the water from the barrels on the wagon to the barrel outside the door, and into the horse trough.

In the evening, Hyrum would water his horse at the river after working all day digging the Blue Bench Canal. She along with all the families around them were anxious for the canal to be completed, or at least get to their area so eventually they would have ditches to bring water to their arid sagebrush covered acres.

She dreamed of having water nearer for cooking, water for washing, and watering the farm animals and she hoped a garden next summer. As it was water was priceless to everyone and each drop was used with caution. "What I wouldn't give for a well in the yard," she thought as she stood up to put the last of the laundry into the heated water. "Maybe next year." She said hopefully.

***

April 1907 *First Signs of Trouble*

Coming back inside from early morning chores Hyrum said, "The snow has finally melted, and the grasses are greening up, do you feel like taking an easy ride around the place and just talk?" Hyrum asked sitting down at the table. "I'd love too," said Isabella, "I love the smell of the sagebrush covered with early morning dew." She said, "Tom can ride with me, and you can put Chase in front of you. I'll feed the chickens when we get back," Isabella said. Riding along the back-property line of their 160 acres they noticed water from the snow melt still sitting in small ponds across the pastures. "I wonder how long that water will keep pooling over there." Hyrum questioned aloud as they turned their horses back toward their cabin.

Several days later Hyrum remembered those ponds and rode back up toward the rise. The areas where some of the ponds had stood were still damp and muddy, and yet some were still holding the spring snow melt. Other parts of the ranch were already dry as if it were early summer. He thought, "I'll talk with some of the more experienced ranchers and maybe Alva, for advice on the best areas to break ground for wheat or alfalfa."

He felt the pressure to get the land under cultivation and seed in the ground for winter feed. "Our money won't hold out long if we have to buy feed for even this small cattle herd when it snows," he thought.

Later that week sitting astride their horses, Hyrum said, "Thanks Al for taking the time to ride clear out here." "No problem Hyrum," Al Murdock said looking across the fields below the low bench where they had ridden earlier. "You are right," Al swept his hand in an arc pointing at the swaths of ground still holding water, "the ground is too wet for crops, their roots will rot, or the plants will develop mold. But they might indicate good areas to put in a holding pond."

"That is what some of the other ranchers are also talking about doing," Hyrum confirmed. "They have these same types of wet places on their land."

Riding back to the cabin, the two men talked about the reservation and how it had changed since Alva Moroni started running cattle on the

Strawberry range years before. A.M. went on talking and said, "It's too bad that section holding water is nearest to the canal, you will have to put in longer irrigation ditches to reach the drier ground to the north." A.M. had been a rancher as well as an Indian Agent at White Rocks for many years and knew the country and it vagaries. Hyrum also knew he could count on his brother-in-law for solid advice.

Isabella opened the cabin door, "hello Al," she said, "It's good to see you. How are your children and Josephine?" "Well enough Tressa, I left Josephine minding the store." "Give them our best, will you?" She asked over her shoulder as she turned to catch Chase who was climbing on the table.

Pointing beyond the cabin Hyrum said proudly, "the yard corral and horse sheds are finally done. The nearby neighbors have banded together to help one another build outbuildings and fencing; especially those of us who haven't a large family or finances to pay someone for the work."

"Having neighbors willing to support one another is a blessing," Alva said. That's good advice on the holding pond Al, it seems I have a lot more work designing ditch locations than I thought. Thanks again Al," Hyrum said, offering his hand, "I've some chores to finish before my shift on the canal, but before you leave come inside for a taste of Isabella's pie."

***

10 Hyrum Chase Nicol about 1 year Thomas Murdoch Nicol about 2 years old

December 1907 *Death Comes*

Evening came quickly to the little cabin on the wide sagebrush covered flat. Hyrum was washing up at the stand by the door when John Holgate rode up the road to the house. A visit this late in the day was never a good sign. It generally meant something was wrong. "Hello John, what's got you out and about?" Hyrum asked drying his face on the sheeting Isabella had tied to the bench.

"I was in town and A.M. asked me to bring this letter out to you. He said a rider brought it in to the store this afternoon, and there was one for Phennie too." That made Hyrum start a little. "Come in and settle a bit, we'd be pleased to have you join us for supper." "No thank you Hy, I need to be getting back home. I've been gone all day." "Thank you for taking the time to stop by, I probably wouldn't have gone into town for weeks the way things are going."

He kicked his boots on the edge of the house knocking off dirt and dust before he walked inside the little cabin. It was snug and Isabella had made it a home. He was very glad they decided to spend the money to put a plank floor in cabin. It made all the difference in the world. He hung his coat and hat on the peg by the door and said, "It smells wonderful in here Tressa." "Who were you talking with?" Isabella asked. "John Holgate stopped by just now and gave me a letter mother sent over, he said a rider dropped it off at the store in Theodore."

Flipping open his pocketknife, Hyrum slipped the sharp blade into the edge of the envelope and slit the top open. Pulling the folded paper from the envelope he sat on the table bench to read. Isabella looked up from the stove as a gasp from her husband told her something was wrong. "What is it Hyrum?" She asked anxiously.

"Father has fallen and is very ill. Mother needs me to come home," she says she also sent a letter to Josephine. "Will you be alright here alone? He asked. "How long will you be gone?" "I don't know, maybe a week?"

"We should come with you, but it is too cold to take the children, and you can move faster on your horse instead of in the wagon." She said, don't worry we will be fine. "

"Once supper is over I'll pack a saddle bag for you." "Thank you, Tress, while you're doing that I'll bring in more wood, and split kindling for you. How is the water supply?" "The water is ok for now, if it doesn't snow too much I can take care of that," Isabella said.

Stars still pierced the dark sky when picking up his saddlebags from the table Hyrum said, "thank you for packing Tressa." "You didn't sleep much last night did you," she asked in reply. "No, not really. I was thinking about my father. I hope Gabriel and the girls are helping Mother and taking care of things for her." "She's a strong woman Hyrum, I'm sure she is doing as well as can be expected." He said, I know, but I'm still worried."

"I will send a letter with a rider when I know how things are," he said as he held her close and gave her a kiss. "Give my love to your mother and father Hyrum, tell them I would be there if I could." "I will Tress." "Please tell them I'm praying for them." The sky was only lightening over the eastern ridge when Hyrum mounted his horse, saddlebags and sleeping gear wrapped in a tarp and lashed behind the saddle. He waved to Isabella as he started for Theodore where he would stop to ask if Josephine would come with him.

Isabella's routine didn't change much being home with the boys. She was often alone, not at night, but Hyrum worked on their ranch, worked on the canal, helped other ranchers in turn for their help. He arose early and arrived home just before dark every day, except Sunday. Sunday she looked forward to with anticipation.

Hyrum had been gone four days, two days to ride to Heber, anything might have happened to his father in four days. Today was Christmas. She and Tom had made cookies and after supper she would read to them the Christmas story from the Book of Luke in the bible. The boys were playing with the wooden horses Hyrum carved for them, so she put some water on to heat and thought she would have a small cup of mint tea. She hoarded it and used it at times like this, quiet and peaceful.

Last fall when she was walking along the riverbank with the boys she had found wild spearmint growing in a shade dappled clearing where it was moist and green. Letting nothing go to waste she pulled off her apron and opened the pocketknife Hyrum had given her when they moved here last year and began to cut the spearmint, leaving enough root and branch that her cuttings wouldn't kill the plant. She folded her apron around the bounty and carried it home in one arm, with tired Chase in the other. She had laid it out to dry in the sun. Then she had broken off the leaves and stored them in an empty fruit jar, for just a time such as this.

She had gotten the boys ready for bed, they had said their prayers and she was about to start reading with them when she heard hoof beats outside the door. She waited for a knock and called "who is it?" "It's A.M. Isabella, I have a letter here from Hyrum."

She quickly opened the door and Alva Murdock, her brother in law came inside. "Did Phennie go with Hyrum?" she asked. "No, she was already in Heber, she is staying at our daughter's home, she hasn't been feeling well." "I'm sorry Alva." He just nodded his head, and pointedly looked at the envelope he had handed to her.

"Oh," she said, and pulled her knife out, opening the envelope exactly as Hyrum had done those few days before. "Did Phennie send you a letter too?" "No, I expect this one from Hyrum will do for us both." Opening the envelope two sheets of paper came out. One addressed to Tressa, the other to A.M. Hyrum and Josephine had sent messages.

Hyrum's letter said, "Tressa, I arrived here safely two days ago. Only hours before Father died. I was able to talk with him and Gabriel and I gave him a blessing. His funeral will be on the 26th and we'll bury him with the rest of the family. Mother is doing well and sends her love. I will try to be home by Sunday or as soon as I may. All my love, Hyrum"

Death of Thomas Nicol.

Another pioneer of this valley has joined the great majority. At 6:45 last Monday evening, December 23, Thomas Nicol died after an illness of about ten days, resulting from a fall. Funeral services were held in the stake tabernacle yesterday afternoon. A wife and four children survive him.

Thomas Nicol was born in the parish of Weymss, Scotland, Nov. 22, 1821. He was a son of Thomas Nicol and Elizabeth Dryber. He joined the Mormon church in Scotland in 1845, and four years later emigrated to America with his wife and child. His child died during the voyage. He landed at New Orleans without means but through the kindness of strangers he fared well and obtained money to pay his passage to St. Louis. Here he stayed for three years and earned enough money to repay the money he borrowed and bring him and his family to Utah. He settled first at Bountiful, Davis county, where he lived for a few years then moved to Salt Lake City. In 1859 he moved to San Pete county and two years later came to this valley where he has since resided. He died as he has lived a faithful Latter-day Saint. He has buried two wives and seventeen children. He has been one of the most progressive and highly respected citizens of this county and leaves a host of friends here.

11 Wasatch Wave December 27 1907 Obituary Thomas Nicol

Alva finished the letter Josephine had sent and said, "Thomas was a good man. I was glad he was my friend." Isabella nodded her agreement. Looking up she said, "A.M. I was going to read the Christmas story to the boys, would you like to join us?" "Thank you for the offer Tressa, but I think I'll ride on back." "Good night A.M.," Isabella said as she handed him cookies wrapped in a napkin. "One for the road and some for later," she said, smiling as she shut the door.

***

July 1908 *Kenneth Crawford*

"He's a healthy boy Tressa, and you are doing well. You'll bounce back just as you did with Tom and Chase." Hanne, her mother-in-law and mid-wife said.

Isabella laughed to herself as she had panicked wondering how she would have her children living on the reservation. Not thinking they could return to Heber City, rough though the wagon ride back was on her. It was so good to be here with Hanne the past weeks while she was getting close to delivering.

Now Isabella was leaning against the bed's headboard, the newest boy in their growing family nestled in her arms. Hyrum had taken the two older boys out riding. They were also taking care of the chores his mother usually did; feeding the chickens, milking her cow, and watering and weeding her garden.

Even in this high upper valley mid-summer was hot, the heat seemed relentless. "Have you decided on a name for him?" Hanne asked. "We like Kenneth Crawford. It's a strong name." "Yes," Hanne said softly, "it is a strong name, strong for another boy growing up on the frontier. Women need to be strong too," she added, as she offered a cool drink of water to Isabella.

***

Fall 1908 *Kenneth Crawford Gets Traded*

Hyrum came in damp from a cleansing swim in the river; he had been working digging the canal. Shaking his wet head he came in humming and swept Chase up off of the floor, tickled him, and turned to Tressa. Tom ran over and said, "I helped momma with Kenneth today." Ruffling his hair Hyrum said, "That's a good boy. You will be a great help to your mother, you are the oldest," he said prophetically. Tom nodded solemnly.

"Tressa how would you like to go to a dance this weekend?" "A dance? I'd love too! Oh Hyrum we haven't been to a dance for so long, I may have forgotten how to dance," she laughed. The light in her face beamed her joy. "It is this Saturday at A.M.'s store, maybe we can stay the night with Alva and Josephine." Hyrum suggested.

For Isabella Saturday could not come soon enough. She cleaned their best clothes and shoes, a little worn, but certainly presentable. She told Tom, "we are going to a party," he only looked at her with his large brown eyes.

The big white tent that was Murdock's Store was filled with people anxious to break the hardness of their lives with some laughter and music. A.M. had moved his stock back making space for dancing. Musicians sat at the edge of the room, and there were some young people on the other side that were offering to care for children for a small charge. Isabella sent the boys in to the rambunctious group, but she saw them hanging back, watching and getting the lay of the land.

She continued to hold Kenneth for a while, until Hyrum asked, "Will you dance with me my beautiful Tressa? " She handed the baby to one of the young women who squealed and said, "He is so cute Sister Nicol." Isabella smiled and said, "Yes he is." Turning her smile toward Hyrum she held out her hand as he led her onto the dance floor.

Several hours later, the dancing stopped and dinner was set around the outside of the tent. Taking her children out of the mob, they ate sitting on a blanket pulled from their wagon. Sending the boys back to play Isabella went and sat by their wagon and fed Kenneth, who was fussing at what he thought was neglect.

Hyrum said to her, "shall we dance a little longer before we leave?" "I could dance all night," she replied, "but I don't think the children would like it that much. Yes, let's dance a bit longer," and she returned Kenneth to the girls watching the children.

Before too long Isabella glanced at rising noise from the children playing in the corner. Tired children were wearing on the patience of the young people caring for them and they were anxious to send them off with their parents. Hyrum and Isabella gathered Tom and Chase while a different girl handed them Kenneth wrapped in his blanket. She told them, "he is asleep, he's slept for a little while even with all this noise," and she smiled.

Tucking Kenneth into his traveling cradle and the boys onto their blankets in the back of the wagon they headed toward his sister's home where they were staying for the night. The evening was warm and stars shone clear and bright to light their way. Isabella picked Kenneth up from his bed in the back and said, "You slept very well didn't you?"

Hyrum who had gone inside to light the lanterns stopped in his tracks when he heard Isabella scream from the wagon. Thinking she had dropped the baby, or fallen off the wagon seat, a number of hideous thoughts ran across his mind as he raced back to the wagon.

Isabella was looking at the baby in her arms who had awakened at her scream and was wailing in reply. "What is the matter? Why did you scream?" "This isn't Kenneth! This baby is not our son!" She cried. In the tumult of leaving the young girl had given them the wrong baby. Hyrum leaped back into the wagon seat and whipped the horses to a trot and headed back to the store. Angry words flowed between them in their worry for their son. By the time Hyrum pulled the horses to a stop in front of the store they had both calmed a little and looking around they found another anxious family pacing in front of the store a crying Kenneth in the mother's arms.

Once the children were exchanged and fearful parents soothed, they began to see the humor in the mix-up and started to laugh. Tom and Chase awakened by the rough stop of the horses looked over the edge of the wagon at their parents laughing and laughing while their mother kept hugging Kenneth, making certain he was really theirs.[xiii]

February 1909 *First Starving Time*

"Once this storm blows itself out I will gather the herd up into the lot," he replied. "I pray they are in the arroyos getting out of the wind. The snow is drifted so high they won't be able to reach any grass; they will be starving soon Tressa."

Later that morning Isabella busy with the care of children and house stopped as she heard boots stomping on the boards Hyrum had laid in front of the door to cut down on the mud being brought inside. She asked anxiously when the door opened and asked, "How many head did we lose Hyrum?" "I haven't rounded them all up, but it seems maybe 10 or 15 percent of the herd," he said as he hung his frozen coat and hat on the wall.

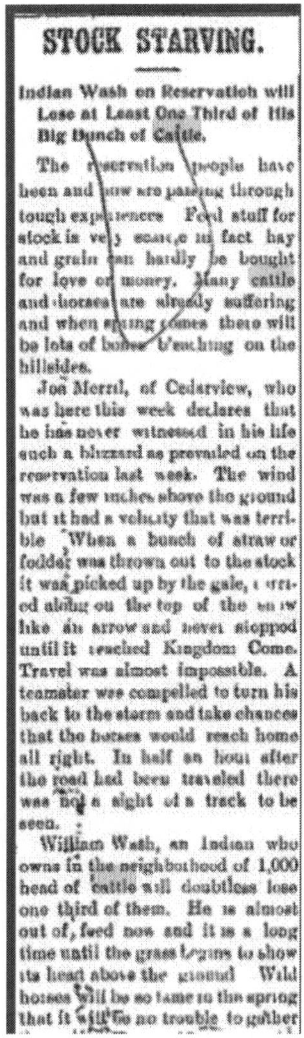

STOCK STARVING.

Indian Wash on Reservation will Lose at Least One Third of His Big Bunch of Cattle.

The reservation people have been and now are passing through tough experiences. Feed stuff for stock is very scarce in fact hay and grain can hardly be bought for love or money. Many cattle and horses are already suffering and when spring comes there will be lots of bones bleaching on the hillsides.

Jon Merril, of Cedarview, who was here this week declares that he has never witnessed in his life such a blizzard as prevailed on the reservation last week. The wind was a few inches above the ground but it had a velocity that was terrible. When a bunch of straw or fodder was thrown out to the stock it was picked up by the gale, carried along on the top of the snow like an arrow and never stopped until it reached Kingdom Come. Travel was almost impossible. A teamster was compelled to turn his back to the storm and take chances that the horses would reach home all right. In half an hour after the road had been traveled there was not a sight of a track to be seen.

William Wash, an Indian who owns in the neighborhood of 1,000 head of cattle will doubtless lose one third of them. He is almost out of feed now and it is a long time until the grass begins to show its head above the ground. Wild horses will be so tame in the spring that it will be no trouble to gather

12 Duchesne Record - Stock Starving 1909

An almost five year old Tom struggled in behind his father his pants covered in snow up to his waist. He stood there shivering as he tried to pull the gloves off his fingers. Taking her eyes from Hyrum she said, "Tom! Come over here quickly! Stand by the fire and I'll help you with your coat. There, let's take off your pants and we'll dry them while you get warm," she said and tugged a blanket off the bed and wrapped him tightly.

"We are about out of feed for the cattle Isabella. I'm riding into town, maybe I'll stop at John Holgate's place and see how they fared during the blizzard." He continued, "I want to see if I can buy any hay or alfalfa. I don't have much hope though," he said as he swung up onto his horse, its nostrils flared and steam puffed out into the icy morning air, tossing its head against the frozen bit between its teeth.

Isabella quickly closed the door and added another log to the stove. "Tom you can crawl in bed under the covers to keep warmer," she said, as she fed he sour dough start and set it in its place next to the stove to keep warm and continue growing.

Later that morning, sitting next to the bed while she fed baby Kenneth, she sang a song her father wrote after he had prayed for the gift of poetry. The poem was written about Scotland and how he was feeling leaving to follow the prophet's call.

It was a song she loved and had heard her father sing many times growing up. He had titled it Oh Scotland, My Country and it was sung to a tune called "Flow Gently, Sweet Afton"[xiv]

Oh Scotland my country, my dear native home,
Though land of the brave and the theme of my song.
Oh why should I leave thee and cross the deep sea,
To a strange land far distant, lovely Scotland, from thee?

How pleasant to view are thy mountains and hills,
Thy sweet blooming heather and far famed bluebells.
Thy scenes of my childhood where in youth I have strayed,
With my faithful companions, my dog, crook, and plaid.

Oh Scotland, my country and land of my birth,
In fondness I'll ever remember thy worth.
For wrapped in thy bosom my forefathers sleep,
Why then should I leave thee and cross the wild deep?

But why should I linger or wish for to stay?
The voice of the Prophet is "Haste, flee away.
Lest judgments o'er take you and lay Scotland low."
To the prophets in Zion Oh, then let me go!

Farewell then my kindred, my home and my all
When duty requires it we bow to the call.
We brave every danger and conquer each foe,
To the words of the Prophet, Oh, then let me bow.

Farewell then, dear Scotland, one last fond adieu,
Farewell my dear brethren so faithful and true.
May angels watch o'er you till warfares are o'er,
And in safety we all meet on Zion's fair shore.
(Author: John Murray Murdoch, 1852)[xv]

She gently laid the satiated and sleeping Kenneth in his cradle and tucked the older boys in tightly as they had drifted off to sleep listening to her melodic voice. Just as she started supper the older boys woke, watching them rub sleep from their eyes she opened the cabin door and felt the quiet that comes when a storm has broken, but the winds hadn't slowed.

"It looks like the storm has stopped boys, bundle up and get your chores done before your father gets home." Hats pulled low, mittens covered small fingers and coats buttoned to their necks the little boys pushed against the piled snow drifts to reach the chicken coop. Each with a hand on the rope that was tied between the house and the shed as a safety line to keep them from getting lost if the storm returned.

While Chase tossed feed out to the chickens, Tom began to carry stove logs two at a time and laid them near the door. Back and forth he went tramping the snow down to a visible path. Chase pulled the cover over the chicken feed box to help keep the mice and rabbits out and stopped to pick up a log to carry to the pile his brother had stacked.

Ferrying the last of the wood into the cabin Tom said, "Mother the cow needs to be milked she started bawling while we were over there." His mother looked up and he continued hopefully, "I can do it, I've watched you and father." His face an expression of determination. "Of course you would be able to do it, but I think your fingers need to grow just a bit more before you'll be able to pull her teats. If your father hasn't returned from town in the next while, you and I will go milk her." Tom's eyes grew wide and he smiled. They shucked out of their coats and boots and she said, "come here, I've buttered you some bread to tide you over until supper when your father comes home."

Twilight pushed gently over the white fields, punctuated by the dark bodies of the cattle pressing together in the feed corral. Their plaintive cries were increasing, and Isabella thought that if Hyrum didn't arrive quickly, she would have to go outside and toss the hay out to them. "Tom and Chase come here and wash for supper," she said, then noticed the silence coming from the corral. "Your father is home boys, let's get ready for supper and family prayer."

Hanging his hat on the peg by the door and pulling off his coat he laid it over the bench near the stove to dry. Hyrum looked over the room and contentment filled his heart replacing the fear that had lingered there most of the day.

Setting bowls of stew on the table Isabella said, "Hyrum, come here and sit down, you'll warm up faster after you've had some supper." "You're right Tress. Boys are you ready?" "Yes Father," they answered, and the family knelt at their benches while Hyrum blessed the day, gave thanks for their lives and the food provided. Once the boys had climbed up on their bench, and were faces down toward their bowls Isabella said, "Tell me what you learned in town Hyrum."

"Well Tressa," he said, "it's like I thought. It appears almost everyone is in the same shape as we are, there is too much snow, and little if any wheat or hay available to purchase even if we had enough money, the prices are sky high. All we can do is pray the snow melts quickly and the grass greens up or we may not have any cattle left once spring comes."

The snow continued and spring didn't arrive until June.

***

May 1909 *First Homestead Patent*

"It was published in the paper this week Tressa," he said as he handed her a copy of the Uintah Chieftain. "By this time next year we will hold the patent on our own land. The notice will be published weekly for a month." "It is something to look forward to," Isabella replied. The winter was long, and this is very good news.

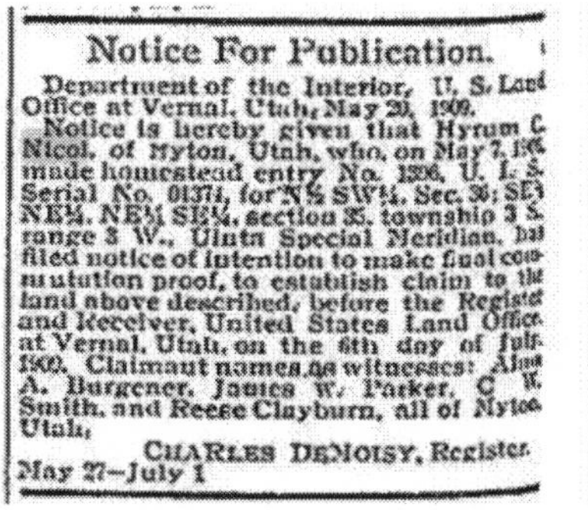

Notice For Publication.

Department of the Interior, U. S. Land Office at Vernal, Utah, May 20, 1909.

Notice is hereby given that Hyrum C. Nicol, of Myton, Utah, who, on May 7, 1906, made homestead entry No. 1206, U. L. S. Serial No. 01374, for N½ SW¼, Sec. 36; SE¼ NE¼, NE¼ SE¼, section 35, township 3 S. range 3 W., Uinta Special Meridian, has filed notice of intention to make final commutation proof, to establish claim to the land above described, before the Register and Receiver, United States Land Office at Vernal, Utah, on the 6th day of July 1909. Claimant names as witnesses: Alma A. Burgener, James W. Parker, C. W. Smith, and Reese Clayburn, all of Myton Utah.

CHARLES DEMOISY, Register.

May 27—July 1

13 *Uintah Chieftain May 27 1909 – Notice of Intent Midview Homestead*

***

"Hyrum? Will you wait after church and take the boys? They have organized a Relief Society and I want to join." "Of course Tress, do you have enough money for dues?" "Yes, I have some of the egg money."

Quietly to herself she thought, "it will give me a chance to spend some time with other women."

Isabella didn't like complaining about their life on the homestead; but it was a solitary one, or as solitary as you can get with young boys around. There wasn't time to visit with other women settlers except when she attended church services and with Hyrum working so hard on the ranch and taking on extra work to supplement their income she was alone with her thoughts too much.

***

August 1909 *Partners*

"I am looking forward to going back to Heber and visiting our families Hyrum," Isabella commented as she put empty canning bottles into the wooden box making certain to tuck rags and paper between them so they wouldn't be broken on the ride over the mountains. Singing as she worked there was a lightness about her as she continued filling boxes with food, clothes, and bedding while Hyrum put their tent in the wagon. He commented, "I hope it won't rain and we can sleep under the stars. I'm also glad the road is much better, nothing is worse than greasy muddy roads, other than being soaked through."

A few days later sitting under the trees in his mother's yard, Hyrum and his mother enjoyed the diurnal breeze gently dropping out of the canyon's mouth. "I miss the cool night breezes; the winds are hot, dry and at times it seems never ending out on the ranch."

Hanne, never one to dally about a point turned to him and said, "I asked you here Hyrum to suggest a business proposition. Age is catching up with me and I won't be able to continue to mid-wife and nurse as much as I do now, I need some income and buying a homestead next to your place will do well for income when I am older."

"Are you certain you want to do this?" Hyrum asked. "Of course. I have thought about it since Kenneth was born. I need somewhere to put my money as an investment and a homestead in proximity to yours is a wise course. I can purchase cattle and you can run them with yours and when they're sold, I will have a profit." "It will benefit both of us." Hanne said succinctly.

"Gabriel and I will accompany you home and will go with me to Vernal to make the purchase." [xvi] With that pronouncement Hyrum and his mother became unofficial partners in an expanded homestead on Holgate Flats.[xvii]

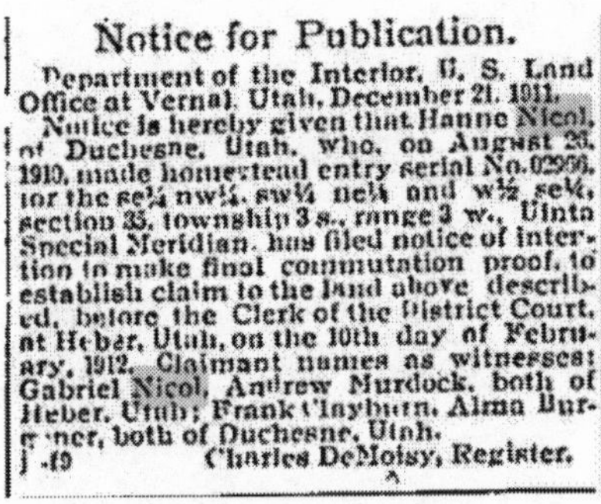

Notice for Publication.

Department of the Interior, U. S. Land Office at Vernal, Utah, December 21, 1911.

Notice is hereby given that Hanne Nicol, of Duchesne, Utah, who, on August 26, 1910, made homestead entry serial No. 02956, for the se¼ nw¼, sw¼ ne¼ and w½ se¼, section 35, township 3 s., range 3 w., Uinta Special Meridian, has filed notice of intention to make final commutation proof, to establish claim to the land above described, before the Clerk of the District Court, at Heber, Utah, on the 10th day of February, 1912. Claimant names as witnesses: Gabriel Nicol, Andrew Murdock, both of Heber, Utah; Frank Clayburn, Alma Burgener, both of Duchesne, Utah.

j 19 Charles DeMoisy, Register.

14 Hanne Nicol Notice of Intent for final Midview Homestead

March 1910 *More Land*

"I think we should buy those additional quarter-sections and connect our land with mother's Tress." Hyrum declared. "Are you certain we should buy more land?" Isabella questioned as she sat down at the table, wiping her hands dry on a cotton flour sack towel. Laying it aside she looked over at the figures Hyrum was carefully writing.

"If the price is low enough we can do it. I admit money will be tight, and we'll use most of our savings, but," he said justifying his argument, "we need more land to run our cattle, there isn't enough feed even between Mother's homestead and ours."

"If that's what you think we should do Hyrum. I'm sure we will get by," she said standing and pushed the bench away from the table. Isabella picked up her towel and returned to setting the kitchen aright after breakfast.

Hyrum Nicol Government Released Patent on second Midview Homestead
Property adjacent to original homestead.
N2NE4:NE4NW4 Section 35 Township 3S Range 3W
Accession Nr: 120396 Document Type: Serial Patent State: Utah
Issue Date: March 21, 1910

***

May 6, 1910 *Death Comes by Telegram*

"I've got a telegram for you," John Musser said as he leaned down from his saddle. Dusting his pants off with the hat he pulled from his head he reached into his coat pocket and handed the folded paper to Hyrum. "I was in Theodore today and they asked me to bring this by on my way home. Wasn't certain I wanted to be the bearer of bad news; not much good news is sent by telegram," he opined. "Care to get down and have a drink of water John?" Hyrum asked. "No, I need to get going. Thanks all the same."

"Thank you John," Hyrum said, holding the paper in his fingers like it was hot. "I'd better take this inside and share it with Isabelle." "You're welcome Hy," John said and nudged his mare toward the road. "Let us know what we can do to help will you?" "Certainly will John. Thanks again," he said and turned toward the cabin.

"Open it Hyrum. Don't keep waiting," Isabella urged, as she caught Kenneth racing across the room and reached for the rag to wipe dust from his face. "I wished he would walk so I wouldn't have to carry him and now all I do is wish he weren't walking. He doesn't walk, he runs everywhere."

"What is it Hyrum," she asked, "I'm running on like a stream." Stopping herself, she slowed and looked at him standing near the door. Then he said, "I'm sorry Tress, your father died this morning. His funeral will be on Wednesday."

The pronouncement hung in the air, Hyrum stood waiting for her tears. She surprised him when she smiled and exclaimed, "oh how happy I am for him! When we saw him last summer he said he was wearing thin and wished to go home. How I will miss him." Then she paused, "I wonder how mother is doing. I imagine she is happy for him too, but very sad to be the last one left."

Looking around the cabin, seeing Kenneth, she said, "We wouldn't make it back in time for his funeral, would we?" "I'm afraid not Tress," he said, shaking his head. "Are you alright with that?" He asked. "I will have to be alright with it since we can't change it can we?" She said a bit sharply. "Oh Hyrum, I'm sorry. Although I am happy for father, I am sad for me and my family, we will miss him." "I know you will Tress and he knows how much you love him."

Suddenly she said, "I'm going to take a walk. Then I'll write mother a letter," she was talking as she briskly moved through the door shutting it softly behind her. "Where is mother going?" Tom asked. "She needs some time to think, and I'm certain she will pray. Your Grandfather Murdoch died this morning." Tom asked, "Is he with Muz now?" "Yes son, he is. Your Mother is happy for him and sad for herself so she is taking a walk."

"Go outside with Kenneth and Chase for a while." "Alright Father," Tom said, taking his youngest brother by his pudgy hand lead him outside".

JOHN M. MURDOCK.

Funeral Services Held Sunday Afternoon.

Patriarch J. M. Murdock died at his home in Heber Friday morning, May 6, 1910, at 9 o'clock, of general debility. The end came peacefully, Mr. Murdock, surrounded by members of his family, dying without even a struggle; thus ended the earthly career of one who has been a useful citizen and an energetic worker for the betterment of the community in which he lived.

Funeral services were held Sunday afternoon, May 8th, at 4 o'clock, in the stake house at Heber, under the direction of the Wasatch stake presidency. The line of march from the family residence was headed by members of the highpriests' quorum, over which Mr. Murdock had presided from 1802 until a short time prior to his death. These were followed by the stake presidency and patriarchs. Then came the casket borne by the counselors of the bishoprics of the three Heber wards. The surviving wife of Patriarch Murdock and his brother William, now the only living member of their family, came next followed by the

family, came next followed by the

children, grand children, relatives and friends. The stake house was beautifully decorated with potted plants and the stand draped in white. Appropriate music was furnished by a mixed chorus and male quartette under the direction of Prof. Whitaker. The speakers were Patriarchs Thos. Hicken, John Duke, N. C. Murdock, and Abram Hatch, Attewall Wootton, and Jos. R. Murdock, James C. Jensen and E. D. Clyde of the stake presidency each bearing testimony of the faithfulness and sterling worth of Brother Murdock.

Deceased was the father of 22 children and his descendants number 101 grand children, and 66 great grand children. He was born at Grasswater, Ayrshire, Scotland, December 28, 1820, and came to Utah in 1852. In 1860 he moved his family to Heber where they have resided ever since. He conceived the idea and supervised the building of the first school house in the valley and was always an energetic worker for the upbuilding of the community, having taken an active part in all public enterprises. He has lived an honest, upright life and the memory of his many kind acts and noble deeds will ever be cherished by his numerous posterity and friends.

15 Wasatch Wave May 7, 1910 –John Murray Murdoch Obituary

***

March 1911 *Protest Letter*

The group of ranchers stood together in front of the Pioneer Store their voices rising and falling as they discussed a letter to the editor of the Vernal Express that had been published the week[xviii] prior. "Well I do not agree with what Mr. Smith wrote," protested George Odekirk. "We do need our own county." "I agree," said Hyrum. In the hubbub of conversation someone said, "We need to write our own letter to the Vernal Express and state what we have been saying here. If we don't then his words will stand encompassing every one of us living here around Theodore. We can't wait years to have our own county." "I agree, I agree," assents echoed around the group of men.

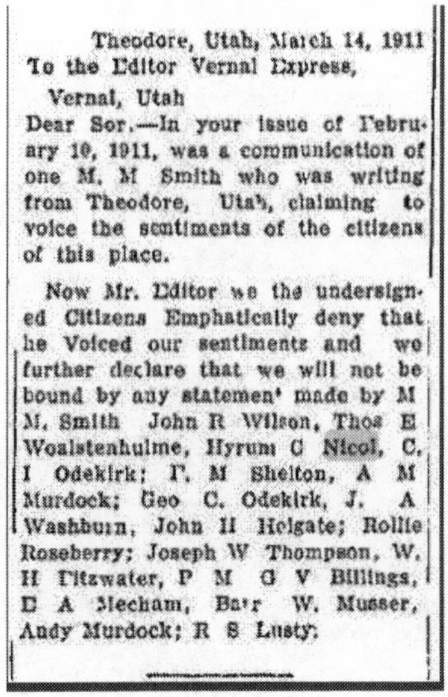

Theodore, Utah, March 14, 1911
To the Editor Vernal Express,
Vernal, Utah
Dear Sor.—In your issue of February 10, 1911, was a communication of one M. M Smith who was writing from Theodore, Utah, claiming to voice the sentiments of the citizens of this place.

Now Mr. Editor we the undersigned Citizens Emphatically deny that he Voiced our sentiments and we further declare that we will not be bound by any statement made by M M. Smith John R Wilson, Thos E Woalstenhulme, Hyrum C Nicol, C. I Odekirk; F. M Shelton, A M Murdock; Geo C. Odekirk, J. A Washburn, John H Holgate; Rollie Roseberry; Joseph W Thompson, W. H Fitzwater, P M G V Billings, E A Mecham, Barr W. Musser, Andy Murdock; R S Lusty.

16 Duchesne Record March 14 1911 Letter to Editor in Rebuttal

A voice in the crowd said, "We should ask the other ranchers nearby for their opinions also; see if they want to add their names to the letter."

***

June 1911 *First Official Patent – Midview Homestead*

"Our second patent is official Tressa," Hyrum said, as she took the paper he held out to her. "Time certainly flies doesn't it Hyrum?" Isabella asked. They had purchased the land, its 160 acres bordering around their original homestead from the Land Office in Vernal in March last year. We're becoming regular land barons or rather land barren aren't we, the sour comment slipping out before she caught it. "I'm sorry Hyrum. I shouldn't have said that. You work too hard for me to belittle your efforts in our behalf." "I didn't take offense Tressa. You know," he said chuckling a bit, "you aren't too far off the mark."

***

VERNAL 03285. 4—1023-R.

The United States of America,

To all to whom these presents shall come, Greeting:

WHEREAS, a Certificate of the Register of the Land Office at VERNAL, UTAH, has been deposited in the General Land Office, whereby it appears that full payment has been made by the claimant

HYRUM C. NICOL

according to the provisions of the Act of Congress of April 24, 1820, entitled "An Act making further provision for the sale of the Public Lands" and the acts supplemental thereto, for the NORTH HALF OF THE NORTHEAST QUARTER AND THE NORTHEAST QUARTER OF THE NORTHWEST QUARTER OF SECTION THIRTY-FIVE AND THE NORTHWEST QUARTER OF THE NORTHWEST QUARTER OF SECTION THIRTY-SIX IN TOWNSHIP THREE SOUTH OF RANGE THREE WEST OF THE UINTAH SPECIAL MERIDIAN, UTAH, CONTAINING ONE HUNDRED SIXTY ACRES,

17 Patent # 03285 Vernal Land Office

Walking down the dirt road toward the Duchesne River, Hyrum and Isabella heads kept leaning together in earnest conversation. Keeping her eyes on the boys racing around she turned quickly back to him when he said, "to lessen our financial worries Tress we could sell. Tress?"

Indignation in her voice and her eyes wide and as she whispered a tightness seemed to radiate from her whole countenance. "We have spent almost our last dollar to buy more ground, we can't just fold our tent and leave," she said stiffly. Looking around she called Tom and Chase back toward them and said, "Tom, you and Chase take Kenneth and start toward home, we'll follow right behind you. Stay to the road, and keep your eyes open for snakes she warned, walk away quickly if you see one. "

Seeing the boys were on their way toward the cabin she was able to focus on Hyrum continued, "the new property is holding water just like the homestead. We lose money each field we clear and plant." Dejectedly he continued, "It is useless! Trying to put in crops here no matter how much we pray for bountiful harvests won't work. The ground is only fit for grazing, and with no field crops we won't have feed for a herd large enough to make any money," he concluded his voice winding down."

Helping Isabella sit near the bank of the river Hyrum picked up a handful of rocks, tossing them in the water one at a time and watching the ripples be quickly caught up in the rapids. The only sounds over their own quiet breathing was the soughing and gurgling water rolling across the hidden rocks below the surface. Finally he spoke, "if we have another winter like Oh-Nine we, as well as the cattle, will starve. I just don't see any other way. I have to get a job and just run the herd as best as we can."

"I know Hyrum, I know how hard you work to keep the ranch going. I'm sorry I was angry. I am as frustrated as you are," she said. Peace again between them they knelt together, Hyrum taking her hands in his they began to pray.

"Father in Heaven, we have followed your spirit to settle in this country. We have cleared the land, and put in ditches and brought water to the thirsty ground, but as you see the land holds onto the water and doesn't drain. Our alfalfa fields produce so little that the cattle will have no winter feed. We have looked at our options and think we will move to town, continue to run our herd, and I will look for work to support our family and to save enough money for winter feed. We thank thee with deepest gratitude for your support and blessings on us and our family all the days we have lived here. May we have thy continued support as we look forward to a different future than what we first envisioned when we came to the Reservation. We desire to do thy will and ask for thy direction and help to obtain employment. In all things Lord, Thy will be done. In Jesus' name, Amen."

Standing up, Hyrum reached for Isabella's hands gently pulling her up from the ground. Hand in hand they turned toward their cabin, Isabella wiping the tears from her face. She whispered, just loud enough, "Let's continue to look forward with faith Hyrum, we are not asked to do more than we can do. I believe that."

Looking toward the cabin she saw Tom and Chase feeding the chickens and heard them laughing as Kenneth tossed his handfuls of millet around the chicken coop. "Those boys are good hands," Hyrum said, "they work hard."

"Good work boys, thank you for looking after Kenneth. Oh! You brought in wood for the stove too." "We wanted to surprise you Mother," they said, looking down at the toes of their dusty worn boots. "You did boys, you certainly did," Isabella touched each lowered head as she walked to the stove to serve the soup simmering there.

***

Later that night after Isabella had cleared the dinner table, and the boys were washed up and tucked in bed Hyrum came in from checking the stock and closing them into the corral for the night. He watched her working non-stop and touched her hand as she started on another trip across the room. "Here Tress, sit down a minute, I've been thinking a lot about what we talked about."

Sliding her chair next to him, she sat down looking intently at him as he said, "I'm feeling that tomorrow I should ride into Duchesne and see if I can find a job. I don't know what I can do, but I know I'll find something." A gentle smile crossed her face as she said, 'I've been feeling the same way Hyrum. I'm not frightened any longer about the debt and the ranch or the cattle. It will all work out. I know it."

The next evening long after the sun had set Isabella leaned near a kerosene lantern reading the scriptures when Hyrum rode into the yard.

She set aside the book and walk out toward the corral. "I have some dinner covered for you," she called as she walked toward him watching as he fed his horse, hung the saddle on the rack, and rubbed him down.

Looking over the horse's back he told her, "Pope's Pioneer Supply had an opening, I can work for them a few days a week. Full-time if we move into town. I left word with Alva to keep an ear open for a house we can rent or buy. We have to have something a bit larger than this cabin he said looking around. The boys seem to take up all the space and most of the air some days."

He continued staring off into the darkness as though his mind was somewhere else. Then he shared his thoughts with her, "A.M. and Josephine ran their cattle operation on the Strawberry while living in town and from White Rocks, he did it for years. We can do the same thing; run our cattle here while living in Duchesne."

Taking a breath Isabella said, "This is an answer to our prayers for help, isn't it? I feel peaceful about the decision."

***

"I so enjoy your visits Hyrum," his mother said as they sat beneath the fruit trees next to her snug home. "I do too Mother," he said. "Isabella is with her sisters canning and singing isn't she?" Hanne's face lit up with the memories of seeing Isabella and her sisters gathered around the piano singing and laughing. "Yes she is Mother.

The weeks here rejuvenate her, she misses her family so much and they make such a fuss over the boys who think they are in heaven. They roll on the lawn and climb trees and pick fruit. That's what we hope for Duchesne; that it will also grow like this beautiful valley."

"I remember Father telling me that this place was sage brush when he came here." "Yes," she said, even when I came years later there were few trees planted." "You and Father made it grow and that gives me hope we will have success." He said, "I love coming home and sitting on this porch in the shade with you," he smiled at her. Comfortable silence drifted between them and then softly he said, "I miss Father's advice." Straightening up in his chair, he pulled his shirt cuffs down and then said, "I have something to talk over with you Mother it is about the ranch."

He plunged in speaking quickly and laying out their plans. "Mr. Fortie, the manager of the Pioneer Supply Store has offered me a position and Isabella and I have decided to move into Theodore. We've thought a lot about it and after much thought and prayer this is the direction we think will be best for us. We know that the homestead ranch will always be a small operation. You know it's almost impossible to grow our own feed out there because of the soil, or should I say lack of soil suitable to agriculture," he grimaced as he thought of the ranch so well situated between two rivers and ground that held water like a dish.

"The additional land we bought gives us more grazing ground, but it isn't going to be hugely profitable, it holds water too; we won't be growing acres of alfalfa there either. All we can do is hope the winters will be milder, so our money to buy feed will go farther, else the cattle will eat most, if not all of the profits from any of the fall cattle sales."

"Here is my question Mother, do you still want to continue running cattle with us? I think we could buy you out if you'd like." Hanne paused for a bit, thinking over the situation Hyrum had laid out, then said, "For now I'll stay the course Hyrum. Beside which you'll need my 160 acres to graze the herd."

"I have faith in you and your abilities to accomplish what you've set your mind to do." Hyrum reached across the table and touched his mother's fingers. "I hope you're right Mother. I hope you're right," he said again under his breath; soft as a prayer.

Seeing his pensive face Hanne changed the subject. "Did you see Phennie before you left Duchesne Hyrum?" Hanne asked. "No, not recently. She is busy with the children and with Al called as the Bishop she's kept busy helping with the store and their other interests."

Thoughtfully he added, "Josephine and Alva have been such a support for Isabella and me, like she always has been. They are always there and I don't know what we would do without their help. I doubt there is any way we can ever pay them back for their kindness and support."

"Once when I was attempting to thank them Phennie said that they are only sharing what God has given them and if we felt to pay them back we could do the same. She told me they try to live like King Benjamin in the Book of Mormon taught his people when he said, '*God, who has created us and on whom we depend for our lives and all that we have and are and who gives to us whatsoever we ask him for in faith, believing that we shall receive, then how ought we to impart of the substance that we have one to another*[xix]. We are grateful to be able to help wherever we can."

"That's just like them isn't it? They care for me also." Then closing the subject she said, "before you leave I have some things put together to send back with you for her. She works so hard, and hasn't been as healthy as she once was." "Of course Mother," Hyrum laughed, "as long as it isn't a full wagon load, there won't be any room for the boys."

***

December 1910 ***A Calling***

Sitting around the stove in their little kitchen Isabella mused,"it will be strange not having A. M. as our Bishop. It will be strange with the new stake being organized too. But he'll be wonderful as a part of the new stake's high counsel. He has overseen so much change and growth in the ward and the town." Receiving no response she said, "Hyrum, did you hear me?" He turned his head slowly, "yes Tressa I heard you." "What has your thoughts in its grip?" Isabella asked.

"I was just thinking that I am already overwhelmed with the homestead, working at Pope's, and now this new calling is going to take more of my time. How will we, especially you, manage?" He asked, his forehead wrinkling over dark eyes his brows drawn together as his gaze focused on her face. "Bishop Billings has the mantle of his calling from the Lord Hyrum, he wouldn't have called you to be his counselor without the Lord's confirmation that you are who He wants serving with him." [xx]

After a pause, Isabella continued, "besides, I grew up with a father who was always engaged in community affairs, helping neighbors, running the sheep and he was fully engaged in the Lord's work. I know what it is like. Don't worry the Lord will provide," she said with a smile full of confidence in him and confidence in her testimony of the goodness and strength of God. Hyrum nodded toward her his face losing its tenseness and he reached over and took her hand, "you are an angel Tressa," he said. "You constantly help me keep a positive perspective."

***

December 1911 *Back to Town*

Isabella was a city girl, she admitted only to herself as she finished emptying the last of their moving boxes. Living full-time in town though it was only 12 miles from the ranch had lightened her spirits considerably. There were people around to talk to that weren't children. Hyrum was so engaged at work, the homestead, with church and community business that he was often not at home.

She looked around their new rented home, once again Alva and Josephine had come to their assistance and wasn't she happy that they had this house available. It was large and the boys were only a few blocks from school.

They were all settling into a routine; Hyrum working during the week and then they took care of the homestead on the weekend. They had never thought of naming the place, it was just the Nicol Homestead in Midview. Maintaining the ranch meant driving or riding out there every week to ensure the cattle's water supply was sufficient, adding fencing, digging ditches, and planting where they could. Now the cold weather had slowed the ranch work and Hyrum had stopped working directly on the Blue Bench Canal which opened up a bit of his time.

***

Winter 1911 *Primary Organization*

"Bishop Billings asked to see us this evening," Hyrum said, when he came in the door after work. "I told him we will come over after supper." "Alright, she replied, "I suppose Tom can care for the boys while we are gone."

"We are glad to have you back in town," the Bishop of the Duchesne Ward, George Billings said, offering his hand. "Come into the parlor and have a seat. Isabella, he turned toward her, "Hyrum told me you've settled in well. How are your boys doing?" he asked. "We're getting used to a different rhythm Bishop. I think the boys like the move." Isabella went on, "it's been hectic but we will make it work with the Lord's help."

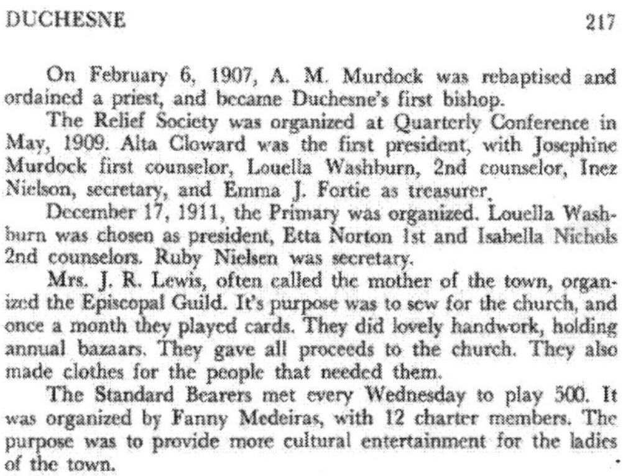

DUCHESNE 217

On February 6, 1907, A. M. Murdock was rebaptised and ordained a priest, and became Duchesne's first bishop.

The Relief Society was organized at Quarterly Conference in May, 1909. Alta Cloward was the first president, with Josephine Murdock first counselor, Louella Washburn, 2nd counselor, Inez Nielson, secretary, and Emma J. Fortie as treasurer.

December 17, 1911, the Primary was organized. Louella Washburn was chosen as president, Etta Norton 1st and Isabella Nichols 2nd counselors. Ruby Nielsen was secretary.

Mrs. J. R. Lewis, often called the mother of the town, organized the Episcopal Guild. It's purpose was to sew for the church, and once a month they played cards. They did lovely handwork, holding annual bazaars. They gave all proceeds to the church. They also made clothes for the people that needed them.

The Standard Bearers met every Wednesday to play 500. It was organized by Fanny Medeiras, with 12 charter members. The purpose was to provide more cultural entertainment for the ladies of the town.

18 Early History of Duchesne Preserved by the Daughters of the Utah Pioneers

Then Bishop Billings came to the reason he had asked them over that evening. "Sister Nicol, it is time that we organize the children's primary program in our ward. The Lord is calling you to be the second counselor in this organization," he said as he looked in her eyes, will you accept it?" He asked. Without hesitation Isabella replied, "Yes, I will." "Good. Good, I knew we could count on you," he said smiling. Turning to face Hyrum he asked, "will you support her in this calling Hyrum?" And Hyrum answered as did Isabella without hesitation, "yes I will."

Both Hyrum and Isabella had been members of the Primary Association as children in Heber City and they were familiar with the direction and intentions of the Primary; that the children would be taught basic gospel principles and values and to 'be prepared in knowledge and behavior to carry the gospel forward, and to be good parents and citizens'[xxi].

The first Primary Association was organized in the Rock Creek ward in Farmington, a small town north of Salt Lake City by 'Aurelia Spencer Rogers, a 44-year-old mother of 12, who felt strongly that something should be done about the behavior of the neighborhood boys who ran freely through the town day and night. She felt many of these children were not being taught basic principles and values and therefore would not be prepared in either knowledge or behavior to carry the gospel forward, or even to be good parents or citizens'. Primary became a conduit to help children learn good character, principals, and values especially using songs, poetry, and activities.

It seems that younger boys were running a bit wild and Sister Rogers concerned that they needed direction and gospel teaching they might not be getting within their homes discussed her concerns and together with General Relief Society President Eliza R. Snow came up with a plan of action.

With the approval of the Church of Jesus Christ of Latter-day Saints' President John Taylor and after receiving an official calling from her bishop, Sister Rogers began planning for the first meeting of the Primary Association. Since these leaders decided that singing 'was necessary' girls were also invited to 'make it sound as well as it should'. Children ages 4 to 14 were invited to participate in the first Primary.

Under the direction of the priesthood, the first Primary was held in the Farmington Rock Chapel on Sunday, August 25, 1878, with 224 children attending.[xxii]

After their meeting Hyrum and Isabella walked slowly toward home. He listened to her excitement about this new endeavor. "You knew didn't you Hyrum." Isabella queried a statement rather than a question. "Yes, I did," he replied, "but you know I couldn't say anything until the Bishop issued your official call." She went on quickly, "you know how much I love children, and it will be so good for our boys to be around other children and learn more of the gospel of Jesus Christ at the same time. I'm so excited!"

***

April 1912 *Answered Prayer of Faith*

"I don't think I've ever been this ill having a child," Isabella thought as she was attempting to put a meal together. "Chase will you please occupy Kenneth for a while. I need to rest and he is under my feet. Tom will you fill the wood box?"

"How I need a healing blessing," she said desperately to Hyrum. "Although the doctors have said that this baby won't live or that I won't live having it, I do not believe that is true, but I am so sick. I can't keep food down, my body seems to rebel every time the baby moves. I am getting weaker," she softly whispered.

After putting supper on the table she turned to her husband and said, "I have to lay down Hyrum, please care for the boys and get them in bed." As he turned to call the boys in for dinner, she said, "President Smart is visiting Duchene for Stake Conference and I am praying that he will come and give me a blessing," she continued as she lay down weakness prostrating her. "I will ride over to the meeting and ask President Smart to come and give you a blessing," he said compassionate tears welling in his eyes. "No! I need you here Hyrum I am too sick, I don't want you to leave me!" Isabella plead with him. "I have faith God will let him know that I have been praying for his blessing; he will come without our having to find him." Sunday evening passed, and President Smart did not come.

Lying in the dark, growing sicker Isabella desperately prayed as she thought, "I think I really may die."

"Father in Heaven, please hear my plea for a healing blessing from President Smart's hands. I cannot sleep and I have almost given up." At the moment of her almost failing hope, at 2 o'clock a.m. there was a knock on the door. Hyrum opened it and there stood President Smart, who explained, "I am sorry to call so late, but I had started back home when I received an impression to return to Duchesne and come here." "Come in President," Hyrum said, opening the door wider and gesturing him inside.

President Smart went on to explain, "at one time someone in my family received a blessing from Isabella's father, John M. Murdoch, and I want to return that blessing upon the head of one of your children."

Hyrum helped Isabella from the bed and as she came into the room, President Smart was walking the floor and weeping tears as large as huge raindrops, as Hyrum had told him of her prayers. Hyrum asked, "would you please give Isabella the blessing she needs so much? President Smart answered, "'I will give you the blessing you desire, and it shall be by my hands as I am directed of the spirit'."

The next morning when Isabella woke she lay very still she checking herself before she moved, was she still ill? After President Smart and Hyrum laid their hands on her head and gave her the healing blessing she had gratefully fallen to sleep and now, no, she wasn't nauseas, her head didn't ache, she had strength in her limbs, and she felt better! She fairly sang out, "how wonderful is God to give me this blessing of health and He answered my prayers!"

When they heard her moving the boys tentatively entered her room, afraid they would see her sicker than the day before. They gathered around her, grinning as they realized that she wasn't sick any longer.

She said, the awe still in her voice, "I have been healed by the gift of God through the power of His Holy Priesthood." She described what had happened the night before as the boys slept through the night not awakening when President Smart arrived. She told them, "First your father sealed the blessing with the consecrated oil[xxiii], and then President Smart and your father placed their hands upon my head and the President gave me a blessing of healing."

"What a wonderful gift that Father in Heaven hears our prayers! What he did for me is a witness that he is aware of each of us and of our needs. He sent President Smart to me just as I had asked him."

"Oh my sweet boys, I know he knows each of you too! Remember, no matter what, no matter where, you can pray and Heavenly Father will answer. He promised us that he is always with us and hears our prayers."

Later she continued to ponder her healing and the rest of the blessing President Smart had given her. She thought, "such marvelous promises I shall never forget." In her mind's eye she heard him say, "I promise you 'full health' and that 'you will live to have this child and many more'. He said, "'the child you are carrying is a boy and his name should be John Murray[xxiv]. He will be a counselor to Bishops and do a great work with young people'." [xxv]

June 1912 *John Murray Arrives Safely*

Hanne Nicol, Hyrum's mother made the two day journey from Heber City to their house in Duchesne before Isabella went into confinement. She helped shepherd the boys encouraging them to get their chores done, all while she helped with the cooking, cleaning, and doing all the things a home needed to stay running. The boys also took over Isabella's chores which included watering and weeding the garden, and feeding the chickens, all while they took care of the other animals and chores that they did each day.

Still marveling at the fulfilment of prophecy, her health and strength restored, Isabella gave birth June 20, 1912 to the promised boy. She held her swaddled baby as Hanne cleared the room and retold her miraculous healing, "We will name him John Murray, after my father, as President Smart directed during my blessing."

Isabella was propped on her side with the baby next to her when Hyrum brought the boys in to see that she was still well and to give them their first look at their newest brother.

As she looked at each of them Isabella gave thanks. She knew that Tom, age 8, had a load of responsibility as the oldest and she counted on his support with the house and his younger brothers; a responsibility that he carried with little grousing. Chase, age 6, and Tom were best friends and Chase worked hard alongside Tom, while Kenneth, age 4, followed after Tom and Chase and learned his share of the ranch work from them. "Now here I am holding another precious baby boy, John Murray," she thought. Feelings of gratitude filled her heart just as Hyrum leaned over and kissed the top of her head, "we are blessed aren't we Tressa? So very blessed."

***

DUCHESNE CITY.

(By J. R. Wilson)

Pioneer Day began with a salute of eight guns at the dawn of day. At ten o clock a m the DuChesne Brass Band held an open air concert in front of the Opera house. At 10 30 the following program was rendered in the Opera house
Music by the DuChesne Brass Band.
Invocation by Elder H C. Nicol
Song by the Sunday School children, 'Utah'
Address "The Pioneers," Wm H. Smart
Solo, Hazel Dickerson
Drill Exercises of the children, Mabel Stephens, director
Music by the DuChesne Glee Club.
Original Poem, Luella Washburn
Solo, Prof Oscar A. Kirkham.
Music by the DuChesne Brass Band.
Benediction, John A. Fortie
From 1:30 to 6 30 p. m. field sports
The game of base ball between the DuChesne and Myton teams was very good, the result being a victory for the home team with a score of eight to seven
The horse races and Colonel Carver's Wild West Show were well worth seeing
Closing with the grand ball at night, the celebration will long be remembered by all who were present.

19 Duchesne Record H.C. Nicol at Pioneer Day Celebration 1912

"I'll be home tomorrow afternoon Tressa. You'll have to take the boys to church yourself, I'm sorry. Saturday is the only day they can meet with us." "Don't worry Hyrum, I have plenty to do. I'll be so busy I may not notice you're not here," she replied with a chuckle. She kissed him on the cheek and turned to go inside the rough sided house.

"Tom, Tom! Come take John Murray and put him down for a nap. Chase, put on your coat and fill the wood box and Kenneth bring me some potatoes from the root cellar so I can start some soup for dinner."

Later that day, sitting near the window to catch the last of the winter's light Isabella held up the dress she was making for John Murray, he was growing so quickly his legs and arms were bursting from the seams of his clothes. Night slowly closed in on the house, the warm orange-yellow glow from the kerosene lantern lit the corner of the room where she sat as she called her boys to come in to her for prayer. The burning lantern's quiet hiss lit the quiet scene. Isabella holding John Murray in her arms her and the older boys kneeling around her knees their boyish voices solemn in prayer as they asked for God's blessings on their father and mother, and they thanked him for all his many blessings. They each asked God to 'help make them a good boy'.[xxvi]

John A Forti and H. C. Nicol went over to the beautiful Fruitland valley last Saturday and remained until Sunday

20 Vernal Express December 20, 1912 John Fortie & H. C. Nicol

February 1913 ***Loss of a Sister***

"Uncle Al!" The boys spilled out into the yard of the house as the horse and rider stopped out front. Alva Moroni touched their heads not noticing their puzzled looks when he didn't rough them up or tease them as he usually did. Isabella looked out the door and seeing the look on his face she called, "Alva! What's wrong?" He replied a seriousness coating his question. "Is Hyrum here Tressa? He wasn't at the store." Taking a breath her said, "I need to talk with you both." "He's eating lunch, come inside. Boys, you stay outside."

"May I get you something?" She asked Alva as she shut the door behind him. But the rest of her words bunched up inside her lips when Alva's eyes filled with tears. He shook his head swallowing quickly then he spoke his voice hoarse from hold back his emotions. "Hyrum, Ida called." A sob broke through and the words, "Phennie passed away this morning"[xxvii] sucked all the air from the room. Isabella turned first to Hyrum frozen in place at the table and then to Alva, not knowing which one to comfort first. She stepped beside Hyrum, placing her hands on his shoulders gently squeezing while tears rolled from her eyes. "Alva I am so sorry, so very sorry. We knew she was ill, but were not expecting this. Hyrum, oh Hyrum I'm so sorry."

Josephine Nicol

Josephine, nicknamed Phennie, was the oldest of Hyrum's siblings and 18 years his senior. She married Alva Moroni Murdock the year after Hyrum was born. Of his 11 brothers and sisters only 4 of them had survived the brutal world of pioneer life; Josephine Maria, Sarah Matilda, Hyrum, and their youngest brother Gabriel Blake. All of these thoughts flowed through Hyrum's heart as he took a deep breath, slowly stood, and embraced his brother in law.

His heart filled with thankfulness and love for his sister, swiftly seeing her steady and loving hand in his life. His heart broke with sympathy and love for his brother-in-law who was such a stalwart figure in their lives. In those few moments he felt his heart calm and he was comforted by the peace of the Holy Spirit which fueled the thanksgiving he felt.

Giving voice to the overwhelming love coursing through him, he said, "I am so grateful for the sealing powers of the Holy Priesthood and of temple marriage covenants that can bind our families together for eternity."

Oh how grateful he was for his testimony of the hereafter. The knowledge testified by the spirit of truth that the Prophet Joseph Smith's teachings of death and the hereafter were true and real. It comforted him to know that those who pass on are only on the other side of a very thin veil and 'that same sociality that exists here exists there'.[xxviii]

The comforting peace of the Holy Ghost descended upon their hearts as they knelt in prayer and thanksgiving for Josephine. Asking God with full confidence that He would send His peace and comfort to them and their families, as they felt the separation in mortal life from sister and wife, become a reality.

***

February 1913 *Loss of a Job*

Not long after returning to Duchesne from their mid-winter's journey to Heber City for Josephine's funeral, Rock Pope, the owner of the Pioneer Supply store where Hyrum worked came in from Salt Lake City. Taking Hyrum and John Fortie aside he told them that he and his son Marcellus would be taking over management of the store. He thanked them for their fine and diligent work for him and told them he felt he needed to be in Duchesne and that Marcellus needed to learn the merchandising business.

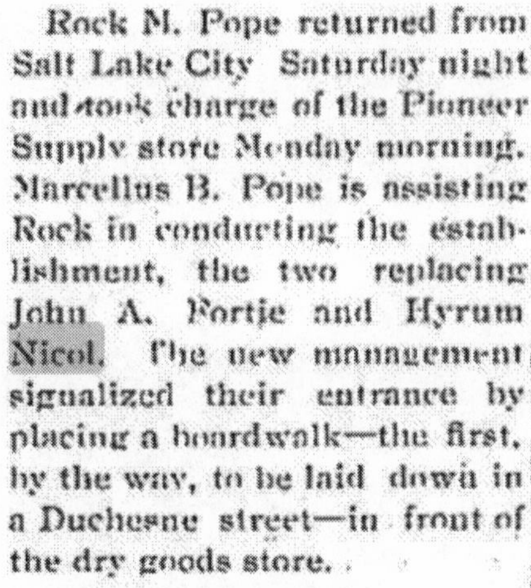
Rock M. Pope returned from Salt Lake City Saturday night and took charge of the Pioneer Supply store Monday morning. Marcellus B. Pope is assisting Rock in conducting the establishment, the two replacing John A. Fortie and Hyrum Nicol. The new management signalized their entrance by placing a boardwalk—the first, by the way, to be laid down in a Duchesne street—in front of the dry goods store.

21 Duchesne Record February 1913 – Fortie & Nicol replaced

Later that afternoon Hyrum comforted his wife; "we knew it could happen anytime Isabella." He reached across the table and took her hand, "Brother Pope and his son have taken over the management of the store from John. And as Marcellus is working with him there isn't room for two helpers. We will have to see it as an opportunity for us," stopping in thought before continuing, "though I don't know what that might be right now."

Swallowing the lump that filled her throat and wiping her hands on the faded kitchen towel she was holding, Isabella marshalled her faith and said with quiet conviction, "Hyrum, the Lord has never let us down. He has always opened doors when we have been in need; he will do so again."

Duchesne's
Complete Store
It is our plan to conduct a GENERAL MERCHANDISE STORE in every sense of the word and we are pleased to inform the public that each line is complete and new goods are arriving weekly.
We handle
Dry Goods, Groceries and Hardware
Pioneer Store
R. M. POPE, Manager
Duchesne - - - Utah

"You're right Tressa. He has never let us down." Later, after an almost wordless lunch, Hyrum said, “I will start asking about for possible positions, and in the meantime I will ride out to the ranch. With the weather so dry and not much snow I’ll be able to get some of the work done that I’ve been putting off being so busy at the store. I’ll take Tom and Chase with me and we’ll probably stay out for a few days or a week.”

“They have school Hyrum, you will have to go alone. We will come out for the weekend.” She told him. Shaking his head he said, “You’re right Tress, I just depend on their help and company. Turning toward the door he ask, “would you put together some food and goods for me to take? Though there isn’t much snow the flow ditches must be choked with ice and I’ll check the fence along the river’s edge.”

“Before I leave I will talk with a few folks in the morning and let them know I’m looking for a new position.” Isabella reminded him, “The boys and I will follow later in the week Hyrum.” Her chair squealed across the plank floor as she pushed away from the table. She said, “I’ll make a second batch of bread, so that you’ll have enough until we arrive.” Knowing her kitchen and the recipe she had memorized since she was a young girl there were no wasted motions as she pulled out flour, salt, sugar, and stirred the sour dough starter she kept warm and growing by the side of the stove.

***

April 1913 *Back at the Store*

Isabella looked up from the fire she was tending to see Hyrum's horse canter into their yard. She stood up slowly from where she was on her knees adding logs to the fire. Rubbing her back and stretching she looked up inquiringly when Hyrum hurriedly swung out of his saddle. "Tress!" He called. "We have an answer to our prayers! Brother Pope asked me to come back and help at the store," his excitement shown from his face as he almost leapt from the saddle.

"Hyrum! How wonderful! I was almost ready to worry, our supplies are that low. But the Lord opens windows, he always does!" Isabella said, the confirmation of her faith made her eyes sparkle with dampness. The moment didn't last long as she turned in time to catch up John Murray as he tottered toward the fire she was tending to heat water for the next tub of wash.

Looking around the house and over at the corral Hyrum mentally listed the chores he must complete before the start of the week when he would again be behind the counter at Pope's. The dry winter was a worry. The grass that should be at least ankle high and greening up was still winter dry. The ground hard packed and the cattle showing the wear of the long dry winter added to his concern.

"Kenneth!" He called, "come get John Murray before he falls into the fire." Kenneth ran around the corner of the house, dust clouds trailing his feet. "Take him inside and play with him." "Yes sir," said Kenneth to his father and left holding tightly to his wriggling brother.

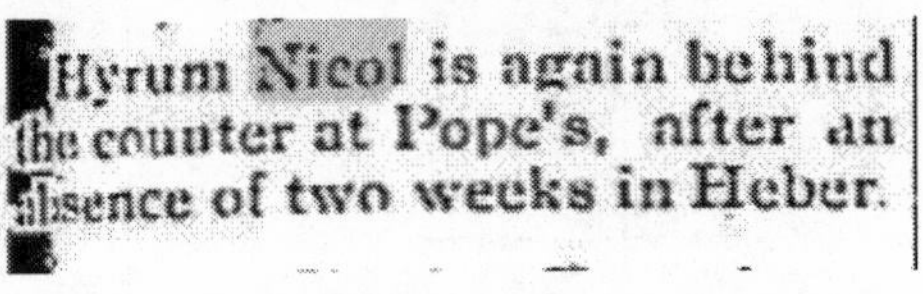
Hyrum Nicol is again behind the counter at Pope's, after an absence of two weeks in Heber.

22 Duchesne Record June 3, 1913 – Hyrum Nicol returns to Pioneer Supply

Looking around the winter barren yard he asked, "where are Tom and Chase, shouldn't they be helping with the wash?" Isabella, swirling clothes through the simmering water said, "They are turning the garden over and clearing out the winter weeds. With this mild weather I want an earlier start on preparing the garden."

"Dry winter, dry spring. I hope we get some rain soon I don't relish hauling water for the kitchen garden when I do plant. The weather is so mild Hyrum, I feel I could start planting the garden already." "It's still at least six weeks to our normal planting time Isabella." "I know, I know, but I can hope," she said catching a glimpse of Hyrum's eyebrow as it quirked higher and she laughed. They both had come to know the vagaries of spring on the reservation.

While Hyrum was thinking corral and ranch, Isabella held the dripping clothing, moving them into the second tub of clean water rinsing them one piece at a time on the large wooden washboard before wringing them out to hang dry from the line pulled tightly between the house and shed.

Thinking out loud she said, "I will need to make soap soon, we are near the end of our winter's supply." Breaking his reverie and turning toward her Hyrum asked, "Soap? Did you say you need to make soap?"

"Yes Hyrum, I did, I didn't realize I said that out loud," she laughed again.

Jumping onto her train of thought Hyrum said, "Well then the boys and I will start splitting the extra wood you will need, will next Saturday be soon enough?"

"We don't need to start quite that soon," she chuckled, "but within the month. I don't want to be standing out here in the mid-summer heat tending an ash fire. Heating water for the laundry in the summer over the fire is almost too much," she said.

Then he asked, "Do you have tallow saved to make the work worthwhile?"

She looked over her shoulder, as she prodded more clothing down into the simmering sudsy water with the long handled wooden paddle. "I should have plenty to make enough to get us through to fall."

***

Spring 1913 *Calving Season*

"Rock, my cows are nearing calving and I need to be out to the homestead for a week or two. I know it is an inconvenience, I'm sorry." "Nothing to be sorry about H.C. we live and die by our cattle herds out here don't we? I'm certain we'll be alright here. Have you got enough help out there Hy?" "It shouldn't be too bad I'll manage." Hyrum replied, hoping he was right.

"Tress, the boys will just have to miss school, that is all there is to it. I can't work the cows and calves alone," and as he stopped to take a breath Isabella broke in, "I know Hyrum, I'm saying we'll all go." "I'll get everything packed up tonight and we can leave for the homestead in the morning. Did you really think I'd let you go out there without me or the boys?" Reaching out he wrapped his arms around her, drew her close, and whispered in her ear, "You are a gift Tressa. I love you."

"Tom? Get the horses hitched to the wagon." Hearing his father call into the house where he and Chase were helping their mother box up food and other goods they would need for the weeks they were going to spend out at the ranch Tom raised his head and said, "Yes Father," then looked quickly toward his mother for permission to leave. She nodded her head and Tom swiftly turned and headed to the corral. Reaching up to lift the bridles from their place on the hook in the small open-faced tack shed built at the edge of the corral as he passed.

Whistling, Tom called to the horses, and climbed onto the bottom fence log giving him enough height to reach the horses heads. The two horses nickered and sidled over toward him nuzzling his fingers for a chance of a treat. Their velvety noses pushed under his palms and Tom's quick fingers caught hold of a halter pulling one of the horse's head near. Talking softly and patting its nose he deftly slipped the bridle over its ears, settling the brow band down as he slid the bit into her mouth and just as quickly he released the halter from around her nose.

He snubbed the ends of the reins around a fence post and reached for the other horse. She tossed her head from side to side as he grasped her halter and started the process again. Unlatching the corral gate, he slipped the reins from the fence post and led both horses toward the wagon at the side of the house.

One at a time he backed the horses into the traces at the front of the wagon, quickly reaching for the breast strap connected to the trace on one side he wrapped it around the chest of the horse, tying it securely to the other trace.

Making another trip to the tack shed Tom picked up gig saddles and crupper straps. The 4 inch padded gig saddle held all the other harness straps and connects in place. Tom tossed the gig saddle over her back just behind the withers. The horse though taller than Tom by at least 12 inches did not faze him in the least. He had been helping his father with the horses since he was old enough to walk outside on his own.

He reached under the horse's belly grasping the belly band and cinch strap to tighten the gig saddle in place. Just as quickly he flipped the crupper straps over her back, pulled the breeching strap over the mare's flanks, then he flipped the tail over the band and tied the straps together.

In less than 30 minutes from the time Tom whistled the horses toward him at the corral he pulled the wagon in front of the house just in time to help Chase lift their supply boxes into the wagon bed.

***

Isabella shook her head when she pushed open the door to the little ranch cabin. Disturbed dust motes floated in the dim light cast through the door and dirty window. The boys looked at one another and knew the first things they had to do before carrying in the boxes was to start cleaning the dirt and dust from the sparse furnishings left in the cabin when they moved into Duchesne. Each boy knew what was expected of him. Kenneth turned outside and started carrying in split firewood, Chase picked up the broom and began sweeping the cobwebs and dust from the walls and floor, and Tom followed his mother, carrying John Murray, back out the door where he unloaded the boxes and tools from the wagon bed carefully stacking them near the front door.

So when Isabella peered into the water barrel and shook her head at the dust floating on the water's surface, along with a dead mouse and assorted drowned bugs Tom knew what to do. He tipped the barrel on its side and watched the contaminated water swhoosh out into the dry dirt yard.

His father walked over and said, "It's been a while since we've been out here to stay hasn't it?" Then he hefted the empty barrel to his shoulder and rolled it into the wagon. Tom, climb up there and push the barrel to the front and tie it in. Looking at his wife he said, "we will be right back Tress."

"Is the barrel tied tightly?" His father asked as Tom climbed over the back of the wagon seat and sat down. "Yes Father," he replied as the tired horses turned toward the river knowing there was a well-deserved drink of their own waiting a short mile away.

***

"Let's start separating those cows from the steers boys, head them into the crowding pen and we'll filter them out of the range gate. Tress be quick on closing the pen gate I don't want those cows trying to bolt with the rest of the herd and try to keep them quiet," he cautioned. With quiet whistles and an occasional snap from the end of a lariat rope Hyrum, Tom and Chase moved their horses through the herd helping the steers make their way out the gate and onto the open range.

"I wish we had a barn for these cows to deliver in, the corral is a messy place to drop a calf," Hyrum mused. "We might clear part of the tack shed, lay down some straw; it's small, but it might work," he continued to talk out loud. "You say that every year Hyrum. The cattle will do well enough as they have always done. It's their nature; they know how to do this," Isabella offered her brand of straight talk which always brought Hyrum or the boys back to the point.

Hyrum said, "I want to evaluate the cows and get a feel for their time to calve." Later, after a supper of bread and ham the boys stood next to their father, oldest to youngest, with Isabella the other parental bookend. She had John Murray tied to her apron strings to keep him from wandering into the cattle pen.

"Here boys, stand up on this rail and tell me what you see happening." Tom climbed to sit on the top rail of the corral while Chase stood on the bottom rail with Kenneth beside him peering between the log rails.

“What looks different about the cows?” their father prompted. ‘Some of them are a bit restless, and they keep moving around.” said Tom having been a part of this spring ritual since he was Kenneth’s age. Chase pointed to an old cow off by herself away from the main body of the herd and offered, “You said last year that a cow getting close will often go off by herself. Is that what that one is doing?” “You’ve got good eyes boys,” Hyrum said, “we may have more than one calf tonight. That one you pointed at Chase is getting very close. We will need to be ready in case she needs our help.”

As the sun began to set Hyrum continued to watch the old cow, this wasn’t her first calf, and knowing the signs she continued to stay away from the young heifers. “Watch boys!” Tressa said, walking up to stand beside Hyrum, the baby now on her hip. “Remember, when she lays down she’s getting ready, can you see?”

They watched the cow drop to her knees then roll onto her side. Her tail was held up and aside as she continually bent toward her udders. “Look!” Kenneth cried out, “I can see something, is it a hoof Father?” “Yes it is.” The cow softly moaned as the hoof appeared and disappeared every few minutes. They watched enthralled as the hoofs stayed in sight and then the tip of a nose pushed out between them. The cow continued to mewl and then the calf’s head popped out into the air, its tongue hanging to one side, an eye lid flickered and was still again.

With a groan from its mother the shoulders appeared, and the calf’s head lay on the ground; with a gush it emerged to lay stretched on the ground, very still and waiting. Lifting its head the little calf gave it a swinging shake.

Slowly the mother cow stood turning around to see the life she had given the world and bent her head down nudging the calf and began to lick its face and clean its body constantly pushing it to move and stand. Trying to hold in his excitement Kenneth held his hands over his mouth so he wouldn’t scream and startle the new mother.

“I never get tired of watching new life come into this world,” Hyrum said as he continued to watch the rest of the pregnant cows. Pointing across the pen he indicated two young heifers, their first births imminent their agitation with the beginning indications of pain showed as they tried to kick and bump their stomachs.

"I bet you that one goes next," Tom turned to Chase. "What do you have to bet?" Chase asked. "You know I don't have anything, but I still bet that one will go first." Their mother heard this exchange and said, "We don't bet in this family, do we?"

"No Mother, we don't." Then find another way to say what you just said Tom. He looked up into her stern face, gambling was a serious offence and he didn't want a switching. Then he said, "I think that one will go first Chase. That reddish brown one with the white patches on her legs is the one I am going to watch." "That's better," Isabella praised him. "Gentlemen do not bet. Practice makes perfect boys," she said turning back toward the cabin.

"It looks like nothing will be happening for a while," said Isabella, "I'm going to put John Murray to bed. Anyone else want to take a break? I have some cake after if anyone is interested." Six booted feet rushed passed her in their headlong sprint and constant competition to be first to do anything. The door slammed open, before they heard the mother's quiet voice, "wash up while I cut the cake." Six booted feet turned to the wash pan.

Hyrum wet his finger and pressed it down to collect the crumbs remaining on his plate, sticking his finger in his mouth he said, "Tress nothing beats your cake." Hyrum looked a bit guilty when Isabella looked pointedly at his finger. The relative quiet was broken by bellowing and mooing and a great commotion coming from the corral.

Hyrum jumped to his feet grabbing his hat as he opened the door. Running toward the corral he saw one of the young heifers sitting then standing right up and bumping into the fence and the other cows. He saw she was frightened and knew he would have to help her so that she or her calf wouldn't die in the birth process.

Carefully he swung his feet over the fence then uncoiled the lariat in his left hand. He quickly although gently tossed the loop over the neck of the cow. The loop dropping around her neck startled her enough to take her mind from what was happening to her. Hyrum gently tugged on the rope and led her away from the herd tying the lead to the fence where she could move enough but not enough to hurt herself.

Keeping his eye on the heifer tied to the fence, he also noticed several others start the birthing dance. "Tom! Isabella! I'm going to need your help out here," he called. Hearing Hyrum's voice Isabella looked around the room and said, "Kenneth make sure John Murray doesn't wake up." Tom and Chase pulled hats down to their ears and stuck leather gloves into the back pocket of their pants. Tom held the door open for his mother.

"Tom light those two lanterns and bring them over here, it'll be dark soon and it looks like we're going to be out here for a while." His father said.

It seemed after that first cow gave birth it set a timer off on the others around her; their night was long and they were kept busy keeping eyes out for danger. Gratefully they hadn't had any big issues and all the mothers were up and the calves feeding when they washed the grime and offal from their hands and faces, dusted their clothes, and once cleaned and in their nightclothes they sank into their beds asleep almost before they closed their eyes.

***

June 1913 *Election Judge*

"Tress," Hyrum said as he put on his hat and dusted his coat before sliding his arms into the worsted wool jacket. "I don't know how long the County election meeting will last tonight. We are determining election judges for next year."

"Are you still thinking of putting your name toward a position Hyrum," "I may, I've been thinking about it. Since we've been back in town I have liked being involved in community's affairs."

"Election judges have a large responsibility to ensure the vote is honest and private." After a moment's pause he said, "The more I think about it I will put my name in the hat for a position as an election judge."

Later that evening, with the boys in bed, Isabella pulled her chair nearer the lantern's light. She listened to the silence, and bowed her head and prayed with gratitude in supplication. Gratitude for her continued health, their home, for Hyrum again having a paying position. She prayed for her sons, her husband, and the lives they were blessed to have. At the close of her prayer her hands that had been still in quiet contemplation immediately became busy.

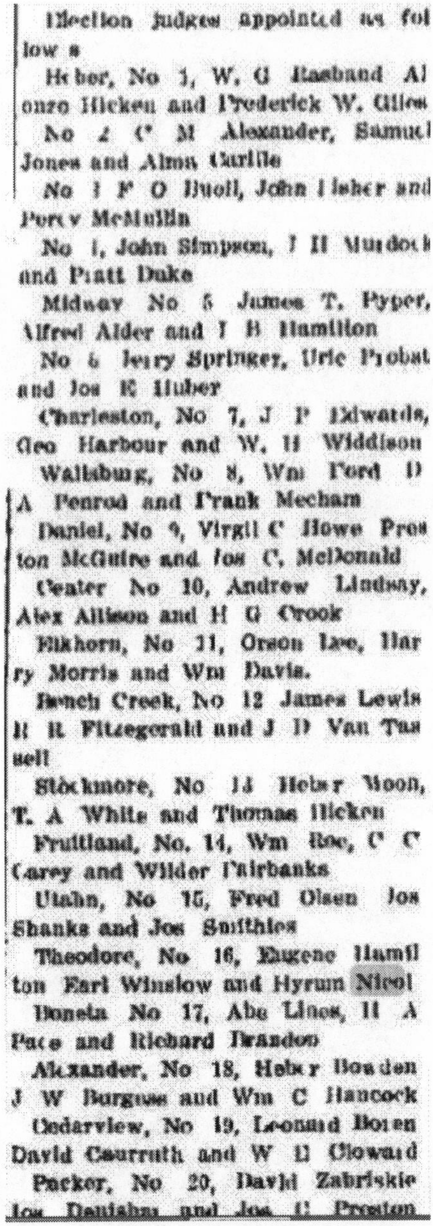

Election judges appointed as follows

Heber, No 1, W. G Rasband Alonzo Hicken and Frederick W. Giles

No 2, C M Alexander, Samuel Jones and Alma Carlile

No 3 F O Buell, John Fisher and Percy McMullin

No 4, John Simpson, J H Murdock and Pratt Duke

Midway No 5 James T. Pyper, Alfred Alder and J H Hamilton

No 6 Henry Springer, Uric Probst and Jos E Huber

Charleston, No 7, J P Edwards, Geo Harbour and W. H Widdison

Wallsburg, No 8, Wm Ford D A Penrod and Frank Mecham

Daniel, No 9, Virgil C Howe Preston McGuire and Jos C. McDonald

Center No 10, Andrew Lindsay, Alex Allison and H G Crook

Elkhorn, No 11, Orson Lee, Harry Morris and Wm Davis.

Bench Creek, No 12 James Lewis R R. Fitzgerald and J D Van Tassell

Stockmore, No 13 Heber Moon, T. A White and Thomas Hicken

Fruitland, No. 14, Wm Roe, C C Carey and Wilder Fairbanks

Utahn, No 15, Fred Olsen Jos Shanks and Jos Smithies

Theodore, No 16, Eugene Hamilton Earl Winslow and Hyrum Nicol

Duneda No 17, Abe Lines, H A Pace and Richard Brandon

Alexander, No 18, Heber Bowden J W Burgess and Wm C Hancock

Cedarview, No 19, Leonard Bowen David Caurruth and W B Cloward

Packer, No 20, David Zabriskie Jos Danielson and Jos C Preston

23 Vernal Express June 13, 1913 Hyrum Election Judge

She picked up a small stocking and slipped the smaller wooden darning knob into its heel. She threaded a large needle with lightweight yarn and set to closing up the hole worn through with busy feet in hand-me down boots.

It was during these quiet times doing her darning, mending, and sewing chores that though her hands were busy in their labor, her mind was freed for thinking, praying, and planning. As the children's Primary second counselor she had another layer of responsibility that pulled on her time and if she didn't plan well, she couldn't get everything completed.

She smiled as she thought about her boys, they certainly didn't shirk their chores, and ranching life was hard. There was always work to do and not much time for activities outside of their chores. The weekly Primary meeting was an opportunity for them to be with boys their own age and participate in activities that built friendships, encourage their testimonies of God to grow as they learned more about following Jesus and his restored gospel.

***

In the midst of her thoughts she heard the steady gait of Hyrum's horse enter the yard. Isabella put aside her pile of never-ending mending and stood to open the door as his boots sounded up the wooden front steps. Looking at the black sky she noticed the usually brilliant nightly star display was dimmed by clouds building around the valley's rim. "Looks like we might get some rain," she commented, "I can smell it in the air." "I certainly hope so," Hyrum said, "the range grasses are as dry as autumn already."

Walking inside Hyrum inquired, "how was your evening Tress?" "All is quiet here." She replied. "I've had time to mend the tear in your Sunday shirt cuff, the one you caught on the fence when the sow escaped last week." She touched Hyrum's arm as he walked passed her and placed his hat on the hook by the door.

"Well?" she questioned twisting around to look at his face, "did you procure one of the judge positions?" She asked as she shut the door behind him. "Yes I did," he said smiling. "Almost everyone who showed up at the meeting and wanted a position got one."

"Theodore is district number 16; each district has 3 judges to ensure that there cannot be a deadlock if an issue arises in the election process. Generally being an election judge means signing in registered voters, explaining the voting procedure, providing ballots, and monitoring the conduct of the election," Hyrum intoned. Isabella asked, "Who else was appointed?" "In our district it is Brother Eugene Hamilton, Earl Winslow and myself," replied Hyrum. "No women were selected?" She asked. "No women were present Tress."

Isabella, always interested the community reminded Hyrum that she had voted in every election since she reached her age of majority. In 1870 the women in the Utah Territory were enfranchised, second by a less than a month behind Wyoming whose Territorial legislators passed women's right to vote in December 1869. There had been much debate at the national and territorial levels about women voting. Isabella remembered her mother telling her about the mass Relief Society meeting the women organized protesting the Collum Bill which was intended to increase pressure upon the Church's practice of polygamy.[xxix]

During that protest the then General Relief Society President Bathsheba Smith championed the cause of suffrage and put forth a motion that 'we demand of the Governor the right of Franchise'. A vote was called on Smith's motion and it carried.[xxx]

Following effective public demonstrations organized and staged by Utah women in protest of the national legislation, the territorial legislature began discussion of female suffrage. Latter-day Saint leaders responded favorably to the idea, as did the national press and the Territorial legislature voted for enfranchisement. Having had the vote for 17 years, in 1887 the United States congress in its continuing anti-polygamy campaign and attempting to curtail the Church of Jesus Christ of Latter-day Saint's influence in the territorial government, revoked the Utah women's right to vote through the Edmunds Act.

The women's right to vote was restored after Utah became a state; the new state constitution gave women the right to vote and to run for office.

***

July 1913 *Moving on Up*

"Hyrum, we've worked together for many years and you're the man I want working with me. I'd like you to come to work at the Express Office," John Fortie encouraged. He had taken the manager's position at the express office after he and Hyrum left the operation of Pope's Pioneer Store the previous spring. "I'll have to think about it John and talk it over with Tressa." "This is an opportunity you can't turn down Hyrum," John reiterated his argument. "I'll think about it John and let you know."

"I have a mind to accept John's offer Tressa," Hyrum mused as they pulled chairs from the kitchen and set them outside in the shade of the house hoping as they did so that they might catch a glow of the setting sun off of the Uinta Mountains to the northeast of town. The mid-summer heat washed over the dirt in the yard and the evening winds began to blow as they settled into their chairs.

"What will it entail Hyrum," Isabella asked, the silk fan in her hand slowly and rhythmically sending a gentle breeze across her turned face, her hair pulled high at the nape of her neck. "Preparing mail and packages, loading wagons and tracking shipments I suppose, John didn't elaborate on the duties."

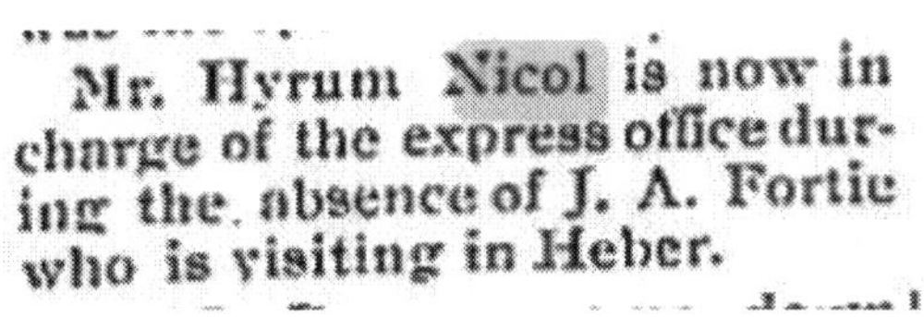
Mr. Hyrum Nicol is now in charge of the express office during the absence of J. A. Fortie who is visiting in Heber.

24 Duchesne Record August 1913 – Hyrum Nicol Express Office

"The pay is better than at Pope's, but from observing John since he took over, there will be some traveling too I suppose. He is gone with the wagons, meeting with the railroad, and he also meets with the Post Master General of Utah several times a month."

Her fan rhythmically sending light bursts of relatively cooler air over her face Isabella looked up at the far mountains as the copper and red sunlight filtered through the growing clouds that had settled down over the peaks which lifted abruptly high above the sagebrush flats. She gazed at the foothills covered in the twisted, hardy pinion pine and juniper trees which provided most of the fuel for their daily needs.

As the light dropped to darkness their conversation turned to the needs of their family, their dreams of a permanent home and a prosperous life. They talked at length of the job offer at the Duchesne Transportation Company and what if any impacts it would have on their boys and Isabella, as well as on Hyrum's ability to operate the homestead. They always questioned changes to see if it would fit within the plans they had for their future.

"I think I should take the position Tressa. The boys are growing so quickly and the homestead is not producing like we had hoped it would." Sitting quietly in the dark Hyrum took Isabella's hand and they began to pray for confirmation of their decision to take the new opportunity that had been presented to them.

Slowly standing Hyrum reached for Isabella's hand to help her from her chair. His face turned upward as he felt moisture drop onto his face. "It's starting to rain Tress!" "Thank goodness Hyrum," she said as little bursts of dust popped up from the ground with each drop of water that fell onto its parched surface.

***

August 1913 ***New Prospects & Weather Worries***

"I am glad you took the job with the Duchesne Transportation Company Hyrum. You seem so excited and engaged in the work, more so than clerking at Pope's." "I am energized Tressa, I can see opportunities for advancement and to have a hand in the growth of the Basin," he replied.

"Tomorrow I will be going to Myton on business for the company. I plan on spending the night at the ranch and will check on the cattle. I'm worried about feed. "You're always worried about feed," Isabella commented. "I know, but that is where our livelihood lies, doesn't it? Then he continued "There is grass, but it isn't nearly as high nor as thick as it should be by this time of year. We need more rain or there will not be enough feed for the cattle to graze through the winter."

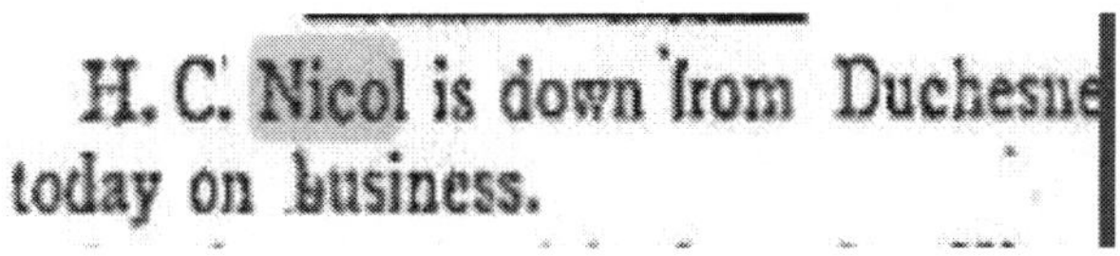
H. C. Nicol is down from Duchesne today on business.

Duchesne Record August 22 1913 H.C. Nicol at Myton on business

***

August 2013 *Building Fence*

"You're back sooner than I expected Hyrum." "Things are alright out at the homestead, there wasn't much that needed my hand that I couldn't do in a half day. The biggest problem is that there are some sections of broken fencing; the cattle must have pushed against the rails to get to the grass on the other side. That has to be fixed quickly."

"I've told John Fortie that I cannot be at work for a few days. The boys and I'll leave Thursday morning. I will need their help to cut new fence posts and poles," Hyrum countered his wife's concerns before she could voice them. Isabella nodded and turned lifting her skirt out of the dust as she walked toward the house.

"Up and at it boys," Hyrum's deep voice echoed up to the loft where his three older boys were sleeping. Morning stars were still visible in the lightening sky when Hyrum heard, "yes Father" along with soft thumps as bare feet kicked blankets free and hit the floor and he heard a whispered, "you stay here Kenneth."

"I have the wagon hitched and your mother has packed what we'll need for the next few days. Bring your bed blankets down with you he reminded them." Urging them on to more speed he called, "we need to get on the road toward the Five Mile Ridge or it will be dark before we get to camp." The last stars were fading from the morning's twilight when Tom, age 9 and Chase almost 8, each holding a large slice of fresh baked bread covered with their mother's jam climbed into the back of the wagon and wrapped a blanket around themselves to keep the dawn's dew and chill off of their necks.

"Hi-ya." they heard their father say as he slapped the reins on the horses' backs and the wagon jerked to a start and began its rattling way up the morning- cold road toward the timber covered mountains 35 miles in the distance.

"Stand back boys!" Hyrum yelled as the 30-foot tall, straight lodgepole pine tree tipped toward the ground cracking at points chopped into its trunk and broke free crashing hard into the dry duff below. Quickly running away Tom and Chase watched it topple toward the ground. Once it was firmly down Hyrum directed the boys and pointing he said, "Chase, Tom, take your axes and start cutting the branches off and pile them to the side and I will start cutting the fence posts."

Hyrum had figured the number of posts and poles he would need to sturdy up the cattle corral and reckoned it would take them at least two days to cut and load all the wood into the wagon. Tom, lost in the swing, chuck, and thump of his axe startled to attention when a branch flipped through the air next to his face. "Watch it Chase," he hollered as he turned toward his younger brother whose swing had caused the dry branch to fly into the air. "Sorry Tom," he replied, "I can't swing and stand on the branch too, I didn't think it would fly up like it did. Are you okay?"

"Yep," Tom replied. He offered, "if the branch is too bushy for you to work alone let me know and I'll come cut and you can stand on it." "Thanks Tom, glad you weren't hurt," Chase replied, then in his next breath he said, "I guess you'll have to come cut while I stand on 'em, these branches are thick."

The boys sat quietly resting against the log pile while their father heated the supper their mother had packed over the fire he had built from the chips and branches of their day's labor. Chase asked Tom if his arms were sore.

"Yep," he replied, "I can hardly move my shoulders."

"Are your arms tired Father?" Chase asked.

"Yes Chase, they are," he said as he rolled his shoulders and stretched out his muscled arms. "Aren't we glad we have arms and bodies that are strong enough to work?" Their father asked as he handed them a filled bowl of venison stew. "You boys did good work today. We will finish up tomorrow and should be back at the homestead tomorrow night."

Laying on their blankets the black sky blossomed with tens of millions of stars. The night breezes rattled the tops of the pines, some towering a hundred feet above their beds. There was a stillness in the heavenly expanse that filled the boys with wonder as they watched falling stars chase one another across the sky. The vastness overwhelmed their senses before exhaustion took them off to sleep.

The rutted and rocky road could be dangerous and Chase watched as their father always kept his foot near the wagon brake while letting the horses make their own way down off of the mountain. Tom, holding tight to the edge of wagon bench swayed with the animal's footsteps down the road. Chase used his father's arm and his brother as twin pillars to help him keep his balance.

"We'll be at the property in a while." Then Hyrum offered, "I have an idea." "What Father?" the tired boys asked in unison.

"I think that Chase, you'll drive the wagon and Tom and I will toss out the posts and poles along the fence line where the corral needs repair. Then we will head straight back to Duchesne. Next week we can dig up the broken posts and place these new ones. I plan on having this fence fixed before we go over to Heber. When we get home in September, before your classes start, we will round up the cattle for winter."

***

Shading her eyes from the sun's midday glare Isabella walked toward the tack shed, John Murray trailing along behind, to find Hyrum under the shade of the shed roof his long legs spread out on either side of the sharpening stone's seat. Head bent and focused on the heavy stone that spun toward him, he held the edge of the axe up and against the spinning stone sharpening its timber dulled edges.

"Tress will you pour some more water over the stone, it's drying out." Picking up the half-full bucket Isabella slowly poured water over the stone as Hyrum continued to work the foot peddle he had attached to the stone to spin it in a steady rhythm. "Where are the boys Hyrum? I thought they would be out here with you." "You'll probably find them around the side of the house gathering sticks to make new flippers. They worked hard the past few days, I figured an hour off of chores would be okay."

Isabella smiled at him, "you are a soft hearted man Hyrum."

"Why did you need them?" He asked. "I thought they might like a slice of bread and jam; I just took the bread out of the oven." "Did you bring me any Tress?" He asked. "No. I thought I could tempt you to come inside and talk with me a while. I've missed you Hyrum."

Behind the cabin the boys were huddled together making plans. "Kenneth your job is to find the perfect sized rocks while Chase and me make new flippers." "I want to make flippers too," Kenneth said to his oldest brother. "I have my own knife!" He proudly held out the small two-bladed bone-handled knife for his brothers to see. "Father gave it to me."

"We know Kenneth, but it isn't very sharp and you could cut yourself with it. After you get the rocks gathered I'll sharpen your knife for you," Tom told him.

"Okay Tom," Kenneth said, kicking the dirt before he turned and climbed the fence. "Remember," Chase yelled at him, "we need a lot of rocks to last all the way to Heber."

"Hyrum will you bring in the big wash tub?" Isabella asked as she finished washing up the dishes. "Tom and Chase start filling the pots and pans with water to heat while I put the dishes away. I want us all to have a good scrub before we leave for Heber tomorrow. I won't have anyone saying we have dirty children."

"They think we live rough as it is, I don't want anyone thinking I'm raising heathens." "As you asked Tress, "Hyrum said as he set the big tin wash tub down by the stove. "I'll help you heat the water, oh I see the boys have already started it."

"Boys let's get our chores done quickly so we may do as your mother asks and scrub up." "Yes Father," they toned together and three pairs of feet followed his large booted ones out the door.

"You take the first bath Hyrum while the water is hottest and then the older boys then Kenneth and John Murray. Once the boys are in bed I will take the last one."

"Doesn't it feel good to go to bed clean?" she whispered to Hyrum as she pulled the covers over her shoulders and snuggled against his back. "I have stacked all the boxes full of empty jars by the front door, and the camping boxes are filled with food, water, and what clothes we will need. I am so excited to see my sisters and brothers," she whispered and quickly fell asleep.

August 1913 *Off to the City*

People will think we are moving there are so many boxes in the wagon." Isabella laughed at Hyrum's complaints as he finally finished loading the wagon. She placed their folded quilts on top of the boxes to make seats for the boys to ride on. "What is all this?" She asked her boys as they leaped into the wagon box with their arms full of slingshots and flippers. "That's not all of it Mother," they said and jumped back to the ground shouting loudly to get Kenneth to hurry. They called, "we're leaving! Hurry Kenny!"

"I'm coming," their five-year-old brother yelled as he rounded the corner with his pockets bulging and struggling hold onto an oversized box filled with rocks. "We can't take all of those rocks with us," Isabella scolded. "They won't stay in the wagon very long Tressa. That's ammunition for the road, don't you know?" "Dump the rocks in the middle of the wagon bed and climb in boys. We're off!'

The early summer sun was just popping over the eastern ridge behind them and highlighting the tops of the sagebrush and glinting off of the windows of the house as their wagon creaked and jerked when their team of horses leaned into their traces and pulled to a start. Mourning doves and meadow larks chirped and chitted flitting through the sagebrush and mountain mahogany. The spicy sweetness of the sage filled the air and Isabella breathed deeply and closed her eyes. She was attempting to remember the name of the yellow- breasted bird that landed on the fence post as the wagon rattled and bumped by as they started up the dirt road. Hyrum turned the wagon west heading toward Heber City and two weeks of family fun.[xxxi] Even if they would have to work picking fruit and vegetables it was still wonderful[xxxii].

"Father?" Chase stepped over Kenneth's legs to stand behind the wagon's bench seat. 'What Chase?" his father asked. "When we stop for the night can, excuse me, may we go swimming? It's hot."

"That would be a fine idea don't you think Tress?" The idea of slipping her feet into a cool stream bed made Isabella smile. "I think so too Hyrum."

Even under the parasol she held over her head which offered some shade and relief from the heat beating down it was defeated by the heat that radiated up from the road.

"We'll stop at the Fruitland Store to water the horses and give them a rest before we start up the grade to the Strawberry Valley." After helping Isabella down over the wagon wheel Hyrum lifted John Murray over the side and gently dropped him to the ground. "Tom, take care of John Murray while your mother rests please."

"Yes, Father," Tom said as he jumped over the wagon's side his boots only clearing his little brother's shoulder by inches when John Murray twisted from his father's grasp and set his toes to take off running. "Here you go John, let's walk by the store and get a drink of water."

"Chase, help me with the horses please."

"Kenneth! Put the rocks down and come help me get our lunch ready."

"Yes ma'am", Kenneth said, dusting his hands off on his trouser legs. Isabella shook her head, "why did we spend all the time bathing last night when we're now all covered in dust?"

"Dust and dirt!" She grumbled to herself. Dust from the course road floated through the air in the wind. Dirt was kicked up by the horses and she didn't want to even mention being soaked through the heat.

She thought, "Well, it was certainly nice to go to bed clean last night at least," as she pulled the table cloth from the basket and set to slicing bread and ham, and setting out jam for a treat. She hoped she wasn't being prideful when she said to herself, "this bread turned out very well." [xxxiii] The smooth evenly browned crust gave way easily to the sharp knife.

It was a steep and steady grade up the mountain road from Duchesne into the Strawberry Valley. The family stopped frequently to rest the horses and take short walks to quell the rattle of the wagon from their bones. When they topped the mountain pass that led down into the Strawberry Valley their view broke wide and clear with the river valley below. Everyone was glad, knowing their camp was not too far in the distance. With a flip of the reins and his familiar "hi-ya," and the horses turned into the flat area not far from the road. Hyrum said, "It's always a quandary, to stop nearer the road, or closer to the river where it's cooler, but there are more mosquitos."

Isabella responded with her own opinion. "Closer to the road please Hyrum. It may be dustier but I won't worry so about John Murray being tempted to go swimming without his brothers around."

"May we go swimming now Father," Tom asked? "Let's get the camp set up, our beds put down, and help your Mother get settled first." "Chase, you and Kenneth take the horses downstream for a drink then hobble them near that grassy stretch by the river, over there," he said pointing to a spot beyond their camping place.

"Put your clothes on the bushes before you jump in the river boys," Isabella called to her anxious as thirsty wild horses to get to the swimming hole.

"No John Murray, you'll be staying here with me. We will go down in a little while and wade in the water while the boys swim." John Murray's face broke into a flood of tears as he watched his older brothers run for the river.

"Hyrum," Isabella called, "will you start the fire and build up some coals before we take John Murray down the hill? He is out of hand."

"John Murray! Come here and help me carry this wood for a fire." Hyrum got his youngest son's attention.

Isabella took a moment to watch her husband and youngest son carrying wood for their fire. The small arms carrying branches his father had broken into pieces easy for the little boy to carry. John Murray's eyes were large and all his focus was on not falling over as he, imitating his father, squatted down next to watch him build the fire.

"It's time you learned to build a fire John," Hyrum said. He picked up a handful of sticks and said, "First we lay the smaller sticks like this, so it looks like a little cabin. Alright, then fill it up with those broken twigs. That's right, just like that."

"Now we put the bigger logs around the little cabin like an Indian tepee. Lean the tops together, like this." Isabella marveled at the patience Hyrum had when he was teaching his sons. "No, John Murray, I will start the fire. When you're a older you can do it yourself. Now, if we laid the sticks just right, and they are dry enough, the fire will start quickly. Stand back and watch."

The fire did start quickly and burned merrily, with a neat pile of wood stacked near at hand. Finally John Murray, pulling at each of his parent's hands his patience at an end, almost ran toward the river. Yelling for his brothers as they reached the river, his parents held tightly to his hand when they stopped short of the bank seeing Tom, Chase, and Kenneth standing quite still watching trout flash around the large boulders that filled the stream bed.

"Boys, you know what to do," Hyrum called quietly. Walk slowly out of the current and move downstream a little. Once we're dressed we'll dig up a few worms and see if we can't catch a few of those beauties for dinner. What do you say?"

Looking west across the long Strawberry Valley toward Daniel's Canyon summit the last of the day's light could be seen filtering through the fir and aspen trees that ringed the valley. "Are you finished with your plates boys?" Isabella asked standing to gather up their dinner remains.

"I'll help you Mother," Tom said, also standing up while reaching for the plate he had set on the ground next to him. "Thank you Tom," she said as she took the dishes from his hand.

With the two of them standing by the wagon gate Isabella had an overwhelming feeling of love for this strong, obedient boy by her side. She reached out and wrapped her arms around him, quickly giving him a hug, letting go just as quickly because a nine-year-old frontier boy did not like to be coddled by his mother.

"Here Tom," she said, "take these cookies and we will have a treat as we sit around the fire."

"Boys, come here for prayer," Hyrum called. "Let's kneel here around the fire." "Don't get too close Kenneth." Hyrum quietly looked around at the bowed heads of his family and his heart swelled with gratitude. "Our Father which are in heaven. We thank thee for thy tender care and the abundance of thy blessings in our lives. We are thankful for the fish we were able to catch for our supper and we are glad that we are all here together and able to travel to see our families which we miss so very much. Will thou please bless them and allow thy Spirit to be with us. In Jesus' name. Amen."

Later when the stars blossomed overhead like a field of wildflowers spread horizon to horizon and the Milky Way glowed in the midst of the heavenly display the boys moved their sleeping blankets nearer the fire where the flames had settled into a bed of red-white hot coals. The boys settled into their beds while sitting on an up-ended log, Hyrum watched the coals glow and crackle gazing up toward the mountains. He said, "I remember my mother telling me a story about the stars she saw from the ship when she emigrated from Denmark. These stars reminded me."

She said she told the group of sisters she had been helping, "I cannot stay below a minute longer." Hyrum began to tell Hanne's story as if they were watching her as she stepped lightly around the few tables bolted to the floor and wove her way around the boxes and bags of her fellow Saints. She almost scrambled up the steep ladder to escape the confined space below the deck.

It was so cramped and smelly, there were so many people in the small space they were assigned below the decks, it was hard to sleep and she was desperate for clean air. Making her way around the carefully coiled ropes and chains on the deck she worked toward the aft of the ship. The night was black and still. She heard the ship creaked as it followed the contours of the waves up and down, up and down.

The water was blended black on black, except for a silver-gold slash across the line of the horizon which quickly disappeared as if she had only imagined it. She stopped and leaned against a large coil of rope. Only a few lanterns burned behind her, and she saw the wake of the ship spreading out to melt back into darkness.

After the cacophony below decks the sea and sky spread out like a blanket a balm that calmed her nerves. She thought, "The Sea is as night-black as the inside of a coal mine, but she wondered just where the glow of light was coming from." She lifted her eyes to the heavens and realized that it was the innumerable stars sending their reflections shining upon the water. The sea was a great mirror filled with stars.

"Have you been inside a coal mine," an inquisitive Kenneth asked, as his father's voice drifted away. "No son, I haven't. But I imagine a place where there is no light from the sun."

Changing the subject Hyrum said, "You know that Grandmother Hanne also pulled a handcart from Iowa City, Iowa to Salt Lake City." "We know Father," Chase replied, "Grandmother told us how sore her feet were, and her shoes wore out, and how very hungry and thirsty she was most of the time. She told us that it took her almost half a year to get to Salt Lake from Odense, Denmark."

"An ocean mirror full of stars," murmured Chase as he turned on his side and whispered, "I wonder if I will ever see an ocean at night?"

"Wake up, wake up it's time for breakfast," Isabella called as she shook out the blankets of her bed and watched three heads pop out from under their covers. "Roll up your beds and put them in the wagon and then come get something to eat. We will be at Aunt Catherine's house before dinner." [xxxiv]

"Have you used all the rocks you brought from home already? "Isabella asked her boys as they climbed into the wagon with their pockets filled with more stones. "Yes, we did mother. We hit everything we were aiming at," they boasted.

"Now did you really?" She queried.

"Well, almost," they replied, ducking their heads to avoid her gaze. "We do have to practice, because practice makes perfect doesn't it Mother?"

Laughing at hearing her own words given back to her she said, "at least you were listening." Turning toward Hyrum she said, "here, take John Murray and then help me up. Let's get going."

***

"We're here!" Isabella called as she and Hyrum walked into her sister's kitchen. "ZCMI, ZCMI," she sang, "Zion's children must increase,"

While her boys filed in behind their mother their cousins started filtering into the room. Coming from their bedrooms doors banging when they heard their Aunt Tress singing.

"I've missed you all so very much," she said, hugging her sister tightly. Touching her nieces and nephews on their heads or reaching to hug one who wrapped their arms around her. She looked over their heads at her sister and asked, "Where is Mother?"

"She is in her chair in the living room Tressa. She's been watching for you all afternoon. She may be taking a nap," her sister replied.

"No. I'm not taking a nap," a smart, though frail, voice called from the room next to the kitchen. "Come here my sweet daughter and let me see you and your family. Oh, it is so good to see your face Isabella," she said, as her daughter peeked around the doorframe into the living room.

Her eyes began tearing up when she lifted her frail arms to embrace her youngest daughter. "I've missed you so much." "I've missed you so very much too mother," whispered Isabella returning her mother's embrace with emotional gentleness.

"Has two weeks passed so quickly Hyrum?" Isabella pined as she topped off the suitcase with the last of her clothes. "We've hardly had time to see everyone with all the picking and preserving we've been doing. How I love my sisters," she exclaimed! "It is so much easier to bottle the fruits and vegetables together, rather than trying to do it myself from our little kitchen garden."

"Oh!" The thought popped into her mind. "I do hope the hired boys have watered the garden as they promised." "They will have done exactly what they said they would do Tress, don't worry."

Raising her hand she wiped her tear dampened cheek, "let's go quickly Hyrum, you know how I cry when I leave everyone here."

"I know sweetheart," he said, reaching over to pat her hand. "But we do have to get home. John is expecting me back at the office by the end of the week."

***

September 1913 *Fall Cattle Round-up*

Hyrum had gathered together a few of the Midview Flat ranchers to help complete the fencing repairs. The boys tried hard, but they were too small to do more than hold the posts upright after Hyrum dug out the old posts. "Thank you gentlemen for your help today," Hyrum exclaimed, shaking hands and smiling to his neighbors. "Let's get a cool drink and some food before you head home. Isabella baked fresh bread and sent a stew over with me."

"Your wife sure makes good bread Hyrum. I could eat the loaf myself," said one fellow as he smeared jam over the second slice he had taken. "I'll let her know you said so Bill," Hyrum smiled. "Thanks again fellows" he called as his neighbors swung booted feet over their saddles, resettled their hats, adjusted their reins, and trotted out to the road.

"Boys!" His three oldest boys appeared from around the corner, "have yourself some stew and bread and then clear things up. Now that the corral fence has been repaired we'll start pushing the cattle down into the pens tomorrow."

"Yes sir," Kenneth replied, while Tom and Chase carried the empty pan and dishes into the cabin to wash them.

The sun had just lightened the sky when father and sons finished their breakfast, quickly clearing up their dishes. Today they would be long in the saddle. "I can't believe how beautiful it is this morning," Hyrum said to his boys as they mounted their horses. Earlier that summer Hyrum had picked up a small mare for Kenneth and he was excited to be one of the older boys and old enough to round up the cattle.

"Let's ride north onto Grandmother Hanne's homestead and start pushing the cattle we find to the corral over here."

The September morning was clear and the night's chill burned off quickly as the boys raced their horses down the road toward the far side of their Grandmother's property. The wide brilliant blue sky was unclouded and the sun soon had them stopping to tie their coats to the back of their saddles. Their hats remained on their heads and gloves on their hands;

these two articles of clothing were as indispensable as a shirt and pair of pants.

"Tom why don't you and Chase take the upper edge of the property and Kenneth and I will ride along the arroyo's edge."

Kenneth called out, "let's ride faster Father!" And he kicked his little mare into a trot.

"Not too fast Kenny the horses will tire out before we finish the push." Reluctantly Kenneth slowed to ride next to his father.

The boys and Hyrum pushed individual cattle they found grazing and headed them slowly into a herd and with gentle swings of a rope shied them toward the corral.

"Good job boys," Hyrum said pushing the last pole into place, closing the corral up tight. "Let's take care of our horses, be sure to give them some grain and brush them down. Tom, take my horse while I get some supper on."

Later sitting down at the table, after blessing the food, Chase asked, "did we get all the cows in today?"

"No, we didn't," his father replied. "Tomorrow we will grid the ranch to catch the strays here, we will start riding off our place and talk with the neighboring ranchers to see if any of our cattle were rounded up with theirs."

"Then we will check the cattle in our pens and separate out any that don't belong to us. I am hoping to head back to Duchesne tomorrow night for church on Sunday.

Chase said pausing to swallow, "that sounds like a lot of work to get done in one day." "It seems like it, but we'll get it done. We always do, don't we?"

"It will be a full day tomorrow. Let's clear up the dishes and then to bed early, Kenneth is almost asleep in his supper," their father nodded toward Kenneth.

Tom and Chase turned toward Kenneth as his eyes fully closed and his head tipped into his empty dinner plate. Pushing away from the table Hyrum stood up and swept Kenneth into his arms in one motion. "Come on son, wake up, and get dressed for bed. Then we'll have prayers. It's been a good day boys. You did a good job," their father praised them.

***

Fall 1913 *Trouble on the Horizon*

That Sunday evening, with the supper dishes washed and stacked on the shelves along the kitchen wall Isabella sat at the table and opened her scriptures. She glanced over at her mending, sighing at the over-flowing basket and shook her head. "Every time I think it's empty it's filled to the brim. I don't know why I expect it to stay empty living on the frontier with four lively boys. I'll work on that tomorrow," she told herself. "Hyrum will you light another lantern and bring it over here please?" Placing the lantern on the hook above her head, Hyrum pulled the bench away from the table and stuck his legs under it as he sat down.

"The boys are in bed Tress," and then in a quieter voice he said, "we need to talk about the cattle."

"Alright Hyrum," she said, closing her scriptures. She slowly put them on planked table top apprehension in her carefulness.

Hyrum began. "The cattle aren't in too much stress from this long, dry summer. Though the ones I hoped to sell to the cattle dealer are only of average weight, not as heavy as we had wished they would be. There just isn't enough grass to support them. I thought the rains we got in June and July would help the grass, but I suppose it was too much too late. You know how many of our ditches collapsed with the heavy rains."

Watching him Isabella nodded, knowing he would get to his real concern once he had his thoughts lined out. Pausing he dreaded the next words he had to share with his hard working wife and partner. "I've figured that we'll have about 50 steers to sell in the next few weeks and they will only bring about five to five and a half cents a pound. As small as they are, most no more than 800 pounds, means it will be about two thousand dollars. Short of what we need to pay off the mortgage. Quite a bit less than we were planning on and remember part of the profit is mother's.

"Some is better than nothing Hyrum," Isabella said. She continued, "we can still purchase breeding from A.M. instead of buying our own bull." "No, that's not what I'm worrying about Tressa," Hyrum replied with an even more serious expression crossing his face.

“With the grasses depleted we will have to purchase hay or alfalfa again to get the rest of the herd through the winter. Instead of freezing to death like the herd did in ‘09’, they will starve to death, unless we can buy enough hay.”

“I read an article in the Vernal Express saying there will be about 20,000 tons of extra hay this year, or at least 20,000 tons more than last year. But with everyone needing hay that surplus will be gone in a heartbeat. I’m estimating I will have to spend at least a third if not a half of our proceeds for the hay.

“If that is what we need to do, then we will do it.” Isabella’s support never wavered. “Let’s try to buy hay now rather than later and then we will just rely on the Lord to see us through.” She encouraged, “why don’t you write your mother so she will be aware of the situation and get her concurrence? We could sell more of our cattle couldn’t we?” Isabella asked.

“I don’t think that would help much,” he replied. “The rest of the cattle are younger and smaller, it would be best to try to keep them alive and hope for better grazing next year.”

***

October 1913

The boys clattered around the kitchen table while Isabella dished hot mush out for breakfast. "I'm looking forward to the Halloween ball tonight. I've cleaned your Sunday clothes," she said, "and if you can arrive home a bit early we can have dinner with the boys before we leave." "I will try Tress," Hyrum replied sitting down and reaching for the butter to melt on to the top of his mush.

"I'm looking forward to the ball," she said again. "It's been a long while since we have been able to attend a dance," and her eyes stilled for a moment as her mind drifted to her youth in Heber City. Dances, buggy rides, picnics and socials had been a regular part of their lives. Her reverie was shattered when John Murray pushed himself off of his chair and went top over tea kettle onto the floor.

***

"I've got to go to Heber and thought Tom could ride with me."

"He has school Hyrum."

"I know Tressa, it's only for a few days and I could use his help and his company."

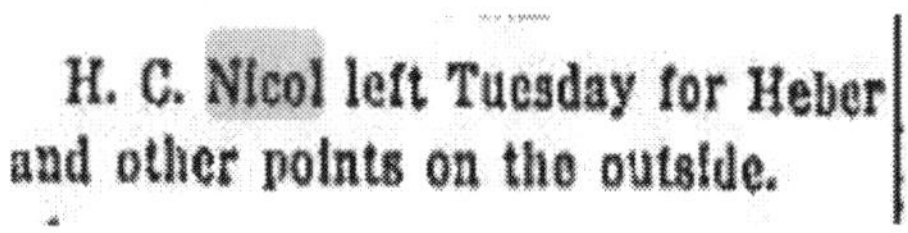

H. C. Nicol left Tuesday for Heber and other points on the outside.

25 Vernal Express October 31, 1913 – H.C. Nicol traveling to Heber

"Alright Hyrum. He will be excited."

"Will you stay at your mother's?"

"Yes, it's always nice to go home and to visit with her. That is when she isn't so busy delivering babies and caring for the sick." "She does have a gift," Isabella nodded in agreement.

***

Hanne looked up toward Daniel's Summit, the pass east of the Heber Valley that led out to the Indian Reservation, Ft. Duchesne, Duchesne, and points east. "Those clouds are hanging heavy over the mountains Hyrum, maybe you should wait until the weather changes."

"I think we'll be okay Mother," he answered. "Tressa will be waiting for us, and we've stayed a few days longer than we planned. She'll be worried."

As Hyrum and Tom moved toward her, intent on saying a final good-bye she took their hands, bowed her head, and began to pray for their safety and protection, she prayed for their horses, and she prayed that they would return home healthy and well. Smiling down at her, Hyrum said, "thank you Mother, your prayers have saved and protected me all the days of my life. I keep them near to my heart."

With those words he turned, lifted the reins, grabbed hold of the saddle horn, stuck his booted foot into the stirrup and pulling himself up he swung his leg over the back of his horse and sat down into the saddle. Waiting while Tom climbed up on the back of his horse Hyrum settled in and gave his mother one last wave and smiled. Home was only two days away and he missed Tressa and the rest of his family. Tom smiled too and waved, he was looking forward to the two-day ride through the canyons home to Duchesne. Tom loved being outdoors and sleeping beneath the black star filled sky.

As they started up the canyon, snow began drifting slowly down, fat lazy flakes that brushed their cheeks and powdered their hat brims. Higher they rode and faster the snow came down, smaller now and sharp, as the wind twisting through the sagebrush pushed into their collars and under their hats, leaving them breathless.

On they rode more slowly. Tom, 10 years old, was hunched into his coat, the reins gripped in gloved fingers peeking from his coat sleeves, trusting his horse to pick the safest route. The snow kept falling, covering him and his horse like a wooly blanket. Finally he could ride no longer; he was sleeping on the back of the horse, stuck in the saddle by legs too cold to feel.

Hyrum knew they could not continue further in the storm. Peering through the blinding white he searched for the cabin that once belonged to a horse thief; empty now, but a haven to wait out the blizzard.

Through squinted eyes peering briefly from under his hat brim, Hyrum spotted the old cabin, south of the road in a little hollow. He hollered to Tom to hang on and he grabbed hold of Tom's horse's bridle and pulled it with him off the road. The horses struggled through the drifted snow to the leeward side of the cabin.

“”Tom, wake up, and climb down!” Tom was almost frozen solid,[xxxv] so much that his father had to pry him from his saddle and carry him inside. Pulling their damp bedding from the back of their horses, Hyrum wrapped Tom up and sat him down next to the small fire he had built with debris scattered inside the cabin.

“I'm bringing the horses inside Tom,” his father said, “they'll freeze in this hollow if we leave them outside in the storm” Nodding his head stretching his hands out toward the fire, Tom huddled near the flames letting the heat melt the snow from his boots and pants.

Once the horses were tethered in the far corner, Hyrum pulled out the bread and cheese his mother had handed him before they left Heber that morning and cut chunks off the cheese and tore pieces of bread which he handed to Tom who was beginning warm up. Pools of water spread beneath their feet from the snow melting from their clothes as it thawed. "Let's try to get some sleep," Hyrum said. "We'll be safe here," and he placed some more wood on the small fire they huddled around.

Once the storm broke the next morning, they continued on to Duchesne through a world of wondrous glittering snow. The winter sunshine glinted from mounded sagebrush hidden below the blanket of blinding white. The snow hid the road and the way home was colder, more work and slower plodding from their horses until they finally dropped from the mountain canyons to the high desert terraces of home.

***

March 1914 *Memories & Surprises*

Living in the fast-growing town was exciting. Although making a living was rough, the citizens worked hard to bring a civilized atmosphere to the frontier. Isabella and Hyrum were involved in political, civic, and religious activities. The school building wasn't far from their house and the boys attended school regularly, and though they had chores, they didn't work quite as hard as they did on the homestead. They were social boys and had a lot of friends.

Hyrum Nicol and Victor Billings, representing the Duchesne Stage and Transportation company, Duchesne, were in Vernal Tuesday and Wednesday in the interest of the company.

Isabella smiled again, she and Hyrum had taken to saying that they had the 'horn of plenty'. They had a wealth of material things; a comfortable snug home, and no little reputation in the community.[xxxvi]

Hyrum's calling as the first counselor in the Duchesne Ward Bishopric had brought many blessings, but it often kept Hyrum busy caring for the spiritual and temporal needs of the ward members. In addition his work with the transportation company included his having to travel occasionally, the homestead ranch took much time and effort. Isabella was left to manage home and children often by herself. She didn't know what she would do without Tom's unflagging help with the house and with his brothers. She also had her church calling, but she didn't complain because of the extra support, physical and spiritual strength and blessings she received from God. She knew she was lifted far beyond her own capacities.

Advertised List
The Duchesne Irrigation Co.
There is delinquent upon the following described stock, on account of assessment No. 12, levied Aug. 18, 1914, the several amounts set opposite the names of the respective stockholders, as follows, stock certificates not yet issued:

Name	Shares	Amt.
H. C. Nicol	160	$79.74
John J. Sellers	130	12.52
Bank of Heber	342	266.75

and in accordance with the law and an order of the Board of Directors of this company dated Nov. 19, 1914, as many shares of each parcel of stock as may be necessary will be sold at public auction at the Musser School house, Midview, Utah, Dec. 17, 1914, at 1 o'clock p. m. to pay the delinquent assessment thereon, together with the cost of advertising and expense of sale.
35-37 Fred S. Musser, Secretary.

26 Duchene Record October 27, 1914
Duchesne Irrigation Co delinquents

She also knew that sharing her testimony to her family was the most important thing she could do. Her most heartfelt desire was for them to come to know Jesus and to choose to follow him. She knew deep in her soul that the restored gospel was truly upon the earth. There absolutely were true and living prophets again in the world.

Isabella loved to share her love of God, her faith in Him and in his son Jesus Christ in quiet moments of conversation. She shared it in family counsel, and she shared her experiences as she spoke in meetings. Isabella sincerely wanted everyone to feel the Holy Ghost witness to their own hearts and confirm the truths she freely shared.[xxxvii]

Shaking her head she focused once more on the mending in her hand, and looked around their peaceful home and gave thanks for God's blessings. Her mind was far away while her fingers pushed the needle through the fabric pulling the edges of the torn material together with stitches so small and neat they were almost invisible.

Their lives were full of spiritual and temporal blessings and although in the midst of their horn of plenty they continued to be plagued with financial struggles. There never seemed to be enough money. They owned their property, but had property taxes and additional assessments on their irrigation shares to pay, as well as saving enough to pay off their yearly operating expense loans. Finances were always tight. She shrugged. Their struggles were part of a homesteader's lot, they did their best and pressed forward.

With her mind deep in thought she didn't hear the door open. "Is it time for dinner already?" She wondered, startled from her reverie. "I was a million miles away Hyrum," she said, standing and making her way toward the kitchen. "Sit down and I'll get you a plate."

"No thank you. I have a surprise for you," he said with a sly grin. Not able to contain his glee he exploded, "I've purchased you a piano!" "A piano!" She exclaimed. "Can we afford one?" "It is second hand, but the sacrifice will be worth it," he replied. Isabella's brimmed with tears of joy. "How I've missed playing and singing together."

"I can teach our boys to play the piano; we already sing together." Just watching her beam Hyrum's heart swelled with happiness. He would do anything for Tressa. And his eyes too filled with tears.

July 1914 ***War on the Horizon***

Turning the pages of the newspaper laying atop the table Hyrum said, "All the countries in Europe are aligning themselves for war. Last month's assassination of Archduke Ferdinand seems to be the lit fuse."

Isabella walked over to lean across his shoulder reading the article he pointed toward. Shaking her head she said, "every time I read of conflicts anywhere I hear in my mind, 'war and rumors of war'. It is in the Book of Matthew when Jesus is teaching of his second coming to his apostles."

"Yes, I know the one you mean," and he quoted " '*And ye shall hear of wars and rumours of wars: see that ye be not troubled: for all these things must come to pass, but the end is not yet. For nation shall rise against nation, and kingdom against kingdom: and there shall be famines, and pestilences, and earthquakes, in divers places. All these are the beginning of sorrows*'."

Isabella shivered, "I hope war does not come to our door," she said softly.

***

Written on the back of the this picture is the following:
"This is the Childrens play tent they have a good time. Tom is always making something. I wish you could see it. The boy standing by Tom with his hat on one side, the little girl and the boy by her are neighbors children also the one just back of John with the paper in his hand. The rest are mine. Can you tell them by their looks? All well hope you are. Don't think that house is ours. Ours is a little bigger than that. I wish I could see you all but don't know when that will be."

Love to all
Tressa

27 Tom, Chase, Kenneth, John Murray & Friends circa 1914

Nicol's In the News

February 1915

On the Nicol and Murdock ranches at Midview operations commenced last week on boring artisian wells. From indications a good flow of water will be encountered.

28 Duchesne Record February 1915 – Nicol & Murdock artesian wells

H. C. Nicol and wife returned last Monday from Provo where Mrs. Nicol was operated upon. The operation has proven very satisfactory and Mrs. Nicol is getting along nicely.

29 Duchesne Record May 8 1915– Isabella Nicol operation in Provo

H. C. Nicol, of the Duchesne Stage & Transportation Co., was up at the station last week looking after business. He reports a severe snow storm which covered the ground to the depth of three inches. This will somewhat retard the drying up of the road on the summit.

30 Duchesne Record May 8, 1915 – H.C. Nicol reports severe snow storm

COUNTY SEAT WILL CELEBRATE

Citizens Decide to Have Appropriate Exercises for Nation's Birthday.

At a citizens' meeting Monday night it was unanimously decided to celebrate the Fourth of July at Duchesne. Details for the celebration were left in the hands of the following committees:

Sports—Ed. Hart, P. Y. Farnsworth, Chas. Odekirk, Mrs. J. A. Washburn, Mrs. L. Stott, L. E. Hume and Chas. Barton.

Finance—Geo. Kohl, W. C. Perry, Homer Brandenburg, T. W. Sweatman, R. M. Pope and M. B. Morrison.

Program—Fred Davis, Mrs. Francis Shelton, Miss Grace Hart, Mrs. H. Nicol, Mrs. J. R. Lewis, L. C. Winslow and Geo. T. Pope.

Advertising—Paul Billings, M. M. Smith, Jake Kroupa, F. L. Watrous, Jackman Herrick and W. H. Fitzwater.

Decorating—James Dalgleish, J. Pope, P. Y. Farnsworth, Guy Hollenbeck, Afton Pope and Mrs. Geo. Kohl.

The sports and program committees are at work and in next week's Record will be contained a full account of the events that will be pulled off. Among other things, however, it is planned to have a baseball tournament that will eclipse anything of the kind ever attempted here. Races also will be prominent features of the day's program.

31 Duchesne Record May 13, 1915 – Independence Day Planning Mrs H.Nicol

"Tressa, the Duchesne Stake quarterly conference will be next month. Will you be okay to provide supper for the visiting General Authorities on Saturday evening?" Hyrum asked. "Bishop Billings' will host supper for them on Sunday before they return to Salt Lake."

"How many people are you talking about Hyrum?" "I believe you should plan on at least ten guests. Chicken and dumplings then, it will stretch far enough."

"Your chicken and dumplings are wonderful Tress." "Thank you," she smiled, "and I'll make lemon pie too."

Stopping a moment she said, "How many people have asked to stay with us for conference weekend?" "Not many yet," he replied, "although I expect we will be wall to wall as usual."

After they had moved into town they were often visited by General Authorities of the Church, as well as political leaders; men Hyrum had met and worked with as a member of the 20th quorum of the Seventy. He had been ordained a Seventy at the time he was called to serve a three-year mission to New Zealand.

Isabella said, "I'm glad we have room to share, it's always fun to have company." [xxxviii]

***

Second from left on back row:
Isabella Crawford Murdoch Nicol
President of the Relief Society

32 Isabella Nicol - Relief Society President Duchesne Ward (no date)

In the News Again

Steer calves for heifer calves. H. C. Nicol.

33 Duchesne Record July 3, 1915 – Cattle for Trade H.C. Nicol

DISTRICT COURT DOCKET

Three criminal and fifteen civil cases are on the docket to be tried by District Court when it convenes in Duchesne next week.

The criminal cases are:

No. 2 State of Utah vs. Clark Elmer. Grand larceny. Ray E. Dillman and J. H. McDonald represent the state and J. A. Wilson the defendant.

No. 3 State of Utah vs. Luray Pace. Appeal from Boneta Justice on charge of larceny of water. John T. Pope and C. S. Price appear for the defendant and Dillman and McDonald for the state.

No. 4. Town of Myton vs. Ethel Beril. Appeal from Myton Justice. R. B. Croix for Myton and E. D. MacDougall for the defendant.

The list of civil cases is as follows:

No. 11. Lee Chas. Miller vs. John W. & Florinda Green. Foreclosure of mortgage.

No. 18. James C. Ward vs. W. A. & Marion Warthen. Foreclosure of mortgage.

No. 22. Ethel Naillon vs. Joseph Naillon. Divorce.

No. 23. J. R. Bywater vs. J. J. Sellers, David Clayburn, C. W. Smith, Hyrum Nicol and 6 others.

34 Duchesne Record September 4, 1915 – On Court Docket

Helper to Vernal

The Duchesne Stage & Transportation company, weathering the greatest hardships, contending with almost impossible roads, fighting the heavy mountain storms, has built a business that has been no small factor in the upbuilding of this great basin.

Starting with a small equipment in the year 1912 this company had to make what was hardly more than a trail over the mountains to Colton, a road that could be traversed by automobile. It cost $8,000 to accomplish this. Realizing the great necessity of a western gateway to this fast growing country they spent the money cheerfully and today have a highway that is a credit to the basin.

In the meantime the business of the Duchesne Stage & Transportation company has grown to a very large industry. From the two automobiles from which the start was made the equipment today consists of ten passenger autos and trucks and all are in daily use. Twenty men are employed regularly. Seventy head of horses, two heavy and two light stages, and six large express wagons are required to handle the heavy mail and express shipments over the mountain. Two stations, Grant station 14 miles out of Helper and Ross station, 24 miles from Duchesne have been es-

building now in the course of construction will allow the handling of mail and parcel post under cover

The Duchesne Stage & Transportation company is a $25,000 corporation. The affairs of the company are ably conducted under the management of A. M. Murdock assisted by Hyram Nicol and Monte Young.

35 Myton Free Press Sept 16, 1915 – Helper - Vernal Transt Co (Hyram Nicol)

REUNION OF DUCHESNE WARD

On December 3rd and 4th, the Church of Jesus Christ of Latter-Day Saints will hold a reunion of Duchesne ward. Dinner will be served from 12 o'clock until 3 p. m. on Friday for all over 14 years of age.

Program during the afternoon and a grand reunion ball in the evening. Everything free. All over 14 years of age are cordially invited to come and enjoy themselves, regardless of faith or creed. Saturday will be children's day starting at noon dancing will begin. Lunch will be served during the afternoon.

Geo. V. Billings
H. C. Nicol
Lester Stott

36 Duchesne Record Reunion of Duchesne Ward

ZION CAPITALISTS VISIT UINTAH BASIN

MANY CONJECTURES REGARDING TRIP.

Oregon Short Line Official and Bishop Nibley Spend Two Days Looking Over Section Between Duchesne and Jensen.

E. E. Calvin, manager of the Oregon Short Line and C. W. Nibley, presiding bishop of the Mormon church, spent Tuesday and Wednesday in looking over the Uintah basin country from Duchesne to Jensen.

On account of the prominence of the two gentlemen in railroad and financial circles, speculation is keen as to the import of their visit at this time. It is certain they were not here on a pleasure trip and in the two days worked every minute of their time in an endeavor to cover as much ground as possible.

The greater part of Tuesday afternoon was consumed in an examination of the Blue bench. They were shown over this tract by M. B. Pope and H. C. Nicol. They made Myton by night and from Myton to Jensen and back to Duchesne by Wednesday night. This was the first trip of either to the reservation, and although they had anticipated from description the immensity of the basin, nevertheless they expressed their surprise and amazement in finding so many thousands of irrigible acres and an abundance of water with which to make every one

37 Myton Free Press September 16, 1915 – H.C. Nicol escorts Zion Capitalists

INDIAN CANYON ROAD TO BE IMPROVED

Hyrum Nicol of the Stage Company left for Helper Wednesday to finish arrangements for working the Indian Canyon road from the South end. All 28 miles from Duchesne to the summit of the range, with the exception of the six mile stretch that was put in excellent condition by contractor Frank Johnson last fall, are to be worked over by the new road machines of the stage company. The aim is to make a wide, smooth boulevard that can be traversed by the chug wagons in an hour and a half under favorable conditions. Helper has promised to make similar improvements on the road out from their town to the Carbon-Duchesne county line. Several thousand dollars will be expended by those who travel over the road constantly, and then the State will be asked to contribute since the highway will be used by thousands of touring automobiles annually as the main entrance into Utah from Colorado. State Treasurer Jewkes is expected in about the close of the week to look over the situation in behalf of the State Road Commission.

38 Duchesne Record September 4, 1915 – Indian Canyon Road to be improved

LIST MEMBERS COMMERCIAL CLUB, FEBRUARY 14, 1916

C. R. Barton
C. B. Lofthouse
Guy Hollenbeck
Geo. H. McKown
Frank Kelso
Dr. J. E. Zimmerman
E. W. Schonian
John Odekirk
Ed. Mackie
Dr. A. Bjornson
Francis Shelton
Rock M. Pope
W. L. Dean
Max Doeben
C. G. Dalquist
W. C. Perry
M. B. Pope
James Grant
Tom Firth
L. A. Hollenbeck
S. M. Playford
John Madsen
Paul Cluff
Fred Davis
Geo. A. Robbins
Henry Bottom
R. W. O'Toole
Ed. Hart
M. D. Morrison
Paul Billings
E. S. Winslow
M. M. Smith
James Dalgleish
A. W. Clemons
Frank McFarland
John Pilling
O. J. Smith
Dan Powell
John B. Drew
H. C. Nicol
J. A. Wilson
T. W. Sweatman
C. I. Dickerson
J. C. Jensen
Steve Shelton
F. L. Watrous
M. L. Marsing
Wm. H. Fitzwater
Walter O'Toole
Monte Young
Geo. Kohl
M. S. Wooley
Harvey Partridge
R. W. Kroupa
Geo. S. Bowers

M. M. SMITH, Secy.

39 Duchesne Record February 16, 1916 – Commercial Club List of Members

February 1916 *Surprises Ahead*

Steady blasts of winter wind buffeted the frame walls shaking the home's single decoration, the mirror on its nail reflecting the lantern light in dancing waves across the opposite wall.

Yesterday's snow was blown solid against the western windows almost blocking what little light was able to penetrate the clouds which continued to darken the sky in anticipation of another round of snowfall.

Isabella, using both hands, almost heaved herself from the chair near the stove. "Uhhg" she groaned, finally standing straight, or as straight as she could carrying her fifth child into the seventh month.

Wrapping her arms beneath her stomach she slowly walked to the counter poking the rising bread dough to test its readiness. She took a deep breath, rolled up her sleeves, floured her hands, and punched the dough down to begin kneading to shape the dough into loaves.

"Tom, will you come and take over the kneading please? I can't get close enough to the table."

"Of course," Tom replied standing up from the corner where he had been cleaning his pistol.

Holding her hand over the top of the wood stove Isabella called to 10-year- old Chase. "Will you please add another log to the fire and bank it back a bit, by the time the bread rises again it should be the right temperature."

"Push the dough together in the middle Tom or the loaves will not rise correctly," she said.

A particularly hard blast of wind rattled the windows and the frigid air skirted across their arms while they worked.

"Momma, Momma," four year old John Murray tried to get her attention by holding on to her skirts. "What is it John?" She asked, wishing only to sit back down. Her back hurt, and her feet and legs felt like the skin of a sausage just before it pops.

"What can I do Momma? Can I help too?" "Of course you can," Isabella tiredly smiled. "Will you sing me a song while I rest a while?"

"Oh yes Momma I can do that," said her beaming four-year-old.

"When will Father be home?" Kenneth inquired.

"Within the next day or two. I suspect the snow is much higher on the mountain and it may take them longer than they thought to get into where the cattle are snowed in."

"Mother, the bread is in the pans," Tom told her. She asked, "Did you put the towel over it?" "Yes, ma'am," Tom answered.

Later the older boys Tom, Chase, and Kenneth, tugged on their coats, gloves, and woolen hats hoping for some protection against the February storm. With their faces down against the wind, and coat collars turned up they opened the door stepping out into the quickly darkening evening to do their chores.

Following the single snow-packed path from the house's door into the lean-to shed that housed their milk cow and horses, they turned to their chores. Chase started forking hay into the manger. Tom took the milking bucket and stool over to the cow carefully placing his hand on her flank, talking slowly while placing the stool beside her and the bucket below her udders.

Taking off his gloves he blew briskly to warm his already cold fingers. Then pulling gently on her teats a slow stream of warm liquid sang into the bucket. Kenneth fed the remaining hens huddled in their small coop and then took up a shovel to help Chase finish clearing the stalls.

With the speed and ease of chores completed daily over many years they finished up, trooping together toward the house. The wind whipped the dry snow that stung their bare faces, causing them to wince and squint and walk faster; trying not to spill the precious milk before they reached the door.

Several days later when the storm finally blew on toward the east, Hyrum stepped through the frame house's door to find his sons huddled together to their mother who was reading to them on the bed. After hugs and expressions of relief at his return, Isabella slowly slipped off the bed and carefully walked toward the kitchen table.

"The cattle are moved down back to the flats, he said as he followed her into the kitchen."

Slicing bread, pouring milk and ladling stew into bowls she said, "Hyrum, I'm very glad you are home. I can hardly do anything anymore. I feel like I'm going to explode. I can hardly walk because my stomach has gotten so big. I know it is still at least a month or more before the baby will arrive! What will I do?"

Stepping up behind her he carefully wrapped his arms around her shoulders and whispered to her. "You are beautiful Tressa, I love you."

"Would you like me to have the doctor come by tomorrow just to check up on you, to ease your mind?" He asked. Relief flooded her and her voice shook when she said, "if you would do that Hyrum yes, please."

***

Lowering his stethoscope, the doctor patted her arm and said, "Well Mrs. Nicol, you appear to be doing well, though I am concerned about the swelling in your legs. I suggest that you spend less time on your feet and no more lifting." Looking up from placing his stethoscope into his bag and seeing her concerned expression he said, "I don't want to give you more to worry about, but I believe that you are going to have twins. There definitely are two distinct heartbeats. I thought there were the last time, but I couldn't be certain and didn't say anything until I could be sure."

Watching the blood drain from her face the doctor walked quickly to her side, asking her to lay back against the pillows and take a few deep breaths. "Hyrum," Isabella's shaky voice called, "will you please come in? "

The doctor repeated his findings to Hyrum and the news slowly settled into Isabella's consciousness. Quietly she said, "I had a feeling that was the case. My sister has had twins also". The doctor went on to tell them that with twin births they should expect an earlier delivery. He also told them that there was a higher risk to their survival, especially if they were born too early.

Once the news of twins spread through the Duchesne wards, offers of daily help were quickly accepted. When each sister came in the house they carried additional items for the babies, covered dishes and warm bread were brought to alleviate Isabella's need to cook. Neighbors were quick to call the younger boys over to their homes for a few hours, offering Isabella much needed rest.

The weeks moved slowly by for her. Once the thought of putting her feet up and resting a while was a wonderful dream, but now she was restless, as well as uncomfortable. She had all of her mending completed; she had made new dresses for the babies, knitted stockings and blankets and all the while she wished for her mother, or her sisters to be able to share this time with them. But her mother wasn't well and didn't move much from her place at her sister Catherine's home, where she went to live after Isabella's father John Murray died almost six years before.

Her sisters all had homes and families and the trip was still tiring although the motor car service had reduced the 2-day wagon journey to only 5 or 6 hours. Hyrum's mother, who had delivered her other children, was aging as well and wouldn't be coming for this birth. Isabella missed her mother-in-law's efficient and loving care before and after the births of her boys. She wasn't expecting girls, not with already having four boys; it just didn't feel like girls.

***

RECORD IN THE BASIN

Roads are Drifted Full and Many Sheep and Cattle Snowed in on High Ridges.

Until its record is beaten, January, 1916, will go down in Uintah basin history as the month of the "big snow." January, 1909, has easily held the honors up to this year. By the cattlemen of this section it is estimated that there are at least twelve inches more of the "beautiful" than seven years ago.

For the past five days cattlemen have been on the move and are still moving—moving the range stuff to feed. Many cattle are snowed in on the higher ridges of the Indian canyon and Strawberry country and this week and the weeks following will be consumed in breaking trails to the isolated stock driving it to feed yards.

A. M. Murdock arrived in Duchesne Sunday with three hundred head, which are being taken to Hayden. Men are after the rest of Mr. Murdock's stuff and these too will be driven to his home ranch and elsewhere and fed until winter breaks.

Half of the C. R. Barton bunch will be taken to the Spratt ranch on the Duchesne. Mr. Barton believes he has enough hay in Lake canyon

was passenger traffic on the main line of the Denver & Rio Grande. Nevada experienced the worst part of the storm and the Western Pacific, which was opened to traffic Wednesday after being close on account of landslides, is again closed indefinitely by snowdrifts and slides.

Every railroad entering Salt Lake experienced trouble and the city traction line was delayed for more than two hours in the morning getting started. Cars were from ten to forty minutes late, although all lines were operating.

In the Bear River canyon snowdrifts ten feet deep defied the rotary snowplows for twelve hours. Trains from the north were held at Collinston, and those from the south at Brigham City. Trains for Cache valley were also held for more than twelve hours on account of the snow. On the main line many drifts through out southern Idaho caused delays. This is the first time the Bear River canyon has been blocked in years.

Avalanches in Canyons

The Union Pacific had much trou-

---

been magnificent. And it has been no child's play to keep wheels a turning, and runners running between Helper and Vernal. Five o'clock in the morning has seen the employes of the company driving and again breaking trails through drifts which the day before,

Half of the C. R. Barton bunch will be taken to the Spratt ranch on the Duchesne. Mr. Barton believes he has enough hay in Lake canyon to tide over the remainder of his stuff.

Many of the Lusty cattle are snowed in on the ridges. These will be reached during the next week and taken to feed. Brown brothers and Allen Davis have enough hay to take care of their bunches as has G. V. Billings in Sower's canyon. Stott and Nichols have taken their stuff to Holgate flat. Chas Odekirk is feeding his in Duchesne. Wm. Craver moved his to Antelope more than a week ago. "Doc" Thornberg and the Allen brothers have been feeding for the past week.

Not since 1909 has it been necessary for the cattlemen of this section to feed anything but weak stuff. And at that time no feeding was done for the simple reason that there was no hay to speak of in the west part of the basin and what was hauled in from Vernal sold here for $40 a ton. The loss among cattle the following spring amounted to between ten and fifteen per cent.

While there is considerable hay in this immediate section, the producers of it have steadily advanced its price until $12 and better is being asked for it in the stack. Feeders are therefore finding it to their advantage to drive their stuff to the larger hay producing country to the east where a number of contracts have been closed for $6 per ton.

Freight and passenger traffic in the intermountain country was tied up for periods ranging from twelve to thirty-six hours on account of the severe storm which has been raging through the states of Utah, Idaho and Wyoming. The sole exception our southern Idaho caused delays. This is the first time the Bear River canyon has been blocked in years.

Avalanches in Canyons

The Union Pacific had much trouble in getting trains over the Sherman hill. A rotary plow preceded each passenger train. In the Weber canyon a snowslide effectively blocked all traffic over the road for hours. The Park City branch of the Union Pacific was snowbounded Thursday morning, and no attempt was made to operate trains over it. No freight traffic was attempted either over the Oregon Short Line or the Union Pacific yesterday.

The Denver & Rio Grande did not attempt to move a freight train in twenty-four hours. The coal mines in Emery and Carbon county are shut down, as they cannot get cars. One track was kept open over Soldier summit by the continuous use of rotary snowplows. Passenger trains were brought through, but no freight trains were sent out from terminals.

The Western Pacific was blocked by a slide at Wells, Nev., and by other trouble in the Feather River canyon. In addition, snowdrifts at many points on the line impeded traffic.

The Southern Pacific trains from the west leaving coast terminals Thursday were six hours late, and those leaving yesterday were indefinitely late, snowdrifts in the Sierras being responsible.

Confronted with the largest snowfall in the history of the basin at one time, the biggest drifts and most unfavorable traffic conditions, the Duchesne Stage & Transportation company has overcome each and every obstacle and won the admiration of every resident in the Uintah country for having kept an open gateway to and from the outside world.

Its work during the past week has and runners running between Helper and Vernal. Five o'clock in the morning has seen the employes of the company driving and again breaking trails through drifts which the day before, and in many instances a few hours before, had been open highways.

The Uintah line, after having made a most gallant fight against the forces of nature, was finally snowed andj drifted in, and as a result mail for Vernal is temporarily being routed over the Duchesne line.

As far as Duchesne or Helper was concerned the stage leaving Duchesne Thursday was lost from eleven o'clock Thursday night until late in the afternoon the following day. For that length of time it dropped completely out of sight and it was not without a great deal of apprehension that local residents waited for news of it. The storm, which commenced Thursday afternoon, filled the roads so full of snow that five hours were required to travel between the ranger's station and Leavitt's on the Willow creek slope. It arrived at the latter place at 11 o'clock p. m. and with Dick Nye as driver attempted to make Helper. In the Willow creek canyon an immense drift was encountered and the party, including Mr. and Mrs. Jake Kroupa and baby and Mrs. Carl Johnson and Mrs. Homer Brandenberg and baby, decided to camp in the timber, which is plentiful along the creek. A roaring fire was built and at daylight Nye got on one of the horses and made for Castle Gate. At that place he met Less Gardner, headed this way with the mail. Gardner succeeded in bucking through the drift and made Leavitt's about the middle of the afternoon, giving Duchesne the first news that no accident had occurred and that the outgoing party was safe.

40 Duchesne Record 1016 Record Snow Nicol Moving Cattle

March 6 1916 *the Twins, Alva & Alma*

The light was breaking on the eastern horizon when Isabella, who had slept little the night before, shook Hyrum's shoulder, "Hyrum, wake up. You'll need to get the doctor. I've been in pain most of the night and I think it's time for these babies to arrive soon."

Carefully folding the bedding back, Hyrum came quickly to his feet, slid on his woolen pants, pulled on his stockings, and was buttoning his coat as he leaned over Tom and shook him awake. "Tom, get up and start the fire and take care of your brothers while I go to get the doctor. Your mother is almost ready to have the babies."

"Yes sir," Tom said hastily climbing out of the warm nest he had been sleeping in.

Adding kindling and split logs to the stove and starting a pot of water to boil for their breakfast oats he woke his brothers. "Chase, Mother is going to have the babies. You and Kenneth do the morning chores, I'll come help after I get breakfast started."

"John Murray, get dressed and go see if Mother needs anything."

Knocking gently on his parent's bedroom door John Murray whispered, "Mother, Mother, do you need anything?" He slowly peeked around the door and saw his mother's face pale and slightly damp and he saw she was breathing hard.

"Mother! Are you alright?" He almost yelled. After what seemed a long moment while John Murray held his breath his mother answered him. "I'm alright. It hurts to have a baby and I'm going to have two," she winced and held still before she said, "I would like a drink of water if you will bring me a cup John."

Running quickly toward the kitchen he asked Tom to pump him some water, then speedily returned, relief on his face when his mother gently touched his hand and told him thank you. Now you can go help Tom and have some breakfast."

By the time the doctor arrived, all of the boys were sitting at the table, finishing their oats and bread. "The chores are all done Father," Tom reported as his father walked past them with the doctor by his side. "Fine boys, fine," said a distracted Hyrum. "Will you please take John Murray and go to visit the neighbors? They are expecting you."

By dusk, the pale winter sun filtered down over windblown patches of ice and snow outside their house, and Hyrum walked up the block to bring his sons home. News that Isabella had given birth to twin boys galvanized the women's Relief Society. Again covered dishes of potatoes, beef, stews and soup, fresh bread and cakes began arriving. The Relief Society sisters were quickly remaking the bed, helping Isabella into fresh clothes and caring for the infant boys.

Isabella lay exhausted on her bed, the quilts settled over her small frame. As fatigued as she felt she was grateful for the blessings of sisters. Though her own sisters and family were a hundred miles away, the Lord provided a family of sisters through His church.

She knew that for a while they would be there to assist with the additional work of two babies. At that thought she almost stopped breathing. Two babies! A prayer instinctively passed from her lips full of appreciation for her safe confinement, the arrival of healthy appearing babies, the care of the doctor and her Relief Society sisters. She prayed for strength to recover and to be able to care for their ever expanding family.

At the end of the day, Isabella pulled a quilt higher around her arms and asked of the men in her life who encircled the bed around her. "What shall we name them?"

***

April 1916 *Heaven Calls Again*

Isabella drifted asleep, a babe in each arm, the past month since Alva and Alma were born had given her little time for sleep. She dozed knowing her oldest son 12-year-old Tom was caring for his brothers, the house and chores. His father was working and though Hyrum came home for dinner his job was demanding; the mail and freight had to be delivered on time.

Tom was just moving to open his parent's bedroom door to ask if his mother needed anything when he heard the kitchen door open and his father's footsteps crossed the creaky wooden floor. "Hello Father," a surprised Tom said turning toward him. "You're home early."

His father nodded thoughtfully and asked if his mother was doing well. "She was trying to sleep a while ago, I was just going to check on her." "That's alright son, I'll do it," Hyrum said softly and turned to open the pine door.

"Tressa," he whispered, "are you awake?"

"Yes Hyrum, I'm just closing my eyes. What are you doing home so early?" There was the briefest of pauses, such that Isabella's eyes opened and her gaze pierced him.

Swallowing slightly he said, "I received a telephone call from your sister Catherine. I'm sorry Tressa. Your mother passed on last night." [xxxix]

"Oh Hyrum! Oh Hyrum!" Tears became sobs escaping from Isabella's throat.

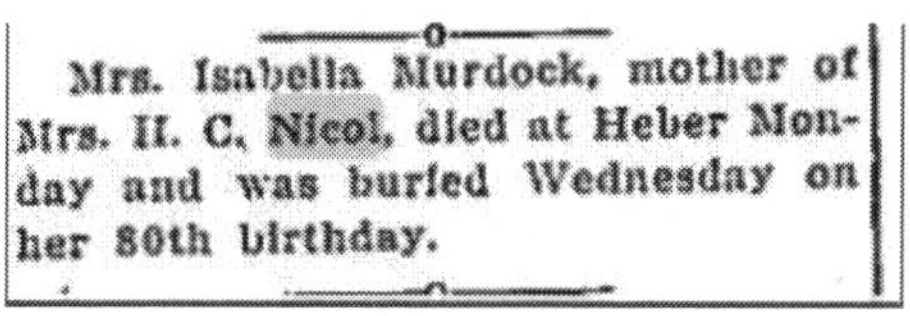

Mrs. Isabella Murdock, mother of Mrs. H. C. Nicol, died at Heber Monday and was buried Wednesday on her 80th birthday.

41 *Duchesne Record Death Notice Isabella Murdoch*

"I'm sorry sweetheart; let me put the boys in their cradle," he said reaching for a bundled baby.

Tears ran from her eyes, heartbroken at the news. Hyrum sat on the edge of the bed, pulled her into his arms, and held her, gently patting her back until the sobs slowly subsided and her eyes had no more tears.

He continued soothingly, "Catherine said her funeral will be on Wednesday."

Tears flowed afresh as she softly whispered against Hyrum's chest, "I can't go to her funeral." "I know, I know," he consoled.

"Catherine said she went to sleep and was gone in the morning." Isabella broke in, "Wednesday would be her 80th birthday." As the words left her lips she began to weep more gently this time.

"She will be so happy to be with Father again," she spoke as if to herself. "She has missed him and Muz so much since they died. I can see her now, flying toward them both, arms out-stretched and joy on her face."

"I will miss her Hyrum, but with my testimony of God's plan of salvation, I know I will see her again. I will hold her again and we will laugh and sing as we have always done."

"God is good to us, isn't he Hyrum?" Taking a long breath she said, "I will be okay now, thank you for coming to tell me

Another Pioneer Called

Isabella Crawford Murdock, better known as "Aunt Bella", died at the home of her daughter Mrs. David W. Hicken, Monday, April 10, 1916, of general debility, being 80 years old on Wednesday, the day of the funeral.

Aunt Bella was one of the early pioneers of this valley, having come to Heber when a young woman and married John M. Murdock as a plural wife in 1862. To this union seven children were born and grew to manhood and womanhood in this community. They are Mrs. Margaret A. Hawks, who died in Idaho leaving a family of six children, Mrs. David W. Hicken of Heber, James C., a member of the high council, Brigham, bishop of Farnum, Idaho, Robert, who died of typhoid fever at the age of 21, John M., now on a mission in New Zealand, and Isabella C. wife of Hyrum Nicol of Charleston.

Funeral services were held at the stake tabernacle Wednesday afternoon, April 12th, the services, which were well attended, being conducted by Bp. Crook of the Heber 3rd ward. The following songs: "Though Deepening Trials Throng Your Way," "Sister Thou Wert Mild and Lovely," and "Nearer My God to Thee" were sung by a mixed quartette consisting of Enid Murdock, Emma Carlile, Frank Epperson and Francis Carlile. Beautiful bouquets of flowers covered the casket, many coming from friends unable to attend the funeral.

The first speaker was Bishop Joseph A. Rasband of the Heber 2nd ward. He said that the departed sister had been a member of the 2nd ward ever since coming to Heber, until about a year ago when she was transferred to the 3rd ward. Said he had known Sister Murdock all his life. She was congenial and pleasant, always endeavoring to do good in the face of continued ill health. We have no occasion to mourn the departure of such as Sister Bella.

Henry L. McMullin said he knew the departed sister to be a righteous woman who has lived a righteous life. She joined the Church of Jesus Christ of Latter Day Saints when a girl of 17 years of age in her native land—Scotland, and left all relatives and friends who were near and dear to her and came to America for the gospel's sake. She worked in the factories of the eastern states for a number of years to earn money to come on to Utah. Spoke of the state of peace and rest for the righteous after death as told us by the Prophet Alma who said an angel had revealed these things unto him. Said that Sister Murdock had merited and would receive the blessings of the righteous.

Wm. Lindsay said he had known the departed sister for more than 50 years and knew her to be a good woman. Testified that the family relations existing in the Murdock family were of peace and pleasure. At the departure of her son John M. to fill a mission in New Zealand she said that she might not live to see his return, but rejoiced that he was going in the service of the Lord.

James C. Jensen of the stake presidency said he had been thinking ever since the opening song of the brevity of life which reminds him of the saying "Is Life Worth Living." In the death of one such as Sister Murdock, the answer to this is "Yes." The posterity she has left, the fruits of her labors, all testify to the worth of such a life. What joy will be on the other side at meeting with her husband and companions who have gone before! All honor to such women! Her life is a testimony that life is worth living. The emaciated form lying before us will not always be the tabernacle of her spirit, but the spirit will attract to it until every particle will be restored to a perfect womanhood in the resurrection. The spirits of our ancestors are not far away. If Aunt Bella could give utterance to her greatest desire now, it would be that her posterity may remain faithful in the service of the Lord.

Bishop Crook said he had been intimately acquainted with the Murdock family, and wished to testify that the family of John M. Murdock had lived in peace and harmony notwithstanding there were two wives rearing families together. Admonished the children to emulate the good works of their parents. In behalf of the family, he thanked all who had assisted in any way during the sickness, death and burial of the deceased.

Interment was made in the Heber cemetery.

42 Wasatch Wave April 12 1916 – Isabella Murdoch Obituary

and for holding me. You can go back to work and I'll lie here a while longer and remember her."

"I love you Hyrum." Pulling her closer again he kissed her gently and replied, "I love you too Tressa."

"I once thought having an infant was hard, but now," Isabella shrugged her shoulders, and opined "I would say a single baby is a breeze. Having twins is a tornado. I've found that the little tricks I used before often don't translate to twins; not enough arms," she said laughing with her 77 year old mother-in-law.

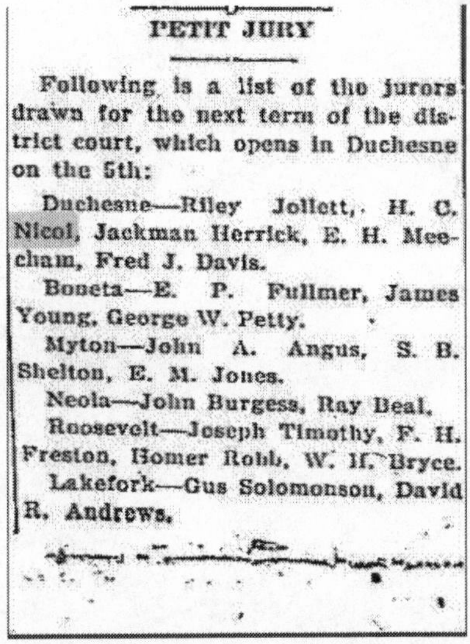

PETIT JURY

Following is a list of the jurors drawn for the next term of the district court, which opens in Duchesne on the 5th:

Duchesne—Riley Jollett, H. C. Nicol, Jackman Herrick, E. H. Meecham, Fred J. Davis.

Boneta—E. P. Fullmer, James Young, George W. Petty.

Myton—John A. Angus, S. B. Shelton, E. M. Jones.

Neola—John Burgess, Ray Beal.

Roosevelt—Joseph Timothy, F. H. Preston, Homer Robb, W. H. Bryce.

Lakefork—Gus Solomonson, David R. Andrews.

43 Duchesne Record May 20 1916 – H C Nicol on Petit Jury

"Hyrum and the boys have been so helpful, the neighbors and sisters were wonderful when the babies were first born, but they have their own families to care for and I don't feel I can keep asking them to keep helping me."

"I've been homebound since they were born you know and I miss getting out. Now with Hyrum so ill with the rheumatism he can't get out of bed, it's been harder to get anything done. It's a trial, but like always the Lord gives us strength to continue." She commented with spirit and conviction.

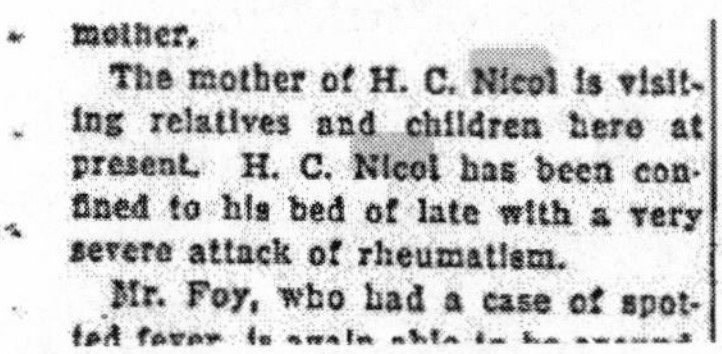

mother.

The mother of H. C. Nicol is visiting relatives and children here at present. H. C. Nicol has been confined to his bed of late with a very severe attack of rheumatism.

Mr. Foy, who had a case of spotted fever is again able to be around

44 Myton Free Press June 16, 1916 Sickness & Visits

"I'm so happy you were able to come to visit," she said returning the hug her sweet mother-in-law gave her. Then Hanne said, "I can't do heavy work like I used to, but I am very good at holding babies." And she winked.

***

September 1916 *Moving to Helper*

On the mend and back at work Hyrum knew his responsibilities were causing a hardship for his family. Isabella needed help constantly with the twins and boys, the house, the garden, and the many chores she did to keep up the home and family in what was still a frontier.

Tom was a stalwart help, he was twelve and carried greater responsibilities. Hyrum was often out of town. Thinking and praying about how he could manage all of the duties in his life he had spoken with Alva Moroni, his brother-in-law who had offered some suggestions that he hadn't thought about.

Mulling them over he went home for dinner and dreaded to tell Isabella that he was leaving again. When he told her the news her generally gentle disposition grew vexed. "Hyrum, we cannot survive here without your help!" Isabella bluntly said to the news that he would be going to Helper again for a few days to work with the railroad.

"I know Tress, but it's my job."

"However," he spoke hastily before she could come at him with another argument. "There are some options I have been thinking about."

"And what would that be?" She couldn't quite keep the irritation from her voice.

"I could quit the transportation company which is what I've been thinking about doing."

Isabella broke in, "Hyrum we can't afford for you to quit working."

"I know," he said, "I wouldn't quit working, I'd find another job that didn't require traveling. I know you need me here."

He paused again. "There is another option. Al suggested that we move to Helper where I would be on-site for the road work, transportation, and mail delivery, at least through the winter. Remember how many times I was snowed in at Helper last winter?"

"Move?" Isabella's heart dropped. She had such a good support system here with the church women's Relief Society, and her friends and neighbors had been diligent in helping her as a mother with twins.

"It is move Tress, or I quit this job, or I continue to go back and forth every week," his voice raised in frustration. In the silence that followed his outburst, he said, "I'm sorry I raised my voice."

Then he offered, "Shall we pray for help to make the right decision? I know any of them will be disruptive for us, we know how much this position has been a blessing; but my thoughts say that moving may be the best option for right now."

Later than afternoon, Isabella knelt next to the babies' cradle and poured her heart out to her Heavenly Father. She told him all the reasons she wanted to stay in Duchesne, and how hard it would be to move with small babies. They would be leaving their home, although it was rented property, it was home. She told him her fears, and her desire to be a good mother and wife. She cried and sat and read the scriptures for a while, hoping to hear an answer to her prayers. Then she left the twins sleeping and went into the kitchen and turned the risen bread dough out on the counter and began kneading it. Kneading it much harder than usual.

"Kenneth and John Murray, will you clear the table and fill up the wood box please?"

"Yes ma'am," they said in unison.

"Tom and Chase watch the twins while your father and I take a walk. We won't be long."

Hyrum guided Isabella out the door, gently touching the small of her back as they stepped down into the yard. With no preamble Isabella spoke out, "I've been thinking and praying all afternoon Hyrum," she said, as they gravitated close together, reaching for one another's hands, and began to walk slowly down the hard-packed street. "I don't have a good feeling about leaving Duchesne, but I also don't have a bad feeling about moving to Helper. I'm feeling that this decision is up to us." "What do you think Hyrum?"

"Well, I think it may be a good move for us. It is a promotion of sorts and we could use the extra money."

"What else is new Hyrum?" Isabella queried with a twitch of her lips. Walking silently along, each in their own thoughts, the cooler than warm evening breezes pushed against their faces. Hyrum broke the soft silence. "If you haven't received a definite no to your prayers and neither have I, I believe we should take the leap and move to Helper. It's also a good time to make a move as the school term will start next month."

With some trepidation in her voice, she tried to keep it from trembling and said, "If you believe that it is a good choice I'll stand by you all the way then Hyrum." "Good," he said, "during my trip this week I'll look for a home for us and I'll let A.M. know our decision before I leave."

Isabella just nodded her head, fighting the bubble of fear which rose in her heart.

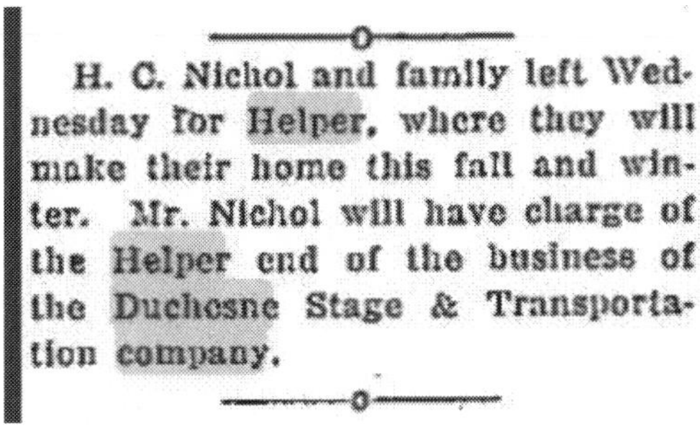
H. C. Nichol and family left Wednesday for Helper, where they will make their home this fall and winter. Mr. Nichol will have charge of the Helper end of the business of the Duchesne Stage & Transportation company.

45 Duchesne Record September 16 1916 – Moving to Helper for winter

Later that night, lying in the dark Chase whispered to Tom, "what do you think about moving to Helper Tom?"

"Don't know Chase," he answered quietly. "If Father and Mother are certain it will be a good thing, then I will believe them." "Guess I will too," Chase said, and turned to face the wall and he murmured to himself, "I hope Father finds a house in town."

"It will be an adventure boys, a new experience." Hyrum watched the stolid faces of his sons, their eyes holding his. "I know you aren't happy about moving, but you'll make new friends when school begins. Have faith boys everything will work out just as it should," he said encouragingly.

When the wagons were loaded with their household goods, and the infants Alva and Alma laid gently into the cushioned cradle behind Isabella's seat, Hyrum finished tying their crate of chickens and his riding horse to the back of the last wagon.

Climbing up beside he wife he turned toward the older boys now in their saddles, gloved hands holding the reins of their horses in readiness for his "hi-ya" to start. "Hi-ya!" Hyrum twitched the reins against the backs of the horses, and the wagons rattled and the move to Helper Utah began.

"***

December 1916

H. C. Nicol has been looking up business interests in our midst for the past ten days. He says they like Helper but like Duchesne better.

"I know we thought I wouldn't be traveling as much as I did, but it is my job and I have to go into the Basin. I'll be gone about a week or so. The road needs repair before the heaviest of winter hits and I need to go out to the ranch and see what I can do to help Alva with the herd before I come back."

Isabella just looked at him, nodded, and called the family to the supper table.

"Hyrum I want to say grace tonight please." "Of course," he replied as he and the boys bowed their heads and anticipated her sweet prayer. "Father in Heaven please forgive me for losing my temper and for my frustration with our situation. I know it is through your grace and blessings that Hyrum has a good position, that we have our health, and that we have such abundance in our lives. Please bless this food, that it may nourish and strengthen our bodies, that we may do thy will. In Jesus' name, Amen."

H. C. Nicol came in from Helper Thursday to look after some of his Duchesne interests. Mr. Nicol speaks highly of Carbon county schools and his boys are making excellent progress in their school work. Mrs. Nicol is enjoying good health but is anxious for the school term to close that she may return to her home here.

46 Duchesne Record December 23 1916 – Anxious to return to Duchesne

January 1917 *Sacrifice*

"I want to thank you A.M. for your help and support, you have always been a bulwark for Isabella and me. Thank you for caring for the homestead and our herd while we're away. I know mother is also very grateful for your care of her holdings too."

Hyrum Nicol has returned from Helper and will hereafter live in Duchesne. Mrs. Nicol and the children will join him as soon as a dwelling house can be secured. Clyde H. Stephens has succeeded Mr. Nicol as manager of the railroad end of the stage company business.

47 Myton Free Press Jan 25 1917– Nicols return to Duchesne

"Isabella and the boys aren't happy living in Helper. She misses her friends and the Duchesne society. Caring for the babies has kept her from interacting much with the Church women, or even the neighbors. It's best that we move back here."

Alva Moroni looked at his brother-in-law and said, "You do good work Hyrum, so I'm sorry to tell you that I don't have any position open here at the transportation company. If you move back you won't have a job."

"What with the new owners and their changes, and the automobile and bus fleet taking over the freight, well, things change," he said, nodding toward the automobiles outside the window. "We knew that was a possibility A.M. I've been looking for something already, but haven't been successful yet."

Looking out the window and down the street Hyrum asked, "Do you still have the rental house?" "Yes, we do. In fact, Ivy and I were talking just the other day about selling it and consolidating some of our holdings."

Mr. and Mrs. H. C. Nicol and family, who have spent this much of the winter in Helper, will move back to Duchesne at once. They and their household goods will be in during the coming week.

48 Duchesne Record January 25 1917 – Back from Helper

"Isabella and I couldn't afford to buy it, but we've saved enough money for rent for a few months until we can get settled, would that be alright?"

“Of course you can rent the house again Hyrum. Remember that Ivy and I will do our best to help you get settled back in.”

“Thanks A.M.,” Hyrum reached out and shook his hand brother-in-law’s callused hand. Tipping his hat he said, “I’ll head back to Helper and will bring the family back at once. Isabella already has the house there boxed and wrapped up for the move home.”

***

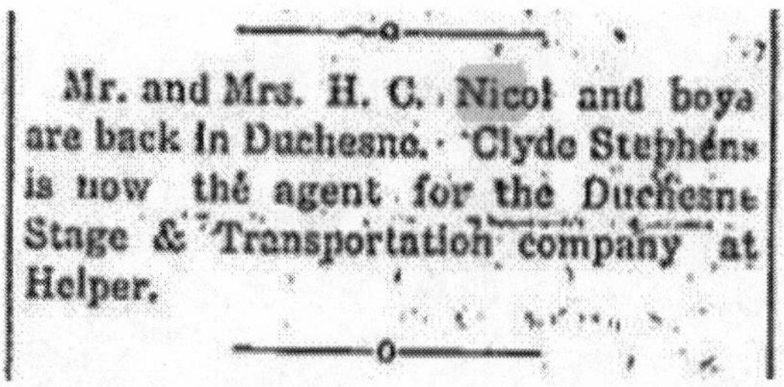

Mr. and Mrs. H. C. Nicol and boys are back in Duchesne. Clyde Stephens is now the agent for the Duchesne Stage & Transportation company at Helper.

49 Myton Free Press January 25, 1917 – Nicol replaced

“Careful, careful,” Isabella warned the men carrying in her precious piano. “Please put it back along the wall, right where it was before; that is perfect.” She was bustling back and forth with her coat, hat, and gloves on in the winter cold, pointing and directing where the boxes, beds, and remaining household goods were to be put.

The solitude of the past 4 months was swept away as friends and neighbors flowed in the door to welcome them back with love, bestowing a special glow about her smiling face. “I’m so glad to be home Hyrum,” she sighed gratefully.

“I know you sacrificed your desires for our happiness.” He replied, “I will always do what is best for you Tressa. God has always watched over us and we’ve learned that no good deed goes unrewarded, don’t we know?”

Shutting the door on the last of the volunteers Isabella called out, “Chase build the fire higher; I want to take the chill off of the room before I take off my coat. Kenneth and John Murray fill the wood box again.”

“Father,” Chase said, after placing another log in the stove, when we went to Helper someone must have taken some of the woodpile. It is not as high as I remember it being.”

"You may be right Chase, a woodpile standing alone is mighty tempting to some people. They think stealing is easier than doing the work themselves."

"Here's a lesson. When someone chooses to become a thief for whatever reason they will soon find that stealing only hurts them. First, they've stolen something that isn't theirs and it lets evil into their hearts. Second they are made the weaker for having taken it because the next time they are tempted to steal, it becomes easier and easier, until they are securely in the hands of the Devil."

"And in jail when they are finally caught." Chase inserted, his tongue in his cheek.

His father turned and gave him a look that brooked no nonsense, and went on, "there's a reason God gave us the Ten Commandments. Paying attention to them and trying to follow them keeps us in God's army. What number is Thou Shall Not Steal?"

Kenneth, keeping his ear toward their conversation said, number eight!"

"That's right Kenneth," Hyrum went on again telling them that honesty and hard work makes you strong." His face cracking into a smile he said, "Plan on getting stronger on Saturday. We'll go cut more wood."

"No Hyrum, I need Tom to help me with the babies; you'll have to just take Chase and Kenneth."

"I want to go too," John whined a little.

"Don't whine John," his father said, "and yes, you may come too. You aren't that little anymore."

Tom looking on stoically said, "Yes Mother, I will be glad to help you," as he tried to keep disappointment out of his voice. His parents had instilled in their children the need to give service gladly and quickly and to care for one another. His mother would often say, "we must be of service to each other, to the family, to the Church, and to our fellowman.'" She also taught them that if they would "spend time doing good things for someone else that it would become a habit that would carry on throughout their lives".[xl]

Tom wanted to make his mother proud and help her as she needed. His baby brothers were a lot of work, as was keeping up with the chores. Secretly he envied Chase for being able to ride out with their father, and work on the ranch as much as he did.

Being the oldest wore on him sometimes; the work never seemed to end and sometimes he hated it, but with their large family he knew his mother couldn't do all that was required alone. He quickly turned from his negative thoughts and unconsciously picked up Alva as he crawled out of his crib.

***

Discouragement marred his handsome face and his brown eyes couldn't quite meet hers. Weeks had passed and he still hadn't found a job. Their savings, used for rent and food for their family of eight, were dwindling at an alarming rate. Isabella knew Hyrum's pride was hurt. He wasn't able to provide as he had been doing and the long winter kept them cooped up together most of the time causing friction between them and shortness of temper with the children.

"Can we, excuse me Mother, may we go outside? Chase and me want to go slide behind the wagons." "Chase and I," Isabella corrected almost without thought.

"I want to go too," Kenneth said, standing up from the table where he had been reading.

"Can I go too?" John Murray asked, jumping up and running for his coat.

"You're too little John, you'd fall under the wagons," Kenneth said.

"Would not."

"Would too."

"Stop that boys!" Isabella sharply reprimanded them.

"No, John Murray you better stay here. You and I will play the piano and you can sing with me." Looking miffed at his mother's attempt to divert his attention he asked again as his brothers threw on their coats and hats and ran out the door.

"Run!" The urged each other to more speed, in case their parents changed their minds. Their booted feet squeaked over the compacted snow where wagon and automobile tracks crisscrossed the street.

Even watching the backs of his boys as they slipped and slid up the road couldn't lighten Hyrum's mood. "Mother I don't want to play the piano," John Murray piped up again. "May I go out too? I won't slide behind the wagons, I'll go over to George's and maybe we can fix our snow fort."

"Yes, yes, John. Go on outside," his mother said. "Button up your coat before you leave," she reminded him absently her eyes already turned toward her husband.

Isabella reached over and took his hand which was laying palm down on the table, his strong fingers slowly drumming against the tabletop.

"Would you like to talk Hyrum?"

"Oh Tress, I don't know what to do!" He burst out. "It seems there isn't anyone hiring and I am almost ashamed to walk into another business or ask another friend if they have any work I might do," he finally paused and took a breath.

"It is winter Hyrum, we will be fine for a while longer," her soft encouraging voice gently rained on his discouraged soul. She continued, "The cattle and the homestead are faring as well as can be, we have enough food and our needs are met."

"Those are great blessings. Have faith Hyrum, God has something good in store for us, I know it. If we work together, continue to pray and do all we can to care for ourselves, the Lord will provide." She patted his hand again and stood up when she became aware that her husband's eyes were looking far away at things which were not there.

***

February 1917 *Health Crisis*

The noise of boots kicking against the front step, freeing mud collected from the boys' feet on their walk home from school brought Isabella's head up from the mending she had in her lap. The front door flew open almost without warning and the cold wind rushed inside along with her four boys. Jostling around one another to reach the coat and hat rack they, almost in unison, said "hello Mother."

"Hello," she cheerily replied.

"We heard you singing when we came up the stairs," Kenneth told her as he walked into the kitchen to where she sat near the stove. "I love it when you sing!"

She smiled and said, "There is fresh bread to tide you over until supper," and watched their cold nipped faces burst into smiles. She picked up the stocking she was mending and turned back to her work while the boys sliced and jammed rather thick pieces of bread.

Looking up she saw Tom, her oldest, buckling on his pistol belt. "Where do you think you're going wearing that?" She pointedly looked at him as he slid his pistol into its holster.

"To shoot rocks Mother."

"Not today son, "she said. "You have chores to do and I need your help with the babies while I pack."

"What are you packing for Mother? Where are we going?" he asked.

"You won't be going anywhere. You have school," she said folding her blue Sunday meeting dress and laying it gently into the suitcase laid open on the bed.

"Grandmother Hanne is very ill and your father and I are going over to Heber so we can help care for her. We will take the twins, but you will be in charge of things here. You can

The mother of H. C. Nicol is re-ported very low at her home in He-ber.

48 Duchesne Record February 3, 1917 Hanne Nicol Ill

call on Aunt Ivy if you run into trouble."

"Don't worry Mother, everything will be alright. I'll take care of things here." Tom assured her with confidence.

"Did you hear that Chase and Kenneth? I'll be in charge."

"None of that contention in this house Tom, you know better than that!" his mother quickly reprimanded her oldest son.

"Yes, Mother," Tom sheepishly replied. Then he asked, "How long will you be going for?"

"Until she is on the mend I suppose. Uncle Gabriel and Aunt Stella are there now. She isn't doing well at all."

Closing her suitcase Isabella walked into the kitchen, holding her hand over the top of the stove she moved the stew pot to a cooler section. "Is she going die Mother?" Chase asked as he walked toward her licking jam from his lip.

Answering her son truthfully she said, "We hope she will get well, but I don't know if she will die. "

Tom saw his mother swallow hard, then as if strengthening herself she briskly said, "let me finish this while you get your chores done please," and she sat quickly into her chair and picked up the darning basket.

Lifting a small stocking that was almost patched from the pile she wove the needle and yarn through the edges of the hole while she slightly pulled the edges together, smoothing the yarn flat to ensure the patch would be as lump-free as possible when the wearer put it on.

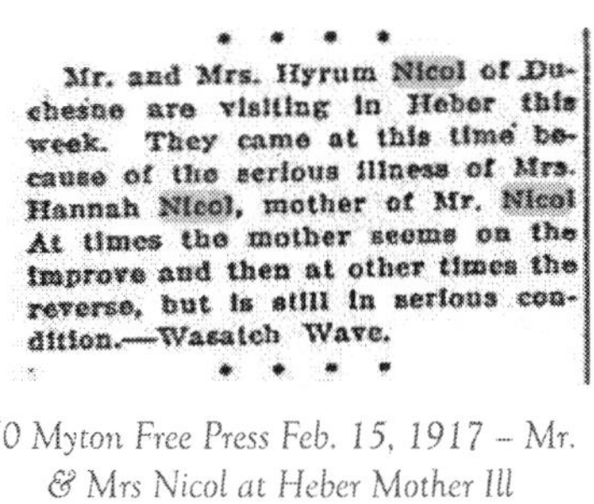
Mr. and Mrs. Hyrum Nicol of Duchesne are visiting in Heber this week. They came at this time because of the serious illness of Mrs. Hannah Nicol, mother of Mr. Nicol At times the mother seems on the improve and then at other times the reverse, but is still in serious condition.—Wasatch Wave.

50 Myton Free Press Feb. 15, 1917 – Mr. & Mrs Nicol at Heber Mother Ill

April 1917 ***America Joins the War***

"It doesn't seem real, does it Hyrum? Our country is actually going into the war against the Germans?" Isabella questioned.

"Neutrality only works if every country recognizes it, and avoids hostile actions towards us," Hyrum replied. "Germany certainly hasn't done that. They have been increasingly aggressive against our shipping vessels. That cargo ship Housatonic[xli] was sunk just days after Germany broke diplomatic relations last week after all the appeals and warnings for them to abide by their agreements."

He went on, "No one wants war less than I do. I want to continue to live in peace as we have enjoyed peace here under neutrality. But I would fight if necessary to bring about peace to the world, when that might be the only way to bring the aggressors to bay. They have been fighting over there for three years with no end in sight."

He took his teaching tone with her, and said, "Remember that column in the paper last week? President Wilson has been adamant about finding a way to end the conflict in Europe and it seems diplomacy is falling on the Kaiser's deaf ears. The speech he gave to congress that we read in the Record last week showed clear reasoning."

As I said, "I am in agreement with this decision to go to war. Every man has to register for the draft, and that means me too." Lifting his eyebrow he said, "yes, I know I'm too old since they are only taking young men 18 to 25 years old. But all of us older men have to register.[xlii] I have heard that there would be deferments for those men in agriculture, at least for now."

Isabella said thoughtfully, "these past years what with the army fighting down in Mexico, and now the war in Europe, and what appears to be a revolution starting in Russia that scripture in Matthew keeps coming back to my mind. You know the one, we've talked about it before, 'wars and rumors of wars'. I am comforted knowing we've been warned. The outcome isn't in our hands. It's only a beginning of things to come."

"I understand what you mean Tress. God knows all things and we need to seek his guidance and peace always, not just in troubled times. We won't make it through the hard times or make it back to live with him if we are overcome by the darkness and evil around us."

"I agree Hyrum. I'm going to add that to my prayers. Shall we add it to our family prayers? She asked.

"Yes, that would be a good thing, a very good thing," he replied.

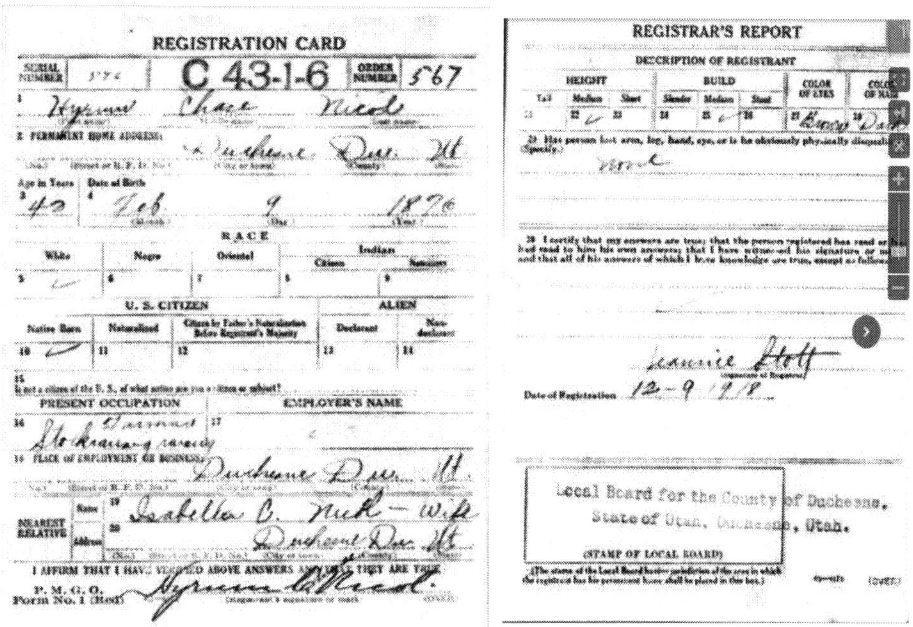
REGISTRATION CARD

SERIAL NUMBER 576 | C 43-1-6 | ORDER NUMBER 567

1 Hyrum Chase Nicol

2 PERMANENT HOME ADDRESS: Duchesne Duc. Ut

Age in Years 3 42 | Date of Birth 4 Feb 9 1876

RACE

White	Negro	Oriental	Indian: Citizen	Indian: Noncitizen
5 ✓	6	7	8	9

U. S. CITIZEN: Native Born	U. S. CITIZEN: Naturalized	U. S. CITIZEN: Citizen by Father's Naturalization Before Registrant's Majority	ALIEN: Declarant	ALIEN: Non-declarant
10 ✓	11	12	13	14

15 If not a citizen of the U. S., of what nation are you a citizen or subject?

PRESENT OCCUPATION: 16 Farming Stockraising | EMPLOYER'S NAME: 17

18 PLACE OF EMPLOYMENT OR BUSINESS: Duchesne Duc. Ut.

NEAREST RELATIVE: Name 19 Isabella C. Nicol – wife; Address 20 Duchesne Duc. Ut

I AFFIRM THAT I HAVE VERIFIED ABOVE ANSWERS AND THAT THEY ARE TRUE

P. M. G. O. Form No. 1 (Red) Hyrum C. Nicol

REGISTRAR'S REPORT

DESCRIPTION OF REGISTRANT

HEIGHT: Tall	HEIGHT: Medium	HEIGHT: Short	BUILD: Slender	BUILD: Medium	BUILD: Stout	COLOR OF EYES	COLOR OF HAIR
21	22 ✓	23	24	25 ✓	26	27 Brown	28 Dark

29 Has person lost arm, leg, hand, eye, or is he obviously physically disqualified? (Specify.) None

30 I certify that my answers are true; that the person registered has read or has had read to him his own answers; that I have witnessed his signature or mark, and that all of his answers of which I have knowledge are true, except as follows:

Jeannie Stott (Signature of Registrar)

Date of Registration 12-9-1918

Local Board for the County of Duchesne, State of Utah, Duchesne, Utah.

(STAMP OF LOCAL BOARD)

(The stamp of the Local Board having jurisdiction of the area in which the registrant has his permanent home shall be placed in this box.)

(OVER)

51 H.C. Nicol World War I Draft Card

***

March 1917 *An Unexpected Offer*

Alma Moroni, his new wife Ivy, Isabella and Hyrum were visiting together in the Murdock's pleasant parlor. Ivy said, we are so glad you are back in the Basin and we can visit like this. We missed and worried about you while you were gone."

The spring evening was mild and the first stars were beginning to shine when the conversation turned to their homesteads in Midview.

"The new artisan wells we had dug are pumping water out at a good steady rate," A.M. said. "It's been a boon certainly, the cattle have better access to water and we didn't lose any to the river." Hyrum replied.

"The wells are flowing steady, the pools we dug around them are filled. The pools are doing the job, but so do the fields; water turned into the ditches and fields takes a long time if never to soak the soil."

"True, the water is only getting in a few inches down. The alfalfa fields are pretty sparse." "That's what I have seen also," A.M. replied.

Thoughtfully shaking his head Hyrum said, "Nothing has changed. No matter how we try to improve the homestead, it stays the same. We can only raise what cattle the land itself will support, small and nothing more."

Alma Moroni looked over at his wife, and she nodded at him while Isabella looked quizzically over the head of the baby she was softly patting on his back.

Looking between them A.M. said, "Hyrum and Isabella, Ivy and I have a proposition to offer you." There was a pause while he waited for their full attention. "We would like to buy you out of your homestead. You know we bought your mother's place last December and with your homestead Ivy and I would have almost a full section for our cattle. I'm getting older and I want to consolidate our holdings into a more manageable ranch. We believe this would benefit you two and benefit us also."

Glancing at his wife Hyrum asked, "What are you offering us Alma?"

"This is what we propose." He paused and then began, "we have 80 acres in Sowers' Canyon about fifteen miles south of town that has a small log house on it, and 60 acres north of town up the Duchesne and," he paused, "we would also sell you the house you are currently renting from us."

"The Sower's Canyon property is ranch land, you'd have to dig wells, but Antelope Creek isn't too far from the place. It isn't too far from Bishop Billings' ranch. There is a lot of additional land available from the Department of the Interior around the ground out there that you might pick up for additional property. The 60 acres up the Duchesne is good ground for alfalfa or hay."

"Ivy and I have other properties that produce enough grass and hay that not having irrigable land over in Midview won't be an impact for us," Alva continued.

After several silent moments, Hyrum swallowed hard before he said, "that's an unexpected offer Alma. It's not as if we haven't talked about selling the homestead." Looking over at his amazed wife he said, "Would you mind if we spent some time thinking it over before we make any decision?"

"Take your time Hyrum, there's no hurry. I've always said, I'm here to help any way I can."

"Alma Moroni has always been unfaltering in our behalf Hyrum and has always seen our needs often before we have. Let's ride out to the Sowers' Canyon property and see how we feel once we're there." With unusual abruptness she said, "We can go tomorrow, and make a day of it."

"How does that sound boys?" Tom and Chase looked wide-eyed at their parents; "all of us?" Tom asked. "Yes, all of us. It's a big decision, don't you want to see where you might be living?"

It was morning twilight, just before dawn broke over the eastern ridge when Isabella woke the boys. The stove was hot and a large pan of oats was bubbling and there was an air of anticipation abounding in the house. After months of worry, and dead-ends each way they turned, this offer seemed a doorway out of the darkness.

***

Isabella looked at the small log cabin, sitting so forlornly in the middle of the dusty patch of ground, as Hyrum turned the wagon into the rutted path. As they drew closer her heart sank and she felt her optimism flee. Her mind raced back 11 years and she saw her younger self in the little cabin on their Midview homestead with an infant and toddler; all alone while Hyrum built fence, dug wells and ditches, cleared fields and worked building the canals and she almost cried.

Hyrum glanced at her as he pulled the horses to a stop and he knew what she was feeling by the stoic expression that had covered her generally smiling face. He knew and could feel her disappointment and he was ashamed that he hadn't been able to continue to provide the life she so deserved. Clearing his throat he said, "Well, let's see what this property might hold for us," and he jumped off the wagon, dust puffing out from under the soles of his boots as he hit the ground.

The boys rode up beside him as the wagon had stopped and climbed down out of their saddles.

"Tressa," he said holding up his hands to take Alma and then Alva. "Tom! Chase! Please come and take the twins while I help your mother down."

"Watch for rattlers!" Isabella warned as the boys began to scatter around the yard.

"I have my pistol Mother," Tom said as he, Chase, and Kenneth started walking toward the little cabin.

"It's not much is it Tress?" Hyrum observed as he pushed open the door. "Let me check inside for snakes before you come in," he warned.

Isabella stepped through the rough doorway into the small two-room cabin her feet falling onto a dirt floor instead of the planks she expected.

She gazed around the dark rooms and looked up seeing the hard dirt bottom of the sod that covered the roof. "No Hyrum, this is not much to look at." In her mother's heart she was asking herself, "how will we fit in this place?"

"And the dirt! Dirt everywhere." She sighed and walked back outside and looked around at the rolling hills of sand and sagebrush. The enthusiasm she had felt when they left their home that morning was replaced with the reality of what starting from scratch again would mean.

"Boys, take the horses down to the creek for water before we start for home. I'll have dinner set out when you get back." Isabella called to them.

Hyrum and John Murray were walking around the small corral next to the cabin while Isabella spread out the large blanket she had used in the twins' wagon box to cover the bed of the wagon. Then she hefted each of the boys over the tailgate and into the wagon to crawl and toddle without her needing to keep them in sight.

She set out the dinner she had packed onto another blanket that she lay down next to the wagon in a slight sliver of shade.

The heat of the early spring day radiated onto her head and up from the ground, perspiration breaking out on her cheeks and forehead. "It's only March, how much hotter will it be here in July and August?" she asked herself while handing the one-year-old twins the end crusts of the bread she had cut and laid out on the napkin next to the leftover roast beef slices and pickles.

Once their dinner had disappeared into her always hungry boys, Isabella stood and began shaking crumbs from the now empty napkins. She carefully folded the linen and placed them lovingly into the dinner box. "We need to be leaving Hyrum, the twins need to rest; it's a long way back to town and I'm hoping they will sleep most of the way home."

"Did it really take us over an hour to get here?" she asked. It would be a long day once they arrived home.

Breaking into her reverie she heard, "Mother, may we start riding ahead?"

"Yes, don't get too far in front of us," Isabella replied and to herself she thought "that will give Hyrum and me time to talk about this proposition."

Before she could bring up her concerns about this piece of property Hyrum beat her to it, his tongue clicking the horses forward slightly faster he said, "I'm not certain what I expected, but it is 'The Basin' and this country doesn't change much whichever end you ride through or which property we use for a ranch. It will be dry, sage brush covered, and hard to homestead."

Isabella only nodded. Hyrum, trying to put a better face on the situation said, "Before we make any decisions I suggest that tomorrow we ride to the north property and look it over. That piece is only 3 miles or so away from the house."

***

The supper dishes were cleared and the boys went outside to finish up their evening chores before she and Hyrum finally had some quieter time to talk. Sitting across the table from one another Hyrum began. "I don't see any other way out of our financial dilemma Tress."

"We know we have to have ground to grow hay and alfalfa or we can't afford to keep our cattle through the winter otherwise. Our resources are at an end and," Hyrum's voice trailed off as the bleakness of their situation began to overwhelm him.

Isabella, seeing the distress in his eyes and hearing the sadness in his voice said, "Hyrum we are not in charge here, you know that. We put ourselves in God's hands the day we were sealed for time and all eternity in His holy temple. We covenanted that we would go and do whatever and however he directed our paths."

"We came to the basin following the council of our Stake President. We have worked hard, and done all that we've been asked to do, haven't we?" Not waiting for his answer she continued, "He knows where we are and what our circumstances are. We have to have faith that he will bring us through."

Hyrum raised his eyes and his heart began to beat a little faster as she continued. "Our life is not meant to be an easy road, we know through revelation that we are meant to be tried and tested to strengthen our faith and testimony in Jesus Christ and to aspire to become the sons and daughters we promised we would be when we die and return home to him."

Her voice became firmer as she said, "we have never gone without the necessities of life, have we? We have never been without a roof over our heads, have we? We have always had food to eat, and clothes to wear. We have both been healed by the power and blessings of the Holy Priesthood. If God has opened this door for us, then we must step through it with faith and hope for a better future."

Hyrum's heart overflowed with the warm witness from the Holy Spirit which testified to the truth to all that his eternal companion said. His love for her was strengthened, his spirits were lifted as the dark cloud of discouragement was dispelled by her never-ending faith in Jesus Christ and his eternal love.

Raising his eyebrows he asked, "Then we do this?"

"Yes, we do this," she replied, looking into his brown eyes as it seemed into his very soul and repeated. "Yes, we do."

52 Sowers Canyon Cabin, circa 2014 Right side addition by subsequent owner

April 1917 *Starting Over*

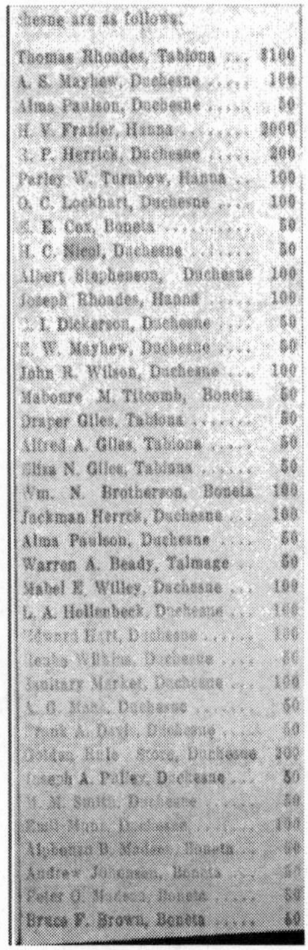

…hesne are as follows:

Thomas Rhoades, Tabiona	$100
A. S. Mayhew, Duchesne	100
Alma Paulson, Duchesne	50
H. V. Frazier, Hanna	2000
[illegible] P. Herrick, Duchesne	200
Parley W. Turnbow, Hanna	100
O. C. Lockhart, Duchesne	100
[illegible] E. Cox, Boneta	50
H. C. Nicol, Duchesne	50
Albert Stephenson, Duchesne	100
Joseph Rhoades, Hanna	100
[illegible] I. Dickerson, Duchesne	50
[illegible] W. Mayhew, Duchesne	50
John R. Wilson, Duchesne	100
Mabonre M. Titcomb, Boneta	50
Draper Giles, Tabiona	50
Alfred A. Giles, Tabiona	50
Eliza N. Giles, Tabiona	50
Wm. N. Brotherson, Boneta	100
Jackman Herrck, Duchesne	100
Alma Paulson, Duchesne	50
Warren A. Beady, Talmage	50
Mabel E. Willey, Duchesne	100
L. A. Hollenbeck, Duchesne	100
[illegible]	100
[illegible]	50
Sanitary Market, Duchesne	100
[illegible]	50
[illegible]	50
[illegible]	200
[illegible] A. [illegible], Duchesne	50
[illegible]	50
[illegible]	100
[illegible]	50
[illegible]	50
[illegible]	50
Bruce F. Brown, Boneta	50

53 *Duchesne Record First Liberty Loan Donations List*

Spring green lined the edges of the road, where sage sparrows called across the open ground giving a lift to the heart and soul. "Spring always makes me smile Hyrum. It just lifts my spirit," she said, "I could sing, and sing along with the birds and if I were younger I would skip toward the land office." He smiled at her renewed enthusiasm and took her hand as they walked up onto the wooden sidewalk in front of the businesses downtown. Once Rock Pope put the wooden boulevard up in front of the Pioneer Store, other businesses soon followed, and were seeing a decrease in the dirt carried into their buildings.

Pulling the chair out for Isabella, Hyrum sat next to her and across from the land office manager who had prepared the paperwork for the sale and transfer of property between Alma and Ivy Murdock and themselves. Once the full exchange was made they had sold their 280 acre Midview homestead for $1,900, and purchased an 80-acre parcel in Sowers Canyon which included the small cabin for $1,000. Including the 60 acres of cleared and fenced property up the Duchesne River for $700 and two town lots including their home in Duchesne for $200. Signing the last of the papers, they stood up and shook hands all around.

Hyrum and Isabella were starting over.[xliii]

***

Sowers Canyon Homestead

"I've sold some cattle to cover the cost of those two parcels of Department of Interior land in Sowers Canyon," laughing as he said, "even at 50 cents an acre the price is too high. But there's no choice, eighty acres isn't sufficient to run a herd of any size out there."

Hyrum answered the questions coming from the group of men standing together outside of the church building after Sunday school meeting. "We've had to do some repairs on the cabin before we could move in." "No, we'll only be out there during the summers. There is no way Mrs. Nicol would allow the boys to miss school." "Yes, we will be moving out there in a few weeks, once the school term is over." "Of course we'll be in town each week for church meetings. You can always count on us, you know that."

"Now boys, you know we cannot take all of the goods from the house. We are taking only enough to make the cabin livable for the summer; I tell myself it will be like our camping trips when we go to Heber." Isabella told the boys after another round of questions about what they wanted to put into the wagon that "I am only taking a few pans, dishes and dinnerware, bedding and mattresses, and a single change of clothing each. You older boys will be sleeping outside."

"Really? They eagerly asked.

"Yes, there isn't enough room for all of us under that tiny roof. Your Father has purchased a large tent that we will put up next to the cabin. If he doesn't have the time you will have to build some frames to keep your mattresses off of the ground."

"Do we have to sleep in the tent Mother? Might we sleep out under the stars?" their questions came so quickly Isabella couldn't keep track of who asked her what. "I love sleeping under the stars and watching them move before I fall asleep," Kenneth claimed.

"I would suppose that would be an option if you'd like, at least some of the time. If it rains, well, into the tent you go."

"Thank you Mother!" After that boon the boys began to feel more comfortable with the move and leaving their friends for the summer.

***

"Hyrum, I am not going to go to church dirty and dusty from a fifteen-mile ride every Sunday. We have to come up with a better plan."

"You've got some ideas already, don't you?" Hyrum squinted at her from under his dusty hat.

"Yes, I've thought of several options that might work. Do you want to hear them?"

"Of course. I'm listening," he said.

"Well, one is that we go into town after work on Saturday, maybe leave a bit earlier, and stay at the house. I don't care if we have to sleep on the floor. I want to have a bath and walk to church clean and I want the boys presentable. We aren't heathens Hyrum, even if we are living rough." Isabella clearly stated her objective.

He nodded, and waited.

"My other idea is to arise very early on Sunday and take baths at the house before going to church." "But," she continued, "that would make for a very rushed morning."

Hyrum C. & Isabella M. Nicol Home in
Duchesne, Utah

54 Duchesne House

Hyrum knew better than to argue about personal things with Tressa. She was raised a lady and the 12 years they had pioneered hadn't changed that. She set high standards, and expected her husband and sons to behave as gentlemen, no matter their living circumstances. He appreciated her tender influence in their lives; he knew he was a better man because of her.

"Tressa, whichever works the best, we can try it both ways. I like being clean before the Lord too."

Spring 1917 *Black Clouds on the Horizon*

Heavy roiling clouds filled the canyon from crest to crest and hung heavy on the tops of the hills surrounding the little cabin. Winds pushed the walls of the tent inward in its single-minded flight to escape. Looking for which boy was nearest she called, "John Murray, is the milk cow in the yard corral?"

"She should be Mother, I'll check on her."

Isabella urged him on, "if she's is, take her inside the lean-to and tie her to the milking rail."

"Tom. Check the tent stakes and tie-downs and make them tighter if you have to. We can't afford to lose the tent to this storm. Help John if he isn't back when you're finish."

"Yes, ma'am," Tom said, pulling his hat down tighter and pushed himself into the wind.

Isabella shrieked when a flash of lightening and bang of thunder hit the field behind them in split second succession. Tom jumped too as he turned searching for John Murray. His gaze took in heavy dark gray and black line of rain marching across the canyon advancing like an army ready for battle.

"John! Get in to the house!" he yelled as his younger brother raced across the yard and pushed around Tom who was holding the door open against the howling wind, ready to slam it shut before the onslaught of water began its assault on the tiny cabin.

"Alva and Alma come here and I will put you on the bed. You must be quiet and stop yelling; it won't help anything screaming and crying."

The two small blond haired boys ran toward their mother, anxious to do her bidding, and secretly hoping for something to eat.

"Tom will you stoke the fire in the stove?"

"I wonder where your dad and brothers are?" she questioned. In her mind's eye she could see them caught in the narrow canyon a wall of water rolling down toward them with no way to outrun it. Saying a silent prayer for her husband and sons' safety, she felt the warmth of the spirit wrapping her heart in peace and an unbidden thought came into her mind; 'they are under the rock ledges to the south waiting out the rain'. With the peaceable assurance of their safety she continued to do her work with a calm and grateful heart.

"Mother," Tom said, "the roof is leaking and not just a little."

"Move the bed away from the leak while I get out the rest of our buckets and pans," she directed. There were more leaks squeezing their way through the loose boards and dirt that served as the roof of their tiny cabin as the ferocious rain continued its onslaught. She placed a bucket under a small stream of rain running through the roof and across the rough log rafter holding up the wood and dirt ceiling before dropping, or rather splashing, to the dirt floor.

The rain continued, the clouds opened sending a deluge of water like a waterfall plunging to earth; it fell, steady, straight, gray, and cold. The heavy clouds dropped lower and lower washing the sodden ground into streams and rivers that ran together until the little log cabin stood alone in the middle of a lake of muddy water.

"Do you think we will get a wood floor here like at home?" John asked.

"We talk about it John," his mother said matter-of-factly, "but I don't think any time soon. I don't worry about it too much, we are only here four months a year," and then abruptly changing her train of thought, "I think it is cool enough to bake a cake," and she turned to the small table and began gathering ingredients.

"John put a log in the stove and push it toward the back, by the time the cake is ready to bake it should be at about the right temperature."

"A cake? In the summer with no special occasion?" Tom realized that his Mother was worried and baking a cake would keep her calm and give the little boys something to keep their minds from the storm. He kept these thoughts to himself and moved another pan in place so he could empty the one already filled from the leaky roof.

The summer storm moved on with the same aggressiveness it had approached with and continued to thunder on across the mountains leaving the canyon dark and waterlogged. The water that pooled around the cabin was quickly absorbed into the bone dry, thirsty soil. Within an hour of the deluge the ground was damp with only occasional puddles found in depressions between the sage brush clumps.

Emptying the last bucket from inside the cabin Tom called to his mother, "Father is coming."

"Just in time for dinner and won't it be a surprise for them to see we have cake for later on?" She smiled.

After supper Isabella and Hyrum walked across the road toward Antelope Creek. "I want to check on my garden," she said as the boys cleared the table and cleaned up after their meal.

They heard the roar of the generally placid creek as it attempted to disgorge the water ripping its banks free with the pressure of the rain swollen stream as it swirled and slammed against and undercut the banks.

"Stand back Tress!" Hyrum warned though they were several yards away from the wild racing water.

"It is almost washed out Hyrum," Isabella bemoaned as she saw the devastation the storm had done to her garden. She could see where the wall of water had cut troughs through the furrows and trickles of water continued to drain into puddles where the drowned and broken plants were only yesterday beginning to show signs of life.

***

Mid-August 1917 ***Berry Pickin'***

"We need a break from this heat Hyrum. Let's go camping so we can gather berries, my jam and bottled currant supply is almost gone."

"Where do you want to go Tress?"

"I was thinking Currant Creek or just up the river canyon where it is cooler. I was thinking we could pack the wagon and leave Monday and not have to drive all the way back out here."

"That's a good idea," Hyrum replied, "the older boys and I need to turn the water into the alfalfa field up on the river property. We may be able to get another cutting before September," he said. "It is settled then, up the river road it is."

"John Murray, help me put these canvas sheets in the wagon along with the other camping tent. I have the bedding rolled, and ready to put in also."

"How long will we stay Mother?"

"I think at least two days."

"I like camping," John told her and smiled as he handed her another bedroll.

Quickly looking around, Isabella's head turned almost on a swivel, "where are the twins?"

"Under the wagon Mother," John said.

"Thanks for keeping an eye out. Those boys can move faster than rabbits startled from under a bush."

Isabella said, "Hyrum, I'll take John Murray and the twins with me and hope to find a shady spot near the berry patches." "I'll not have you go alone Tress. Tom, climb up there and drive for your mother. Chase and Kenneth can help with the irrigation." "Yes Father," Tom replied, looking down at his feet so his father and mother wouldn't see the anger in his eyes.

"Hey Tom," Chase yelled, I put our fishing poles in the back behind the twins' box." Chase knew how much Tom was growing tired of always having to stay behind to help his mother with the children and he also knew how much Tom loved to fish. Standing in the rolling water seemed to calm him and he smiled again. "Maybe when you and John get the tent set up you can catch us some fish for dinner," he yelled over his shoulder. We'll be too tired from irrigating to be of much help."

As the wagon rattled over the washboard roadbed Tom was deep in thought and he didn't hear his mother's voice. "What mother?" He asked. "I wasn't listening."

"I could see that Tom," she said. "I was saying thank you for helping me so much. I appreciate it. You're a good boy."

Tom thought he wasn't much of a boy anymore, he was fourteen. He only said, "You're welcome Mother, you know I'll always help you."

"What do you think of pulling in there, in that little clearing under those cottonwood trees?" Isabella pointed ahead of them toward a copse of cottonwoods. "It looks good Mother, close to the river and I can see from here the bullberry bushes are full too."

Woahing the horses to a stop, Tom jumped to the ground and helped his mother down from the bench before he began to unhitch the horses from their traces.

"John before we start pulling everything from the wagon, hand me the twins' lines," Isabella said, "they are rolled up under the bench."

"Tom hold Alma, back him toward me please." "Alma hold still while I tie this rope through the straps of your overalls." "Good, now it's your turn Alva." "Will you take the other ends and tie them to the bush over there away from the river?"

"I think it was easier when they couldn't walk Mother," Tom laughed, as the 18-month-old twins began pulling at the bushes and toddling toward their mother. The lines were long enough they could wander and short enough they wouldn't be in the way as Tom, John Murray and their mother put the camp together.

Looking around with satisfaction, Isabella said, "the camp looks neat and tidy and isn't it wonderful how cool it is under this shade? Do you want to go fishing now Tom?" Looking up from where he was laying the twigs, branches, and logs for their evening fire he replied, "I do Mother, as soon as I finish building the fire."

John Murray asked quickly, "can I go too Mother?"

"Did you bring a fishing pole?"

"No. But I can use Chase's."

"I don't think so son. If you want to fish go find a good length of river willow. I did bring a roll of line and some hooks. You can go dig some worms over by the bank under the willows after you've cut your pole. Try that bush over there, it looks like it has some sturdy branches."

Evening had slowly darkened around their fire before Hyrum, Kenneth, and Chase rode into camp. "Good timing men," Isabella called lightheartedly, smiling as they swung less than nimbly from their saddles after their long ride up the canyon.

The pinion fire smoke filtered through the dusty green leaves of the cottonwoods overhead. "I'll get the milk and then we can eat. There's a dutch oven stew ready. Chase, after you wash up, will you slice the bread?"

Leaning over the small river inlet Tom had built to keep their food cool, Isabella sighed thoughtfully. Tom was always building something, he had that kind of mind and hands.

Before reaching for the bottles of milk, she soaked the cloth she carried, twisted the water out of it, and felt relief as the coolness of the damp cloth washed away the dust on her face and hands.

Standing next to the fire, calling her family near, they knelt around the campfire while Hyrum gave thanks for the abundance in their lives and for the blessings of Heavenly Father's gifts of safety, guidance, and protection.

As they stood, after their nightly family prayer, their stomachs rumbled, and laughter bubbled, and joy filled Isabella and Hyrum's hearts as they dished stew from the cast iron kettle for their boys. "We are so blessed Hyrum," Isabella whispered as they sat on the log Tom and John Murray had rolled up toward the fire.

That night they didn't sleep in the tent; the air was so clear, and the stars fairly called for them to lay awake and watch the dance the Creator set for them. Isabella felt she was such a small speck beneath that expanse of heaven and marveled that He knew her. She had fallen asleep with the words of Moses from the Pearl of Great Price [xliv] in her mind:

> *And it came to pass that Moses looked, and beheld the world upon which he was created; and Moses beheld the world and the ends thereof, and all the children of men which are, and which were created; of the same he greatly marveled and wondered.*
>
> *And the presence of God withdrew from Moses, that his glory was not upon Moses; and Moses was left unto himself. And as he was left unto himself, he fell unto the earth.*
>
> *And it came to pass that it was for the space of many hours before Moses did again receive his natural strength like unto man; and he said unto himself: Now, for this cause I know that man is nothing, which thing I never had supposed.*

***

"Berry time boys," Isabella called to the tall young men standing on the bank of the river, catching more fish in the quiet of the morning. She bent and untied the twins' from the wagon wheel where they had been pushing rocks back and forth between the spokes. "Tom will you carry the canvas, Chase and Kenneth grab one of the twins, and John carry the baskets," she directed her family like a general marshalling for battle.

"That's right. Spread the canvas around under the bush, be careful not to bump the branches or the berries will fall off onto the ground. Good, that's good."

"Kenneth, you better roll down the sleeves of your shirt, the thorns on these bushes will cut you. Keep your gloves," on she warned no one in particular. "Alright, let's circle the bush all around, now, be careful when you take hold of the branches try not to grab on to the thorns. Now shake the bush!"

The bush started shaking as if the wind was going to pull it from the ground and as the branches whipped in the artificial wind the perfectly ripe Bullberries fell through the leaves to land on the canvas spread below and everyone began to laugh. They kept laughing and shaking the bush until no more berries fell through to the ground.

Down on her knees, Isabella carefully pulled the canvas away from the bush, and once out in the open she said, "Each of you take a corner of the canvas and lift. One, two, three," she counted as the berried rolled into a pile in the center of the canvas.

"John Murray hand me a basket." Taking care not to kneel on the berries they scooped up handfuls of the dark, juicy fruit and dropped it gently into the basket.

Bush after bush they gathered berries; bullberries into one basket, currants into another, and Kenneth exploring further along the river bank called out, "Mother, there's a great big blackberry bush here. It's almost a tree," he exclaimed.

High stepping over broken branches through knee high grasses her skirts pulled high with one hand Isabella and Tom carried the twins, and John Murray held the last of their empty baskets. When they reached the river bank Kenneth, whose lips were already blue from eating the ripe berries said, "it is big isn't it?"

"Hey, look here," Tom pointed to a large track in the mud by the bush. "Is that a bear track Tom?" John Murray asked.

"I don't think I've ever seen one so large before," Chase declared. "Yep, it is a bear track John," Tom replied, as he bent down and spread his hand inside the print that had been pushed deep into the mud.

"How do you know Tom? Is it still here?" John Murray nervously looked over his shoulder. "No, it isn't here now. I've shown you this before John," Tom said patiently. "When the inside is still wet or damp and the outside edge is dried and crumbly a bit it is a day or two old. If the edges are soft and sticky, you better be watching yourself. That bear could be right around the corner."

John's eyes went wide and he screamed because just as Tom said watch yourself, Chase who had been working his way around the blackberry bush while Tom talked, jumped at John Murray's back and growled as loudly as he could.

Shouting in terror John stared at his brother then started to run after him yelling. Chase laughed and easily outpaced him. Heading back toward the blackberry bush Chase almost ran into his parents.

"Hey there! What's going on here?" Isabella's eyes took in the scene in one glance. "Chase do I need to give you a dose?" "Oh no Mother," he exclaimed as he slid to a stop. "Well then stop teasing your brother!"

Isabella believed that a spoonful of 'castor oil cured all ills from a stomach ache, or headache, or whatever. Even to the extent that when the boys were on the offish side, such as doing little things like pushing little biddies in the ditch', castor oil was the cure".[xlv]

***

Sitting on a log, next to the fire he had started in the cool morning light, Hyrum's thoughts were miles away from the filled baskets of fragrant fruit sitting in the wagon bed. They were far from this quiet spot where his family slept, tow-heads peaking from the top of blankets. He thought of his and Tressa's dreams of success on the reservation. He could see people prospering all around them, but it seemed that no matter what they tried to do, no matter how hard they worked, or the sacrifices they made, the advice they took, or how much faith they had in the Lord and his provident hand they could never quite get there.

Just what did he mean by there, he asked himself? There, where hard work and honesty paid the dividends of prosperity and peace of mind. There was where they wouldn't have to mortgage all they owned to make it day by day, month by month, and year by year. There was where he wouldn't have to watch his beloved Tress slowly work herself to the bone. There was where he could be proud of his ability to care for his family.

In the midst of his reverie Isabella sat up, the worn patchwork quilt wrapped around her thin shoulders. "You're up early," she said, knowing he hadn't seen her watching his troubled face, nor that she saw his mask of self-assurance drop over his eyes before he replied.

"I couldn't sleep Tressa. I like the coolness under these trees," he waved his arm encompassing the tall, sweeping canopy of green over their heads, changing the direction of her eyes and the conversation.

Kneeling by the river's edge, scrubbing the last of their breakfast dishes, Isabella started making plans for the week. "Hyrum, I want you to drop me and the twins off in town for the week. I want to make the jam[xlvi] and bottle the currants at home, not out at the cabin."

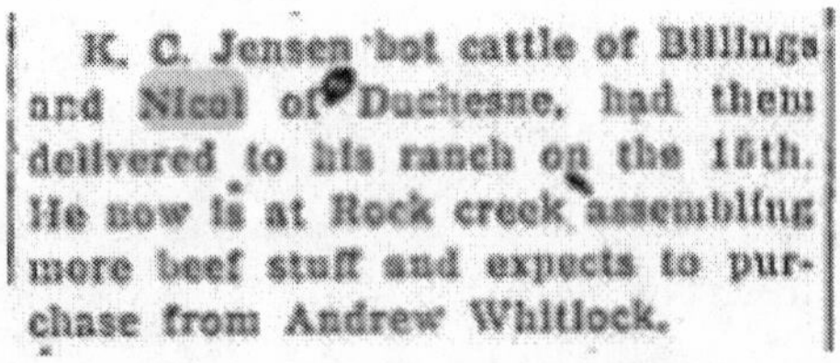
K. C. Jensen bot cattle of Billings and Nicol of Duchesne, had them delivered to his ranch on the 15th. He now is at Rock creek assembling more beef stuff and expects to purchase from Andrew Whitlock.

55 Duchesne Record November 24, 1917 - Nicol selling cattle

"I can see why you want to do that Tress, it will be much easier," he replied. I can manage fine with just the twins." "The boys and I will be home Saturday."

***

May 1918 *More Land for the Sowers Ranch*

Riding into the cabin yard ahead of Hyrum, Chase and Kenneth called out to the cabin. "We're back!" They needn't have called; it was so quiet up their canyon that the sound of their horses heralded their arrival long before the disturbed dust floated high enough to see someone on the road.

"Clean off before you come inside," Isabella said as she stood at the door. "Tom, will you and Kenneth carry the table outside. We'll eat out here."

Watching her husband and sons dust off their clothes, and slap their hats on the legs of their pants she asked, "Was there any problem purchasing the land from the government?"

"No. The land office only wants the money and since we are buying it outright we won't have to prove up like we did on the Midview ranch."

S2 Section 14 Township 5S Range 5W Accession No. 630989

N2NW4 Section 13 Township 5S Range 5W Accession No. 630990

The Nicol Sowers Canyon Ranch now totals 460 acres; a full section plus some," Hyrum said proudly. Then as he walked up to Isabella still standing in the doorway he softly said, "we're on our way again Tressa" and gently kissed the top of her head. [xlvii]

***

Summer 1918 *Coming to Another Crossroad*

"It so is 'so very hot, lonesome, and dry' out here Hyrum, I don't know if I can continue to do this. [xlviii] I mean the moving back and forth from town to this isolated dusty place." She went on quickly, watching Hyrum's jaw tense.

"I know that is what we decided when we made this leap and I'm trying to be strong, but it is wearing on me much more so than when we were younger and more energetic. I remember when no hardship was too hard because I could see a better future. Help me see that future Hyrum. I'm so very tired." She pleaded.

Nodding his head and purposefully relaxing his face, he could feel the release on his teeth when he said, "I know how difficult this new ranching venture is," then his voice wandered off into silence. It broke his heart to see his Tressa working so very hard to care for him and the family. She always tried to keep a smile on her face, though some days she didn't show it often.

"Never mind me Hyrum," she said, attempting to throw off the gloom that seemed to overwhelm her mind and heart. "I'll be alright enough in a bit," she said her eyes narrowing, and her expressive lips pursed in determination.

Looking to change the tone of their conversation, he tipped his head toward Tom and Chase, "take care of the boys and do your chores, I want to take your mother out for a ride before the heat of the day."

"Kenneth saddle the horses for us while your mother gets ready."

"Yes Father," he said as he grabbed his hat from the peg on the wall and walked quickly toward the door.

The early summer morning's air was filled with the last of the night's desert cold and Isabella wrapped her jacket close as she swung her leg over the saddle. She lifted her face toward the east while the sun lifted against the pastel blue sky that seemed to hover over the hill behind their cabin. Shifting to settle more firmly into her saddle, the leather creaked, and that warm horse smell wafted up into her nostrils. Smiling she turned toward the road, nudging her horse with her boot heels, she said, "what do you want to talk about Hyrum? It's early and I have a lot to do."

"It can all wait Tress." He paused, and tipped his head toward his shoulder. "How did you know I wanted to talk?" "It's your way Hyrum, I see the thoughts behind your eyes even when you put on that Scottish nothing-is-wrong face."

"You know me too well," he said. "I want to ride to the outer forty. We will have to pull the cattle into the feed lot even sooner than we did last year. They have eaten every blade of grass and weed fit for consumption."

"Look over there," he raised his leather gloved finger. "There isn't enough grass on all of our land to feed more than 10 cows, let alone a herd large enough to sustain us or allow us to prosper beyond where we are today." "Then that's what we'll have to do then Hyrum," she said matter-of-factly.

"We have yield from the Duchene river property, but I don't think it will be enough, and I don't know where the funds will come from to purchase more. The money from the last cattle sale was barely enough to pay off our feed loans." Frustration emanated from his tense shoulders and his ridged posture. "It's the same story every year. That's what ranchers do Hyrum. Why do you seem more upset about it this time? What are you thinking?" Isabella asked him.

"It's just been so much more difficult this go around, I know. I feel it too, we are not as young nor energetic as we were," he said. "I'm feeling we don't have it in us to continue this way sweetheart," his earnest words poured from his heart.

"I cannot bear to see you suffer and see your health continue to decline under the stress and hard work."

"Then what shall we do Hyrum? We have no money, we have to take a mortgage out each spring just to pay it off in time to take another one," Isabella added cautiously.

"As usual Tress, we are at a fork in our road, maybe more than one fork, I think. Looking at our situation we could just stay the course we are on here in the canyon, and press forward. We might sell everything here and move back to Heber into our little house. A third possibility may be to move to another town or city where there might be more opportunity for work and the boys would have greater prospects." He paused, longer this time. "The fourth option would be to sell this place and stay in the Basin and try again in some other location, possibly up near our Duchesne river property." After the gush of words Hyrum seemed at a loss to continue.

"You've been thinking about this for a while, haven't you? I know that nothing seems right at the moment Hyrum. But we are together, the boys are healthy and doing well in school," her voice also trailed off into silence.

Then she whispered, "I just don't know." "Neither do I Tress," Hyrum echoed. Looking toward one another, and without a word between them, they stopped their horses, dismounted, and dropped to their knees. Heads bowed low, their hearts yearning toward heaven, they poured out their desires and fears to the Lord.

***

Summer 1918 *Shooting Len Nielson*

Heat mirages wafted across the desert ahead of them, dust softly puffed from beneath their horse's hoofs as Tom and Chase rode south and back north, east then west looking for cattle strayed from their ranch. The air carried the occasional morning meadowlark song and the two boys kept an eye out for rattlesnakes that would stretch, out or worse, coil up beneath the sagebrush or in the rock-filled outcrops throughout the ranch.

Tom had his pistol holstered at his side. He prized his pistol and was proud of it and proud of his ability to hit what he aimed at almost all the time. His father had taught him to shoot at an early age as he had taught each of the boys to use weapons for protection, especially riding the ranch; rattlesnakes weren't the only varmints that would and could injure a man or animal.

When his parent's first came to the desert country to homestead, Tom was only two and Chase, riding next to him, was just an infant. They'd moved onto the 'rez' six months or so after it first opened to white settlement in September of 1905. Though Duchesne had grown and had the trappings of a town, with lights, telephones, and electricity. Their ranch in Sowers Canyon about 15 miles from town was as desolate an area now as when the Indians were first confined to the newly designated Uintah Valley Reservation in 1863.

Stopping on the top of a hard-packed sandy hill searching for tell-tale signs of the wandering cattle, Tom lifted his hat and wiped his forehead, wet from the persistent sun pounding down. He pulled his pistol out and shot at a rock a fair piece away; the dust popping just below the target, his steady black mare not twitching when the pistol fired. "We haven't seen a track of those cows Chase. Let's take a break, why don't we ride over to Len's and see if he's seen any strays out his way. It's been a while since we've been over. Besides, the horses could use some rest and water before we move on."

Spotting Len out in his yard, Tom and Chase "hallo'd," as they trotted their horses next to the barn, and climbed down from their thirsty mounts.

"Might we water our horses Len," Chase asked?

“Sure boys, help yourselves. What are you doing this far out in this heat?”

“Searching for some cattle that wandered away from the herd. You haven't seen any strays up this way have you Len?”

“Not up here, but I haven't been out in the back acres for a while, they could be up there, but it's pretty dried out, not much water over that way.”

While the horses drank, the boys and Len leaned against the barn in the shade. “That's a nice pistol you've got there Tom, can I see it?” Len asked.

Tom reached down and pulled the pistol from its holster, flipping it over to hand the butt of the gun to Len. In mid-flip the pistol fired and it was pointed right at Len! As if in slow motion Tom watched the bullet enter in the front and exited the back of Len’s neck. Then Len dropped to the ground.

“What should they do? They were just boys. He didn't want to go to jail, it was an accident.” all these thoughts raced through Tom's mind as he grabbed his horse, flew into the saddle and galloped away leaving Chase staring down at Len. Pushing his horse as fast as she could run through the miles between Len's cabin and theirs, Tom was certain Len was dying or even dead and what was he to do?

His little black horse was lathered and on her knees when Tom jumped from her back and ran to his mother, blurting out "I by accident shot Len Nielson"!

Being the mother of seven boys Isabella had developed nerves of steel where the actions of her sons were concerned, but at this pronouncement she collapsed to the ground.

Tom was breathing hard, tears dry on his face, the twins Alva and Alma started yelling and pandemonium broke loose for a minute and just as suddenly stopped when Isabella said, “stop yelling! Let's kneel down here and say a prayer.” Isabella turned to one of the youngest boys, John Murray and said, “John you say the prayer please.” As they knelt there in the yard, John prayed harder than he had ever said a prayer before. “Please bless Len to be alright. Please bless that Tom won't go to jail. Amen.”

After the prayer, Isabella turned and said, “Kenneth, take care of Tom's horse.” “I hope you didn't ride her to death Tom,” she said, as she and Tom hitched the horses to the wagon.

Leaping as best as a person in a long skirt can leap Isabella was hardly on the seat when she grabbed up the reins and whipped the horses into a cantor turning back up the road to Len's cabin.

Stretched out on the ground Len closed his eyes and knew he was going to die.

Chase yelled, “Len! Len! What should I do? “But Len was clutching at his neck, blood oozing between his fingers, slowly dripping to puddles beneath his head.

All at once, as if it were a picture in his mind, Chase knew what to do! He pulled his handkerchief out of his pocket; stuffed one end in the front bullet hole and the other end into the back bullet hole and held on tight. Slowly the blood stopped running out onto the dirt, Chase didn’t let go, he was also afraid Len was going to die.

Looking toward home Chase saw a rolling cloud of dust and knew help was on the way.

Isabella and Tom leapt from the wagon seat before the horses had barely stopped. Seeing Len’s hand clutching Chase, Isabella bent her head and said a prayer of thanks that Len was yet alive, and that Chase had known what to do to stop the bleeding. It was a miracle that the track of the bullet missed all of Len's major arteries, missed his larynx and missed his spine and major muscles. If Chase hadn't stuffed his handkerchief into the holes he would probably have died from blood loss.

Over the next weeks life on the ranch returned to normal; Tom's horse didn't die, John Murray at age five was certain that it was his prayer that saved Len's life, and Tom and Chase found the stray cattle. Stopping over to check on Len the boys were grateful that he didn't hold any hard feelings; him saying it was an accident, but he was glad he wasn't dead and he supposed that with that kind of thing between them that they'd always be friends.[xlix]

Early Fall 1918 *We Need Soap*

"Hyrum, before we move back to the house I want to get our winter supply of soap made. With these growing boys a batch doesn't last like it used to; if I have enough tallow I'm going to double my recipe."

"Alright Tress, the older boys and I will take a trip up towards the Strawberry and cut a load of Aspen wood and get it split, stacked and ready for you to start burning for ash."

"Will you take the extra eggs into the Pioneer Store and trade them for 2 or 3 pounds of beef suet on your way home from the river property?"

"We will do that too Tress," he replied calling Chase and Kenneth to get a move on.

"Thank you," Isabella told Hyrum and the older boys when they had finished cutting, splitting, and stacking a full wagon bed of aspen logs. "John Murray, will you lay the fire and we will get started. John it will be your job to help me keep the fire burning and keep it within the fire-pit sides."

"I will Mother," he replied, and he began laying the kindling base with small wood shavings, bits and pieces of dry sagebrush, and chips from the wood cutting.

All day and into the night the fire burned, and when the sun rose it caught Isabella feeding the hungry flames until by the end of the second day the fire had consumed the wagon load of cut and split aspen logs leaving a pit full of fine white ash.

Early the following morning, the third day, Isabella was outside, having rousted Tom, Chase, and Kenneth to help setup the lye leeching barrel. The previous afternoon she and John Murray had gathered stones from around the cabin; large and small, and left them in a pile near the fire-pit. Her recipe directions called for straw to create the filter layer, with no hay available she improvised.

"Kenneth will you fork some of that dry hay into the wheelbarrow and bring it over by the fire?"

"Tom and Chase, bring the lye barrel and the saw horses to set it on."

"Good morning John Murray," "she said, "you did a fine job building the ash pile yesterday. Will you go with Chase and bring the lye buckets over here?"

"Good morning Mother," he replied, and turned to follow his brother.

With all the soap-making elements together, the older boys having helped with this process for many years knew their part. They set the lye barrel, balanced firmly on the solid wood planks laid on top of the saw horses. Tom and Chase each stood on opposite ends of the saw horses, themselves balanced, while Kenneth and John Murray handed them up the stones which they carefully placed in the bottom of the barrel mixing, the sizes from large field stones, fist sized rocks, down to pebbles and slinging-sized rocks that would catch and hold any large ash particles that would make their way through the layer of hay or straw.

Once the rocks were laid in place, Isabella and Kenneth handed armfuls of hay up to Chase and Tom who filled the barrel more than halfway to the top.

"I don't think we can press this hay down as hard as you want us to Mother."

Looking up at them she said, "Kenneth, help John up there. Tom and Chase help him inside the barrel; he can stamp down on the hay while we hand you up more armloads."

John Murray gleefully jumped up on the planking, "not so quickly John, you'll tip the barrel over on yourself, let the boys help you in. There you go, hold on to the sides," she said as they all heard his small boots smashing the hay down into a thick pad that would give the lye water another filter layer.

Once John Murray was helped out of the barrel, Isabella carefully began scooping the white ash from the fire-pit into the large ash bucket. She handed the bucket up to Tom who, with Chase's steadying hand, tipped the contents into the barrel filling it almost to the top ring. "Oh, I almost forgot, wait a minute, we need to add the lime," she exclaimed.

Isabella's recipe also called for rain water, but with the dearth of rain that wasn't an option, so dipping a gallon of water from the barrel beside the cabin door she called to Kenneth, "come help me carry this water, it is heavy."

Spilling only a bit of the water Kenneth and Isabella lifted the full bucket up to Tom and Chase who very slowly emptied the water onto the top of the ashes in the barrel. "Don't pour it too quickly," their mother warned, "the ash will puff out or the water will just pour through it and not seep as it should." Watching carefully she said, "That's good."

"Now John Murray, place the lye bucket under the barrel between the legs of the saw horses. That is right, just under the small bung hole; remember we want the lye to drip out into the bucket when we open the plug," she explained. "Putting the wooden bucket under the barrel will catch any lye water that might leak out."

"Tom you put the lid on the barrel before you get down. That's good. Thank you," she said to him and Chase, as they jumped down from their perches.

For three days they continued to add ash atop the already stripped ash and added more water. At the end, their patience paid off, with almost 2 full buckets of lye water.

"John, run and get me a couple of chicken feathers; we have to test the lye."

The boys liked this experiment, they'd seen it many times, and it never failed to make them grin. "Alright John, drop a feather into each bucket, be careful not to touch the lye water."

When the feather floated atop the lye it slowly began to melt away. A disappearing feather meant the lye was good to make the soap. If the feather hadn't melted, then their Mother would have had to boil it down until it had condensed to a strength good enough for the soap.

Isabella had been making soap since she was a little girl and it was second nature to get the right amount of ash and water and she knew just the right amount of time that was needed to distill the lye from the ashes.

"Start the fire again John," Isabella said, "and boys will you move the table outside, by the fire but not too near?"

"Hyrum, will you bring the large iron pot outside?"

"Here you go Tress," he said, as he lifted the heavy pot onto the top of the table.

"I need the soap molds too Kenneth, they are on the shelf in the lean-to."

Unwrapping the beef suet that Hyrum brought home she placed it in the large pot. Stepping toward the fire, pulling her skirts back with one hand to keep from going up in flames, she leveled the coals with a long branch. The coals needed to be spread evenly together to concentrate the heat.

"Here Mother, I'll do that," Tom said, taking the heavy kettle off the table and standing he stood it on its three legs directly on the center of the coal bed.

While watching the suet, the hard fat taken from around the kidneys and loins of beef started to melt. Isabella continued to stir it while the cracklings, the meat bits left from the butchering process, began to separate from the fat and then to darken.

The pot was too heavy to lift with the metal hook they used to take the spider oven out of the coals. Isabella called out to Tom, as Hyrum and Chase had gone out on the range.

"It's time to take the tallow off the heat," she said.

Tom pulled on his well-worn leather gloves and reach over the hot coals lifting the pot with a grunt and set it on the flat rocks his mother had placed on the table top, so the heat from the pot's legs wouldn't burn into the thick wooden table planks.

Taking the long-handled wooden ladle that Hyrum had made for her by drilling small holes though the ladle bottom, she deftly cleared the left-over meat pieces from the tallow, cleaning out all the debris. While the suet had been melting, Isabella had greased the wooden molds so the soap bars wouldn't stick.

"John Murray, stay in the cabin with the twins while we mix the soap. I don't want them underfoot."

"Are you ready boys?" Isabella asked Kenneth and Tom.

"Yes ma'am," they replied pulling on their gloves.

Their mother had put her work gloves on too, as any splash of the lye would burn skin deeply. The boys watched their mother measure out the right amount of tallow into the large wood bucket. Then she had them slowly pour the lye water into the warm tallow while she stirred it continuously while it thickened. She told the boys that the first batch of soap would be the soft soap they used for washing their clothes and for bathing. In the next batch she would add in a small amount of salt which would harden the soap they used for scrubbing and cleaning.

As the soap thickened it became smoother. Before it completely cooled in the bucket Isabella ladled the mixture into the prepared and waiting molds; using flat wooden paddles they firmly pushed the soap into the molds adding more as it became compacted. Finally they used the back of a knife blade pulled across the top to square off the soap with the top of the mold.

Several hours later they flipped the filled molds over and tapped the bottoms; the soap slipped out smoothly, like hot bread from the baking tin. The blocks of soap were lined up across the table top in the sunshine to dry out and they began the laborious chore of cleaning up the pots, kettles, buckets, paddles, and ladles.

Tom and Kenneth rolled the barrel to the side of the corral, trying to keep the rocks and hay from falling out; then together they tipped it over and emptied its contents in a pile. With gloved hands they carefully pulled the alfalfa hay apart from the rocks and carried it to the fire pit to burn. If any of the cattle or horses got into it they would become very sick if not die from the caustic juices created in the lye-making process. They turned the barrel top-side down to make sure no one used it for water or storage. They carried buckets of river water over and washed the lye water from off the rocks and left them in the pile by the lean-to, next year they wouldn't have to gather them up again.

2018 Late Fall *Lessons*

For the remainder of the summer, through the fall's cattle roundup, and their return to Duchesne just in time for the school season, Hyrum and Isabella prayed fervently for guidance. Their financial problems continued, and their minds were a jumble when they looked at the options they thought they saw.

Excited about their first day back in school, the older boys dashed out the door. The two-year-old twins Alma and Alva entertained themselves with some wood scraps, and Isabella was taking a few minutes to read the scriptures that she had laid out before her on the table. In the relative calm of their morning Hyrum was working the figures from the fall cattle sale.

"Hyrum?" Isabella paused waiting for his recognition before continuing. After a few moments she said again slightly more loudly, "Hyrum!"

Shaken from his thoughts he said, head still down, he rather briskly said, "what?"

She replied, "I think this is the answer we have been praying for."

"What?" He said again. He glanced at her and just as quickly as his head went back down his eyes focused on the papers before him.

"I think I've found the guidance we have been praying for." Isabella said a bit more firmly. Hyrum stopped, looked up from his papers, his pencil raised, and asked, "What do you mean?"

Excitedly Isabella said, "We've been praying for guidance to help us make a decision on how to move forward, right?"

"Yes, but I haven't found, thought of, nor felt any answers," he said.

"Neither have I," replied Isabella. "But as I was reading these verses in the Doctrine and Covenants their meaning burned in my heart. Listen to this:

> *'Behold, you have not understood; you have supposed that I would give it unto you, when you took no thought save it was to ask me.*

But, behold, I say unto you, that you must study it out in your mind; then you must ask me if it be right, and if it is right I will cause that your bosom shall burn within you; therefore, you shall feel that it is right.

But if it be not right you shall have no such feelings, but you shall have a stupor of thought that shall cause you to forget the thing which is wrong;"[1]

"Don't you see? The Lord is answering our prayers. I think that is what we need to do. We need to really think about the consequences of each of the choices we have talked about and make a decision. Isn't that what these scriptures are telling us; that we have to determine what we want to do, and then ask the Lord for confirmation?"

"Rather than expecting, you know just expecting him to guide us or tell us what to do?"

Hyrum's face bloomed into a smile. "You are an angel Tressa!" Although we've read that many times and I taught that principal when I was on my mission I never thought to apply it to myself."

With renewed enthusiasm he shuffled the ranch papers together and carefully laid them aside on the tabletop worn smooth with use. "Do you have time to talk now?"

Isabella said, "Finish your bookwork, and that will give me time to mix up the bread, and clean up a little. Then we can sit down and really give it some uninterrupted thought."

The soft morning luster grew into full fall light, brightening their cozy kitchen as it beamed through the windows. The conversation was animated, each one pointing out and clarifying their thoughts and opinions to the other.

"I want to add to that list that we haven't lived in Heber City for almost 12 years. And I don't think we could just ask the renters to leave, I think it may be like our house was to us when we rented; we felt like it was our home."

"You're right Tressa."

They both sat very still as they reread the lengthy lists below each option. As one they looked up and said, "I think we should stay in the Basin." Laughing at the ways they were so closely linked in their desires.

Hyrum said, "Now with that settled we need to decide to stay on the homestead in Sowers Canyon or find another prospect."

Hyrum stood aside as Isabella tipped the bread dough onto the table and they continued talking while she kneaded the sticky dough adding in a bit of flour so that when molded the dough was smooth and pliable for turning into loaves and into the bread pans to rise again.

"Are we in agreement that we will sell Sowers and try again elsewhere, maybe near the river property?"

"Yes Hyrum. We are in agreement."

Hand in hand they went to their room with warnings to the twins to stay outside and not wander away. They knelt in the quiet of their room, hands clasped tightly together and implored the Lord for confirmation of their decision[li].

The months of winter wore on; chores, cooking, cleaning, teaching, praying, church work and Hyrum continuing to search for but not finding another job. Their nerves were frayed with one another and with the boys.

"There's nothing to do about it Tress," Hyrum said, "there have been no good farm or ranch prospects opening up that we can afford, we have to go back to Sowers when school is over."

Once again in their wagon, filled with their summer needs, Hyrum hi-ya'd their horses and turned to the southwest, rattling across the sparse sagebrush covered miles of nowhere, back to the parched and isolated Sowers Canyon ranch.

***

August 1918 *Buying Chervney's Land*

"I was talking to Lewis Chervney at Priesthood meeting this morning, you know they have that property next to our river property. He and his wife are calling it quits and are willing to sell their 60 acres for one hundred dollars."

"They're leaving the Basin?" With a sorrowful shake of her head she said, "so many people have just given up and left through the years."

"We've thought often of leaving too Tress," Hyrum shared, "we know how hard this life is."

Then he said again, "it is only a hundred dollars[lii]. I think we should make the sacrifice and buy the land before someone else takes the bargain."

November 1918

After the 60 acres were purchased from the Chervneys, Hyrum began to talk to all of the landowners around their river property.

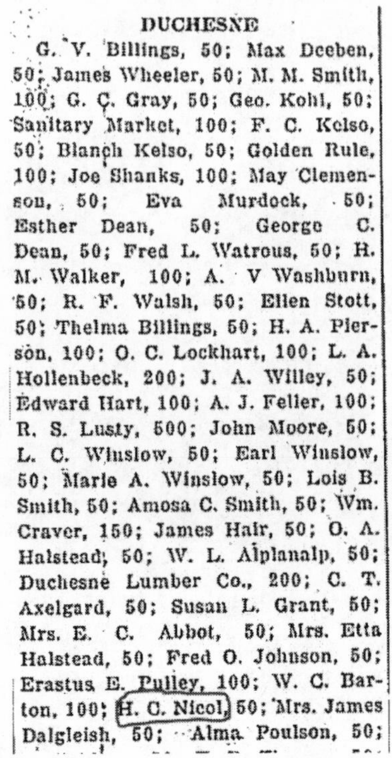
DUCHESNE
G. V. Billings, 50; Max Deeben, 50; James Wheeler, 50; M. M. Smith, 100; G. C. Gray, 50; Geo. Kohl, 50; Sanitary Market, 100; F. C. Kelso, 50; Blanch Kelso, 50; Golden Rule, 100; Joe Shanks, 100; May Clemenson, 50; Eva Murdock, 50; Esther Dean, 50; George C. Dean, 50; Fred L. Watrous, 50; H. M. Walker, 100; A. V Washburn, 50; R. F. Walsh, 50; Ellen Stott, 50; Thelma Billings, 50; H. A. Pierson, 100; O. C. Lockhart, 100; L. A. Hollenbeck, 200; J. A. Willey, 50; Edward Hart, 100; A. J. Feller, 100; R. S. Lusty, 500; John Moore, 50; L. C. Winslow, 50; Earl Winslow, 50; Marie A. Winslow, 50; Lois B. Smith, 50; Amosa C. Smith, 50; Wm. Craver, 150; James Hair, 50; O. A. Halstead, 50; W. L. Alplanalp, 50; Duchesne Lumber Co., 200; C. T. Axelgard, 50; Susan L. Grant, 50; Mrs. E. C. Abbot, 50; Mrs. Etta Halstead, 50; Fred O. Johnson, 50; Erastus E. Pulley, 100; W. C. Barton, 100; H. C. Nicol, 50; Mrs. James Dalgleish, 50; Alma Poulson, 50;

56 *Duchesne Record, October 26, 1918*
4th Liberty Loan Drive Nicol Donates

"I talked with W.L. Dean today and asked him again whether he would sell us their homestead ranch," Hyrum told Isabella as they walked toward their town home from Sacrament Meeting.

The boys ran ahead excitedly involved in something they were planning on building. "He said he would talk with his wife, and decide on a price for the property. That is if they decide to sell."

"I thought because they are building their new home here in town they may change their minds on selling it to us. I told him I would stop by the bank tomorrow afternoon and discuss options," he continued.

1918 Late Summer *All In*

"Let's take a walk Tress. Tom and Chase take care of things here."

Isabella had only time to pick her coat from its peg as Hyrum put his arm out to pull open the door. They turned out of the yard on the outskirts of town and Hyrum began, "I spoke with W.L. this afternoon and he will sell us his homestead, the house, barn, and outbuildings."

"How much?" Isabella asked, holding her breath for the answer. Her voice rose several octaves when she repeated the sum, "five thousand dollars? Oh Hyrum! That's a lot of money! Five thousand dollars is a fortune. Everything we have is all mortgaged already[liii]!"

They had this same conversation for months as they discussed the possibilities of their future. The discussion always ended at the same place; they had to borrow money by mortgaging their existing assets, and through God's grace they had been able to maintain their livelihood, but it was a hard place for them. They wanted to be debt free, and ranching wasn't the way to do that, they had learned over the years.

Isabella continued, "you know we haven't had anyone even interested in the Sowers Canyon ranch." Looking at her husband's face as it began to harden, his lips tightened and the end of his mouth turned down she could feel she had said almost too much.

"Tressa," he started to break into her stream of conversation, but she took a breath and pushed forward quickly. "I know we said we would stay here and try somewhere else, but are we rushing into something so big we won't be able to pay for it? I'm feeling apprehensive, like we're borrowing from Peter to pay Paul."

"I can make it work Tressa. We will build up the herd and before the mortgage is due in five years we will have saved enough money to pay it off. Cattle sales will allow us to pay the interest. I know I can make this work!" His voice raised emphatically.

His words dropped into silence; a silence that spoke more than words as they continued up the road toward the river, their steps grinding grit as their heels sank into packed dirt. The air between them prickled as each one's opinion solidified. Their silence continued as they neared the river bank.

Stopping at the river's edge they stood listening to the rush and babble of the crystalline water while watching it twist and turn over and around the rocks spread out between the banks like a checkerboard. In the midst of her individual turmoil Isabella sat carefully down on a patch of dried fall grass, adjusting her skirts while her eyes gazed at the reflections of the rare greenery along the far bank that wavered in the pools of slow moving currents.

Isabella spoke slowly, her voice calm and deliberate, keeping her eyes on the river's calming currents. She said, "I think I understand your thoughts Hyrum. I do not feel good about such a plan. But I've stood by you all of our days together and I'll stand by you now. I agree that my health is failing with the hard work."

With the sudden break in the silence Hyrum startled and bent his head down toward his beautiful wife, her hair pulled loosely up in a knot at the base of her long neck. Squatting down next to her he recognized the determination in her face.

She continued, "Do I understand what you've told me Hyrum? That we'll buy the Dean's homestead for five thousand dollars, then hope someone buys our homestead in Sowers Canyon and our home here in town? Then we'll mortgage the Heber house and property to cover the homestead value because it isn't worth five thousand dollars and use some of the proceeds for winter feed and fuel? The end of all of that is to hope that we don't drown under the debt?" she asked stoically.

"That's pessimistic isn't it Tressa?" Hyrum countered, putting his hand down and grasping a bunch of dried grass. "If we're meant to be here as we believe, then things will work out the way that it is supposed to be." [liv] Isabella sighed deeply and knew that she would follow her husband's lead as she had since becoming Mrs. H. C. Nicol sixteen years before.

Indian Ranch

Hyrum C. & Isabella M. Nicol Home on
"Indian Ranch" in Duchesne, Utah.

57 Indian Ranch picture circa 1960; to right is Dee Nicol, Tom's wife

November 1918 *Armistice Comes*

"The war is finally over!" Relief and thanksgiving spread through Hyrum like a dam broken from holding back years of fear and sadness. He exclaimed, "Can you imagine the loss of life? How those countries must be shattered? Czars? Emperors? Kings and Queens ruining their countries, killing their people, for what purpose?" He questioned not expecting a response.

With something near outrage he purposely lowered his voice so he wouldn't erupt, "did you know Tressa that Kaiser Wilhelm is the cousin of King George V of Great Britain, and Czar Nicholas II of Russia? I wonder if this horrible war was just a squabble, not between countries, but between cousins who wanted more power than they already had and then they pulled our country into it to finally stop their madness."

Isabella wasn't joining him in his outrage, rather she raised her voice in praise and celebration. She paused in her song and said, "Pride and a thirst for power is the cause of all nations' failings; it's what happened to the Nephite civilization too," said Isabella. "But I am much too happy to worry about the causes of the war" and she began singing her favorite hymns: Now Thank We All Our God.[lv]

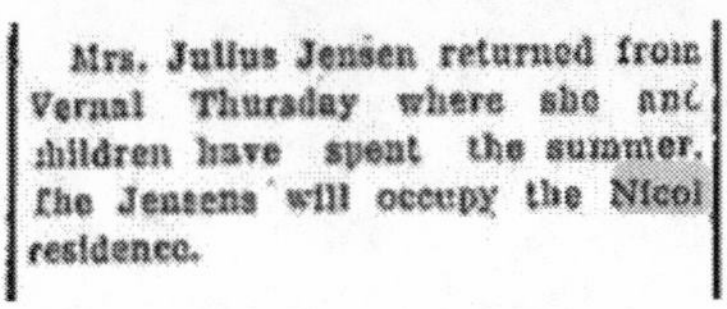
Mrs. Julius Jensen returned from Vernal Thursday where she and children have spent the summer. The Jensens will occupy the Nicol residence.

58 Duchesne Record November 16, 1918 -- Jensen' to occupy the Nicol residence

"I'm going to go over to the cultural hall later this afternoon, the choir is practicing for the victory celebration this weekend." She had joined in the festive mood of the town by adding her voice to the choir in the town's victory celebration'. [lvi]

After the party, family in tow, Hyrum and Isabella climbed up into the seat of their old wagon to follow the river road to their new home. They were happy and the pride of patriotism buoyed up by song and prayer had made the day special.

Isabella had a smile on her face such that she beamed with joy. "I'm so happy Hyrum," she said, even in the midst of all of these changes. "What Tress?" Hyrum turned to face her, my mind was elsewhere.

"I'm happy," she said. "I'm glad the war is over and I am excited that we are going to have another baby," she announced to the wonderment of her whole troop.

Hauling sharply on the reins at the unexpected news Hyrum pulled the horses to a stop and eyes wide, he wrapped his arms around her shoulders, holding her as tightly as he could without squeezing the breath from her lungs, and said, "I love you Tressa," and then he asked, "are you certain?"

"Yes Hyrum," she smiled again, "I am certain we'll be adding another son to our brood."

"You know already it will be a boy?" He asked. "It has to be Hyrum, we live a frontier life and I would hate to have a daughter grow up out here."

The boys sitting behind them grinned at one another. Tom only looked on silently.

***

June 27, 1919 ***Brigham Rue***

Exhausted, Isabella lay back against the pillow. At the age of 43 streaks of gray ran through her once dark and luxurious hair that was loosely braided, and stray hairs escaped from their bonds as she moved it out of the way. The ordeal of childbirth, although different with each child, came down to three intense moments; of course there was the fierce pain, the momentary asking of why was she doing this again, and then the sweet forgetting once the infant was laying bare on her breast, and then the love which overwhelms the heart. The midwife and doctor moved around her as in a dance, the midwife caring for the baby while the doctor cared for mother.

Taking the infant from the arms of the midwife, Isabella held their newest gift from heaven close to her heart, and whispered into his ears, "you've been swept into this mortal world straight from the arms of our Father in Heaven. Remember his love is with you all the days of your life. Remember you are here for his purposes, remember your promises to live up to your blessings and potential."

Shutting her eyes, feeling his soft warm breaths against her skin, she in gratitude thanked Father in Heaven for the safe delivery of this, her youngest son. She thanked him for all of his goodness and prayed that she would be faithful to the end. She asked for blessings that she would be the strong mother in Zion that she knew she had promised to be when she herself came through the veil into this mortal realm.

She knew her sons were powerful spirits with the potential of God within them. Then she prayed for them as she had all the days of their lives.

Hyrum, having come in only a moment before, stood quietly watching his beloved's face, tranquility and peace radiated from her as he watched her lips moving in her silent prayers.

There was light knocking at the door which brought her back from her reverie. Looking up she saw her sweetheart watching over her and she reached out for his hand as she said, "come in." She was tired. Every inch of her body screamed for sleep, but she smiled and called her family in to share these precious first moments of their brother's life.

"What did you finally decide to call him Mother? Father said you hadn't felt any name you thought of was quite right."

"Hyrum why don't you tell them what we decided his name will be."

Lifting his gaze from his newest son, he grinned and said, "His name is Brigham Rue Nicol."

***

December 1919 *Death Reaches Out*

Isabella thought she should have put on her coat before opening the door to winter's grasping cold fingers. Raising her voice to carry with the icy wind she called Alma and Alva in for their noon dinner. Turning her face away from the wind she saw the young telegraph carrier riding up the road toward their house. Her breath caught in her throat, not from the wind but an icy chill spread down through her heart; something was wrong and that young man was bringing her the news.

Standing in the doorway the young man said breathlessly, "Mrs. Nicol?"

"Yes," she replied, "I am," shallowly aware of how calm she was.

The young man stated, "I have a telegram here for Mr. Nicol."

"He's not home right now, I'll take it."

"Alright ma'am," he said handing the yellow envelope into her outstretched fingers. In that moment as she looked at the sealed packet held tentatively between her thumb and forefinger, she observed her finger nails seemingly turning blue, unaware that they were hers.

"Just one moment," she said walking inside, returning quickly she handed the delivery boy a coin. "Will you please take this telegram back and deliver it to Mr. Nicol, he is over at the Bishop's Storehouse."

"I will, thank you ma'am," he said, and swung his booted foot over the saddle of his steaming horse. Kicking it lightly in its flanks, the boy turned the horse away from her and cantered up the road.

Opening the sealed yellow envelope Hyrum pulled out the onionskin-thin single sheet of paper and slowly exhaling, read the single line of black letters:

Hanne passed this morning. Telephone Me. Signed Heber Crook

Bishop Billings watched his first counselor as he opened the telegram envelope. Telegrams seldom brought good news. "Hyrum what is it?"

Hyrum's eyes filled with tears and the Bishop placed his ranch tough hand on his shoulder. "My mother died this morning," he said bluntly. "I need to leave, I'm sorry, I'll try to get back over here to help." "No you won't. Go talk with your brother-in-law. We'll take care of things here."

Isabella opened the door upon hearing Hyrum's horse race into the yard. "What was in the telegram Hyrum?" Isabella quickly asked.

"It was from Matilda's husband, Heber G., Mother died this morning."

"Oh Hyrum! I'm so sorry." She reached out to him, putting her arm around him as he tied his horse to the rail and they walked into the house. They closed the cold outside, but the cold which filled their hearts at the news remained.

Speaking quietly, his voice raspy, "she had been ill for a few days, the doctor had been over to the house and she passed through the veil shortly before Heber sent the telegram. The doctor called it a cerebral apoplexy."

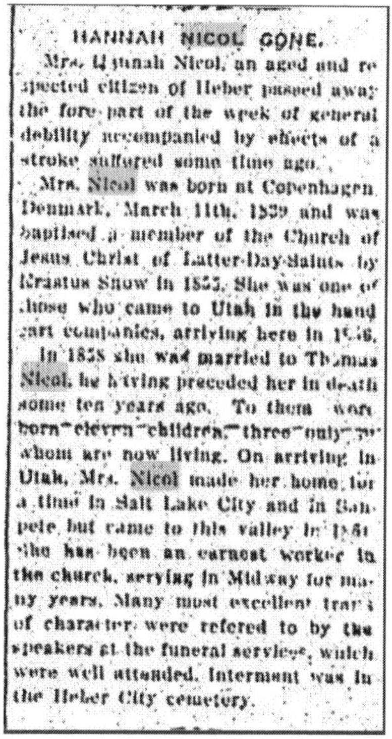

HANNAH NICOL GONE.

Mrs. Hannah Nicol, an aged and respected citizen of Heber passed away the fore part of the week of general debility accompanied by effects of a stroke suffered some time ago.

Mrs. Nicol was born at Copenhagen, Denmark, March 11th, 1839 and was baptised a member of the Church of Jesus Christ of Latter-Day Saints by Erastus Snow in 1853. She was one of those who came to Utah in the hand cart companies, arriving here in 1856.

In 1858 she was married to Thomas Nicol, he having preceded her in death some ten years ago. To them were born eleven children, three only of whom are now living. On arriving in Utah, Mrs. Nicol made her home for a time in Salt Lake City and in Sanpete, but came to this valley in 1861. She has been an earnest worker in the church, serving in Midway for many years. Many most excellent traits of character were refered to by the speakers at the funeral services, which were well attended. Interment was in the Heber City cemetery.

59 Duchesne Record December 1919 – Hanna Nicol Obituary

Looking quickly around as if seeing things for the first time he muttered, almost speaking to himself. "If I leave quickly I can be in Heber for the funeral on Wednesday. I can stay at Gabe's." He startled himself and realized what he had been saying and then turned to Isabella and said, "Matilda has taken such good care of her. She has things in hand. I'll plan on being back here late Saturday."

His tears that had dried on the ride home began again. And as he held onto Isabella, wrapped in her arms, his broken heart was comforted.

Later, as she finished packing his saddle bag with food and his Sunday clothes, she told him, "I wish we could go with you Hyrum. We love your mother. She has been a rock for us to cling to all of these years. I will miss her terribly."

"Where is father going?" Alma asked.

"He has to go to Heber, Grandmother Hanne died this morning."

Alma just nodded his head, he only knew his grandmother from their yearly visits to Heber. As she had aged her trips to the Basin had stopped and her younger grandsons didn't know her well.

When her older boys arrived from school, their coats and gloves were hung to dry and their boots were knocked free of the mix of snow and mud accumulated on their way across town.

Before she could tell them anything Chase asked, "Where is Father?"

"Grandmother Hanne died this morning, I'm sorry to say." The room went quiet as each one stopped and remembered her special way for each of them.

During their family prayer before supper Isabella gave thanks for the loving care and support of her mother-in-law, and offered gratitude for God's plan of salvation and happiness, which knowledge made parting easier to bear. She prayed for comfort and peace of the Holy Ghost to be with them and to protect Hyrum as he traveled in this cold, snowy weather.

***

Slicing ham and setting mashed potatoes steaming in a large bowl on the table, the boys pulled in their chairs and started to fill their plates. Wishing to share a little of their day Isabella noticed that Alma was quiet and was only picking at his food. "What's the matter Alma? Are you sick?"

"No." A little stubbornly he asked, "Why can't we go to Heber with Father? I want to see Grandmother Hanne."

With glistening eyes and a tight throat Isabella said, "We can't see her again until we die." The question didn't go from his eyes. She sat in thoughtful silently asking for help to answer this first important life lesson for her son.

Then she began, "you know that before you were born you lived in Heaven with Heavenly Father and Mother?"

"Yes," he replied.

Isabella paused, "Then we were born here on earth to get a body like Heavenly Father, because we want to be like him because we love him."

Still staring at her Alma remained in his silence, waiting.

She continued, "We come not only to get a body; we come here to learn to choose whether we will continue to love Heavenly Father and keep his commandments, or if we will forget him."

"Like baby Brigham we are little and then we grow older, like Tom and Chase and Kenneth. Then we get older and have families like me and your father. Then our bodies get older and we die. But what is wonderful is that only our bodies die, our spirit goes home to live with Heavenly Father again."

"That is where Grandmother Hanne is now. She is happy, and not sick anymore. She is with Grandfather Nicol and with all of her children and babies that died when they were little. They are all very happy. She is very happy. And though we are sad that we won't see her body here with us anymore, we can be happy that she is happy. We can remember all the good things that she did for us and how much she loved us."

She stopped and saw that the boys were all watching her and watching Alma. Quiet permeated the room and then a smile began to grow on his little solemn face. A great peace filled their hearts and warmed them to let them know that what she taught was true. Though they may not have known what was happening, they knew they weren't sad any longer.

***

Winter 1919 *More Killer Snows*

WEEKLY WEATHER REPORT

By M. M. Smith.

Guess the temperature; what do you think it was last night?!!—"0, 25 below." "I say 23" "40". "36". "All in?" It was 26 below zero the last two mornings. Seems to run in multiples of unlucky 13, (two times 13 last two nights, and three times 13 the lowest on December 3. By the way, that 13 was lucky enough to take the prize, national and international, so far as reported. This does not bar Green River and Canada. Highest was 23. Following is the daily minumum for the past week: -24, -1, -13, -26, -26, -22. Only half an inch of snow fell during the week.

Washington, D. C., reports fair weather, but low temperature for the week. The entire northwest is reported with low temperature. Salt Lake warned shippers against 35 to 25 below in the Wasatch mountains. We will know by the time this paper is out whether we paid our taxes in vain or not.

62 Duchesne Record December 18, 1919 Weekly Weather

WEEKLY WEATHER REPORT

By M. M. Smith.
U. S. W. B.

Minimum temperatures for the past week from Wednesday to Tuesday are as follows: 7. —21. —21. —20, —25, —20, —19. Average of —22 for six days. A remarkable run of temperature, but it is about what we are to expect in January. Mercury went below zero on 25 days last January, with 34 as the lowest. The warmest day of last week was Wednesday with 7 during the night and 29 during the day.

January as a mean is our worst and severest month for relentless temperature. Thus far it is well behaved, this year, as to disagreeable winds, so hard on live stock, which have not suffered any great loss as yet, though some have perished.

It is now thought, at least hoped, that we have reached the apex and are now coasting down the toboggan. Winter ought to be more than half over; at least January is half gone. There is an equivalent of two feet of snow lying on our river bottoms. Of course, it is settled.

And our quail are dead. But that story belongs in the "kicking" column and not in the weather report.

January with us is the most disliked of all the months. It is to be endured rather than enjoyed. We greet it coldly. It goes us one better. Nobody would go through January, if they could drive around. In California they usher the month in with a flower carnival. But with all that, I would not trade the Rocky Mountains for all of California.

Informed that temperature was 25 Sunday morning and 20 Monday A. M., a certain lady insisted that both, myself and the weather machine were off wrong, saying: "Just lots of people say that this is the coldest morning." I replied: "That is why the thermometer was invented. The people can't be relied on as accurate judges of temperature. The changing humidity has much to do

62 Duchesne Record December 25, 1919

WEEKLY WEATHER REPORT

By M. M. Smith.

Following are the daily minimum temperatures of the past six from Wednesday to Tuesday: -19, -15, -15, -12, -9, -9, -8. No precipitation.

After four weeks of hard winter weather, we reached the first almanac winter day on the 21st, the shortest day and the longest night of the year, when the earth, not the sun, reaches its farthest declination north, till the sun shines vertically on the tropic of cancer. The six months day begins at the south pole, and six months continous night at our north pole. Our days will at once begin to lengthen, and our nights will grow correspondingly shorter about three minutes per day. But in spite of the fact that our earth is now three million miles nearer the sun than next June, owing to the obliquity of sun's rays, it often grows colder now for a while.

Some old timers are looking with hope to an expected January thaw. It is noticeable, however, that our January thaws are often delayed until March.

Owing to the deep snow in the bottoms, covering up the bird feed and shelter, it is repor ed that our California quail are perishing in large numbers. I have wired the state game commissioner at Salt Lake recommending that feeding stations be established every six miles along the Strawberry and Duchesne rivers.

62 Duchesne Record January 15, 1920

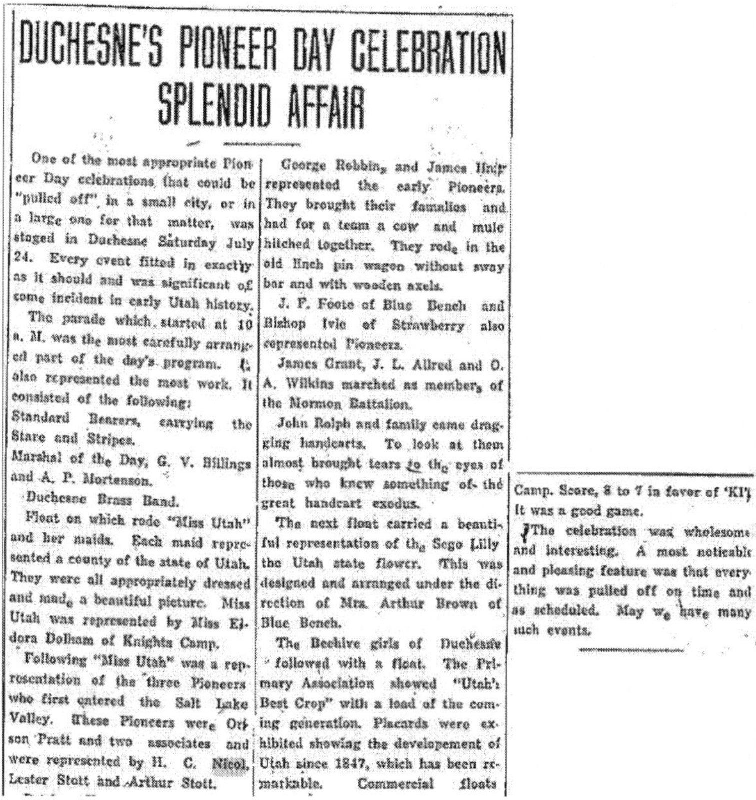

DUCHESNE'S PIONEER DAY CELEBRATION SPLENDID AFFAIR

One of the most appropriate Pioneer Day celebrations that could be "pulled off", in a small city, or in a large one for that matter, was staged in Duchesne Saturday July 24. Every event fitted in exactly as it should and was significant of some incident in early Utah history.

The parade which started at 10 a. M. was the most carefully arranged part of the day's program. (. also represented the most work. It consisted of the following:

Standard Bearers, carrying the Stars and Stripes.

Marshal of the Day, G. V. Billings and A. P. Mortenson.

Duchesne Brass Band.

Float on which rode "Miss Utah" and her maids. Each maid represented a county of the state of Utah. They were all appropriately dressed and made a beautiful picture. Miss Utah was represented by Miss Eldora Dolham of Knights Camp.

Following "Miss Utah" was a represcntation of the three Pioneers who first entered the Salt Lake Valley. These Pioneers were Orson Pratt and two associates and were represented by H. C. Nicol, Lester Stott and Arthur Stott.

George Robbins and James Hnpr represented the early Pioneers. They brought their famalies and had for a team a cow and mule hitched together. They rode in the old linch pin wagon without sway bar and with wooden axels.

J. F. Foote of Blue Bench and Bishop Ivie of Strawberry also represented Pioneers.

James Grant, J. L. Allred and O. A. Wilkins marched as members of the Mormon Battalion.

John Ralph and family came dragging handcarts. To look at them almost brought tears to the eyes of those who knew something of the great handcart exodus.

The next float carried a beautiful representation of the Sego Lilly the Utah state flower. This was designed and arranged under the direction of Mrs. Arthur Brown of Blue Bench.

The Beehive girls of Duchesne followed with a float. The Primary Association showed "Utah's Best Crop" with a load of the coming generation. Placards were exhibited showing the developement of Utah since 1847, which has been remarkable. Commercial floats

...

Camp. Score, 8 to 7 in favor of 'KI'j It was a good game.

The celebration was wholesome and interesting. A most noticable and pleasing feature was that everything was pulled off on time and as scheduled. May we have many such events.

63 Duchesne Record July 1920 - Pioneer Celebration H. C. Nicol as Orson Pratt

Hyrum, looked left and right for his family as he walked behind the float carrying Miss Utah and her attendants. He was portraying Orson Pratt who was the first man into the Salt Lake Valley with the first group of Saints that had crossed the Great Plains and the Rocky Mountains in the great exodus from Nauvoo.

"There he is, there he is, hello Father!" Alma and Alva yelled as he walked passed them.

Hyrum smiled, waved, and kept walking.

The parade continued with families in wagons representing the early pioneers. Then came men portraying the Mormon Battalion and following the battalion a family pulled and pushed a handcart.

Isabella's eyes filled with tears as these people passed by their seats on the edge of the wooden sidewalk in front of Pope's store. Her father John Murray Murdoch and his wife Ann had crossed the ocean and then plains with the Abraham O. Smoot wagon company. Her mother Isabella Crawford and her friends had purchased their own wagon hired a driver and joined a wagon company that wasn't sponsored by the church. Her grandmother, Mary Murray Murdoch had died at Chimney Rock, Nebraska, and was a member of the ill-fated Martin handcart company. Hyrum's father walked the plains with the David Wilkins' wagon company, and Hanne, his mother had crossed the plains with the C. C. Christiansen handcart company.

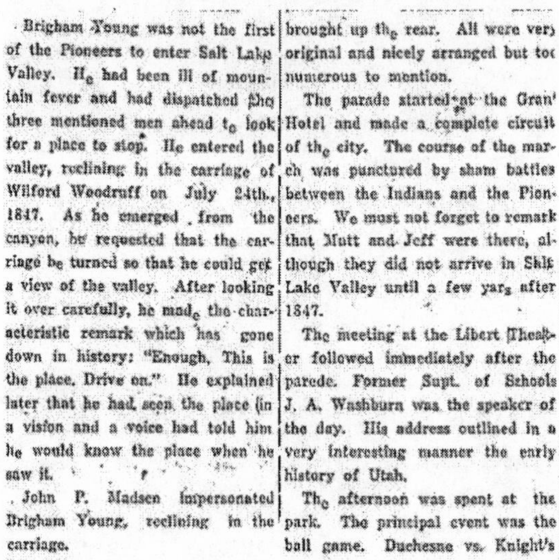
Brigham Young was not the first of the Pioneers to enter Salt Lake Valley. He had been ill of mountain fever and had dispatched the three mentioned men ahead to look for a place to stop. He entered the valley, reclining in the carriage of Wilford Woodruff on July 24th., 1847. As he emerged from the canyon, he requested that the carriage be turned so that he could get a view of the valley. After looking it over carefully, he made the characteristic remark which has gone down in history: "Enough. This is the place. Drive on." He explained later that he had seen the place in a vision and a voice had told him he would know the place when he saw it.

John P. Madsen impersonated Brigham Young, reclining in the carriage.

brought up the rear. All were very original and nicely arranged but too numerous to mention.

The parade started at the Grand Hotel and made a complete circuit of the city. The course of the march was punctured by sham battles between the Indians and the Pioneers. We must not forget to remark that Mutt and Jeff were there, although they did not arrive in Salt Lake Valley until a few years after 1847.

The meeting at the Libert Theater followed immediately after the parede. Former Supt. of Schools J. A. Washburn was the speaker of the day. His address outlined in a very interesting manner the early history of Utah.

The afternoon was spent at the park. The principal event was the ball game. Duchesne vs. Knight's

64 Duchesne Record – Cont. Coverage of Pioneer Day Parade & Events

The lives her and Hyrum's parents had lived were ideals she held herself to: determination, courage, hard work, and most importantly faith in Jesus Christ and the gospel restored through the Prophet Joseph Smith.

She knew deep in her heart that their testimonies of the truthfulness of the restored Church and gospel of Jesus Christ helped them overcame all the obstacles placed before them. These were the ideals she strove each day to instill in her children. Wiping the tears from her cheeks after seeing a couple of her boys look back to see if she was alright, she pointed quickly at the float representing the Sego Lilly.

***

August 1920 Nothing is Impossible

"Mother! Mother!" John Murray yelled into the house, "We can't find Brig!"

"I thought you were playing with him in the yard."

"We were, but he's gone!"

Shaking her head Isabella said, "He is fast on those fat little legs. Go look for him around the pig pens. The old sow with her litter is loose and may eat him. And some of you go to the river; he just might have fallen in."

Isabella, the mother of seven boys on the frontier had seen almost everything with them. Panic had been washed from her nature like the cleansing of muddy feet stepping into a clear mountain stream. She smiled and nodded to the boys' calls that they found Brig and he wasn't eaten by the sow.

The smell of baking biscuits and bacon wafted down the hall and tousled heads and sleepy faces appeared in the door of the kitchen.

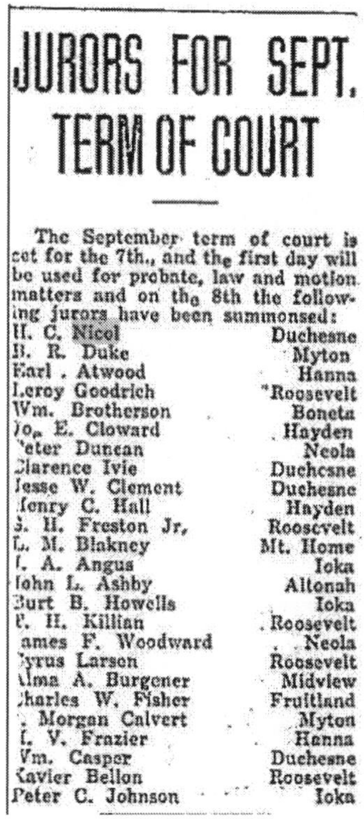

JURORS FOR SEPT. TERM OF COURT

The September term of court is set for the 7th., and the first day will be used for probate, law and motion matters and on the 8th the following jurors have been summonsed:

H. C. Nicol	Duchesne
B. R. Duke	Myton
Earl . Atwood	Hanna
Leroy Goodrich	Roosevelt
Wm. Brotherson	Boneta
Jos. E. Cloward	Hayden
Peter Duncan	Neola
Clarence Ivie	Duchesne
Jesse W. Clement	Duchesne
Henry C. Hall	Hayden
S. H. Freston Jr.	Roosevelt
L. M. Blakney	Mt. Home
I. A. Angus	Ioka
John L. Ashby	Altonah
Burt B. Howells	Ioka
F. H. Killian	Roosevelt
James F. Woodward	Neola
Cyrus Larson	Roosevelt
Alma A. Burgener	Midview
Charles W. Fisher	Fruitland
. Morgan Calvert	Myton
I. V. Frazier	Hanna
Wm. Casper	Duchesne
Xavier Bellon	Roosevelt
Peter C. Johnson	Ioka

65 Duchesne Record - August 1920 - H. C. Nicol juror

"You're up earlier than usual Mother," one of the boys said. "Brig didn't want to go back to sleep once your Father and Chase went out for the mid-night watering turn. I thought biscuits would taste fine." She said.

"Let's have morning prayer before I set breakfast on the table."

The sun's morning pink glow illuminated the hills east of their ranch and the food was gone hardly before it touched their plates.

"We have a lot to do this morning Mother," Tom said as he pulled his hat down to his eyebrows and stuck his gloves into his jeans waistband. "John Murray, Alma, and Alva you'll have to help me since Chase is out with Father."

The door slammed behind the boys as they hurried to their chores and Isabella laughed at the scraped bare plates and pans. She knew she would have to make more gravy when Hyrum and Chase returned. Lifting her head she turned her ear toward the door and she asked the air, "What is that commotion?"

Walking onto the porch she followed the noise as it got louder nearer to the pasture. There she found the boys pulling and pushing one of the horses that had fallen into an irrigation ditch. In the mare's frantic attempts to stand up the poor thing had rolled onto her back. The boys were trying their best, but couldn't help her out.

Surveying the scene she said, "Stop that, it won't work. One of you go get a long pole from the fence. That's right, that one will work." Finding its balance point Isabella lifted the pole and pushed it down the side of the irrigation ditch under the horse's back. The boys watched in wonder as their tiny 130 pound mother walked down that pole and stood in jaw dropping amazement as the horse literally lifted up from the ditch.

"Stand clear of her legs and feet," she called to them and smiled at their wide-eyed, open-mouthed stares.

"How did you do that Mother?"

"Inspiration boys," she replied with conviction. "Remember 'nothing is impossible if we have the desire and fortitude to accomplish the seemingly impossible'." [lvii]

***

"Mother!" Isabella heard the voice pitch that told her to steel her nerves and run. Again she heard "Mother!" She headed toward the tears and cries from the corral.

Her eyes took in John Murray cradling his arm struggling to get up out of the dust. Alva and Alma were covered in the same dust and debris valiantly trying to help him up. 'I'll get up myself," he said, looking up at his mother closing the gate behind her.

Having assessed the situation she turned to the twins, "are you two alright?"

"Yes Mother, we slipped off the horse."

Carefully she knelt down and saw John's arm twisted at several different angles. "Alva started saying, I was sitting behind..." and Isabella broke in, "you may tell me what happened on our way into town."

Taking a deep breath Isabella used her apron to tie John's arm against his body so that the jolting ride into town wouldn't damage it more. Isabella kept the horse and wagon at a slow steady pace to keep his arm from being jostled.

Once they were on their way to town Isabella said, "Alright Alma you may tell me what happened now."

"We were riding triple bareback on the horse, you know John's a good rider and we were holding tight to him and we slipped when the horse shied from something and we fell off,"[lviii] the twins broke in on one another as they told the story to their mother neither one taking a breath until their story was told.

***

October 1920 *More Changes*

Hyrum felt at loose ends since the Bishopric had been released last month. His new calling in the ward choir didn't take the time that being the Bishop's councilor had. He missed the visiting of the sick and needy, working in the storehouse, and generally being involved in the care of the ward family.

What could he do to continue to be of help and be involved in the community? With a start he thought that he would volunteer at the Bishop's Storehouse. That would help focus his mind and calm his spirit; it always did. He was worried, the interest on the mortgages was due. He hoped that he could sell enough cattle to make the money.

November 1920 *Storms*

Snow packed around the windows, the wind forcing it into the cracks and crevices of the house. Hyrum and the older boys stomped their boots and shook their coats all while shoving the door hard against the wind chasing behind them.

"The stock is all right for now; we've chopped open the water troughs and cleared the ground in front of the barn doors. The horses are all in the barn and the cattle are outside in the pasture,"

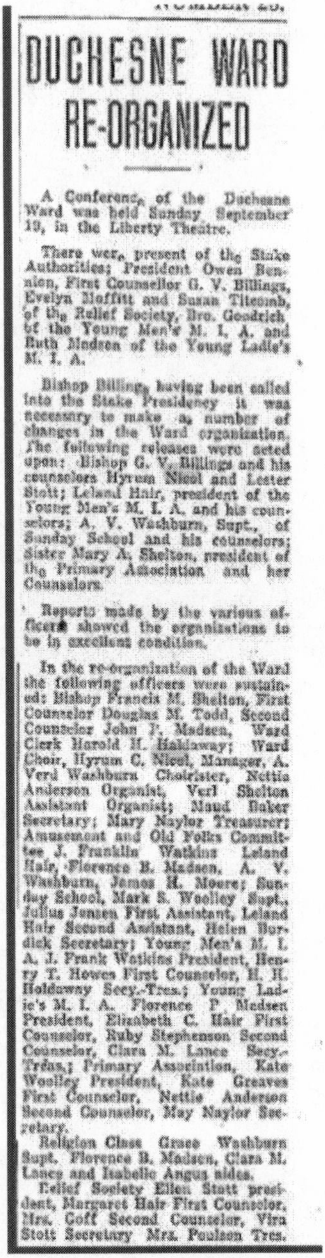

DUCHESNE WARD RE-ORGANIZED

A Conference of the Duchesne Ward was held Sunday September 19, in the Liberty Theatre.

There were present of the Stake Authorities; President Owen Bennion, First Counsellor G. V. Billings, Evelyn Moffitt and Susan Titcomb, of the Relief Society, Bro. Goodrich of the Young Men's M. I. A. and Ruth Madsen of the Young Ladie's M. I. A.

Bishop Billings having been called into the Stake Presidency it was necessary to make a number of changes in the Ward organization. The following releases were acted upon: Bishop G. V. Billings and his counselors Hyrum Nicol and Lester Stott; Leland Hair, president of the Young Men's M. I. A. and his counselors; A. V. Washburn, Supt., of Sunday School and his counselors; Sister Mary A. Shelton, president of the Primary Association and her Counselors.

Reports made by the various officers showed the organizations to be in excellent condition.

In the re-organization of the Ward the following officers were sustained: Bishop Francis M. Shelton, First Counselor Douglas M. Todd, Second Counselor John P. Madsen, Ward Clerk Harold H. Holdaway; Ward Choir, Hyrum C. Nicol, Manager, A. Verd Washburn Chorister, Nettie Anderson Organist, Verl Shelton Assistant Organist; Maud Baker Secretary; Mary Naylor Treasurer; Amusement and Old Folks Committee J. Franklin Watkins Leland Hair, Florence B. Madsen, A. V. Washburn, James H. Moore; Sunday School, Mark S. Woolley Supt., Julius Jensen First Assistant, Leland Hair Second Assistant, Helen Bordick Secretary; Young Men's M. I. A. J. Frank Watkins President, Henry T. Howes First Counselor, H. H. Holdaway Secy.-Tres.; Young Ladie's M. I. A. Florence P. Madsen President, Elizabeth C. Hair First Counselor, Ruby Stephenson Second Counselor, Clara M. Lance Secy.-Treas.; Primary Association, Kate Woolley President, Kate Greaves First Counselor, Nettie Anderson Second Counselor, May Naylor Secretary.

Religion Class Grace Washburn Supt. Florence B. Madsen, Clara M. Lancy and Isabelle Angus aides.

Relief Society Ellen Stott president, Margaret Hair First Counselor, Mrs. Goff Second Counselor, Vira Stott Secretary Mrs. Poulson Tres.

66 *Duchesne Record October 1920 - Duchesne Ward Reorganized*

Hyrum said. "I hope the storm breaks soon."

"Boys," Isabella called out from the kitchen, "bring your school work with you." She could tell by the slow tread of boots down the hall and across the floor that they were not excited by her words. The early winter weather had kept them mostly housebound; the frigid temperatures and incessant winds making it difficult for them to get to school.

"Read and do your next lessons, I want you able to pass any testing that you may have missed because of the weather."

Noting the heads and eyes focusing down on the table, book pages occasionally turning and pencils writing, Isabella returned to her work. Today was Monday, wash day. The cold outside wouldn't stop her in the scheduled completion of her tasks.

Skipping a chore for any reason caused a cascade of chaos to the rest of the week. "Hyrum, will you please run some clotheslines in the front room near the stove?"

"Tom will you help me wheel the washing machine over near the sink?" The heavy steel machine was a joy. Every time she used it she said a prayer of gratitude. She knew there was no way she could wash clothes for seven boys, Brigham's diapers, plus her own and Hyrum's things, by hand.

After selling the Sowers Canyon ranch and moving here, Hyrum had surprised her with this marvel. With its fat round tub and ringer she was able to complete their wash in one day. She sang as she worked. She loved her life.

November 1920

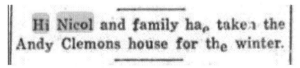

Hi Nicol and family have taken the Andy Clemons house for the winter.

67 *Duchesne Record November 11, 1920*

February 1920 *Horror*

"There isn't anything else we can do Tressa, we have to take another loan to buy more feed. With the early snows and these cold temperatures we've had to start feeding much sooner than usual."

"I know that is what you must do Hyrum, I'm just very worried." Isabella said with trepidation tinging her voice.

"Maybe the weather will break soon, maybe we will have an early spring," Hyrum offered.

"We can hope," she replied, trying not to tinge her words with doubt.

Cold continued to settle deep over the Uintah Basin, freezing when spring should be sending tentative warming forays to break up the winter's hold on the land. The opening of the door sent the flour on the bread board flying and Isabella turned to send threatening words at what she thought were her sons. Seeing Hyrum's expression, the words were bitten back and her hands set the potato she was peeling down on the table.

"What is the matter, your face is holding back something terrible I think," she said cautiously.

Looking around the room, seeing they were relatively alone with only baby Brigham in his chair, Hyrum told her, "the bank won't loan any more money to us Tressa; we can only feed some of the cattle with the remaining feed we have. Feed a few and hope to save some rather than feed all of them for a shorter time and possibly lose them all." Facing her, his brown eyes begged her to understand the hard choices he had been wrestling with, "I've decided to turn the largest steers out to scavenge for themselves."

"Oh Hyrum," Isabella exclaimed, "they will surely die if we do that!"

"They will surely die here," he soberly replied. "I hope to save some of them through to spring; I can't save them all." Despair and anguish carved deeply into Hyrum's face as he hardened himself to the only decision he could make.

Huddled inside, burning coal at a furious rate to keep back the cold, Isabella and Hyrum prayed desperately for help and guidance in this trial.

They joined with friends and neighbors across the basin for some relief from the long, severe winter's toll; they prayed for the survival of their livelihood wandering about on the open range. They prayed that they might find food and shelter and be saved. The winter that started early continued long past spring's advent on the calendar. Most of the ranchers and farmers in the basin faced failure and bankruptcy; the Nicol family was among them.

"We need to ride out and check on the cattle," Hyrum told Tom and Chase.

Isabella continued to hand them extra shirts; they already wore two pair of pants. Wrapping their faces with her shawls, they pulled their hats tight to their ears and walked gingerly out into the frigid air. Riding along the fences, eyes squinting against the glare of the snow on the ground, searching for signs of their herd, Hyrum stopped and pointed at the backs of cattle bunched down in the arroyo, or small wash, "there's some over there," he said.

As they rode closer Tom exclaimed with dismay, "They're frozen together!"

Horror of what they were seeing seared their hearts and souls. With resignation Hyrum said, "Let's go back home. There is nothing we can do out here today." Silently they turned and rode away from death. [lix]

***

It is time to move back to the ranch, Hyrum said, after he and the boys returned from riding the fences.

Isabella nodded her head and mentally began deciding the best way to pack for the move back up the river. The winter in town had been a respite to living isolated with the new baby. The neighbor women were as considerate and caring as she remembered them being each time she had had a new little one to care for.

Thinking out loud she said, "I'll need to get up to the ranch house and get it aired out and cleaned. I hope it wasn't overrun with mice and vermin." "What did you say?" Hyrum asked. "I was thinking out loud I guess. If we're going to go then let's not let the grass grow under our feet."

By the end of the following Saturday, they were again ensconced back in their river ranch. They had begun to call it the Indian Ranch, though when the name first came up or why she couldn't remember. Part of her wanted to argue that each of their homesteads had been an Indian Ranch, but she wouldn't cause any controversy over the name and like the others accepted the name as the ranch's due.

Spring wild flowers and grasses pushed up through the still frozen ground and the sun still seemed thin and cold as May arrived the reservation country. The cool weather helped keep the rotted smell of frozen cattle to a minimum while ranchers worked with icy fingers and toes to bury those closest to the homesteads. The coyotes, other predators and carrion birds weren't going hungry.

Day after day Hyrum and the older boys worked hour after hour repairing winter damaged fencing; sprung barbed wire, and tumbled pole fences broken by the heavy snow. They rode miles, climbing on and off of their patient horses, they pulled barbed wire tight and lifted logs up to reset the buck and rail fences surrounding the rockier stretches of ground. Occasionally they wrapped rope around the carcass of a cow and dragged it away from the fence line, pulling neckerchiefs over their noses to help block the smell.

***

Spring 1920 *Saved by Revelation*

Trying to escape the blistering desert heat that bore down with almost a weight, Tom, Chase, and Kenneth leaned against the shade side of the barn. The irrigation turn was done and the afternoon stretched out beckoning them to hide out and rest, but Chase had other ideas.

"Come on, come with me. I'm going into town and see if I can't find something to do besides sit here in the dirt."

Standing up, dusting off his pockets, he walked to the water trough; sticking his head into the warm water he cleaned his face and hands and turned into the house. "Mother, I'm going into town and see some of the boys. My chores are done," he said quickly before she could ask.

"Anyone else going with you?"

"No ma'am. They're just sitting out in the shade."

"See you later then," she said and turned back to the mending she had finally found a few minutes to catch up on.

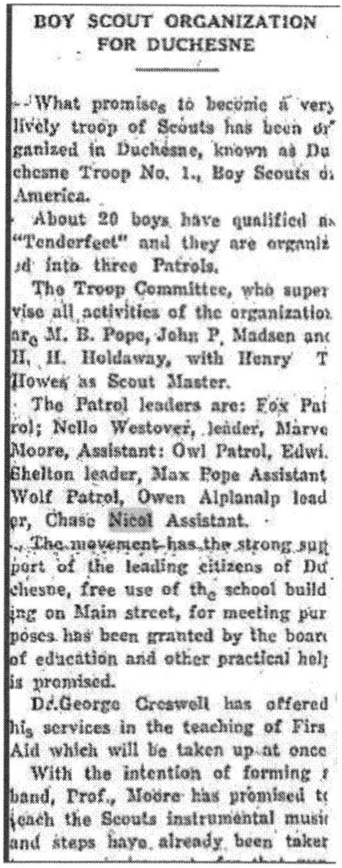

BOY SCOUT ORGANIZATION FOR DUCHESNE

What promises to become a very lively troop of Scouts has been organized in Duchesne, known as Duchesne Troop No. 1., Boy Scouts of America.

About 20 boys have qualified as "Tenderfeet" and they are organized into three Patrols.

The Troop Committee, who supervise all activities of the organization are M. B. Pope, John P. Madsen and H. H. Holdaway, with Henry T Howes as Scout Master.

The Patrol leaders are: Fox Patrol; Nello Westover, leader, Marve Moore, Assistant: Owl Patrol, Edwin Shelton leader, Max Pope Assistant, Wolf Patrol, Owen Alplanalp leader, Chase Nicol Assistant.

The movement has the strong support of the leading citizens of Duchesne, free use of the school building on Main street, for meeting purposes has been granted by the board of education and other practical help is promised.

Dr. George Creswell has offered his services in the teaching of First Aid which will be taken up at once.

With the intention of forming a band, Prof., Moore has promised to teach the Scouts instrumental music and steps have already been taken

68 Duchesne Record December 2 1920
Boy Scouts Org'dd – Chase Nicol Ass't

Buttoning on a clean shirt, Chase headed out toward the barn, "you sure you don't want to come with me?" he asked his brothers a second time. They just waved him off and went back to whatever conversation his question had interrupted.

Tugging his hat down, he started walking the 3 miles or so into town.

Not too far into the outskirts of town, Chase stopped when some of his friends saw him and waved him over.

"What are you in town for?" they asked. "I wanted to get away from the ranch for a while. Even in the shade it's hot."

"What are you two doing?" Chase asked. "We ate some ice cream and we thought we might go down to the river and swim for a while. Want to come with us?"

"Yes sir," Chase's blue eyes sparkled and his face lightened up with a smile. It had been a while since he had taken time to go swimming.

Their conversation wandered from work, to girls, to the movie playing at the theater and finally landed on their Boy Scout troop. Chase had been asked to be the assistant to the Scout Leader and he was working hard to learn new skills to add merit badges to his sash.

The troop had been organized less than a year before and the boys were excited about the new opportunities. Talking and laughing they headed down to the river. Chase and his friends stood on the bank throwing rocks into raging waters that flashed through the generally gentle bend where they swam.

"It must be running high from all those thunder storms. I'm not getting in there." "Me neither, I'm not that good of a swimmer." They continued to toss sticks into the water and watched them bounce and drown in the racing waters.

"I bet you can't climb to the top of the girders." They challenged one another. "Are you crazy? We'll kill ourselves!" "No we won't, it's not much higher than those cottonwoods up the river and we climb those." "I'll climb if you will, I'm not doing it by myself."

***

"Where's Chase?" Hyrum asked when the family had sat down for supper.

"He went into town to see his friends a while ago," Kenneth answered.

"He'll show up sooner or later," Tom added to the conversation.

Supper done and chores complete Hyrum and Isabella sat outside, hoping for a breeze to funnel down the canyon, and watched baby Brigham toddle around the house dragging a rope behind him. He looked almost asleep as he walked. Isabella called him over, picked him up and cuddled him on her lap.

"Alva, Alma it's time to get ready for bed," Isabella called standing up and shifting the heavy sleeping weight of Brig in her arms. Looking down the road Isabella said, "I expect he'll be coming in soon," as she walked inside.

Evening twilight settled into night. Isabella said, "I hope Chase gets home soon. It isn't like him to stay out so late."

Waking with a start Isabella looked around. The house was quiet. Something was wrong. She hadn't heard Chase come in. What time was it? Sliding out of bed she softly went into the parlor and looked at the clock on the mantle. It was past midnight. Something was definitely wrong.

In the stillness of the night she knelt in prayer asking the Lord to guide them in what they should do. Something was wrong. As she knelt pondering the feelings in her heart and worry for her son, her mind was filled with knowledge.

"Hyrum! Get up! Chase is on top of the steel girders over the Duchesne River Bridge and he can't get down. The water is high and the river is raging."

Hyrum immediately arose and began dressing; he knew Isabella so well that he willingly accepted her direction from the Lord. Riding quickly into town, he found the boys on top of the bridge girders, cold and scared as Tressa had said. He helped them down and returned Chase and his companions' home safely.[lx]

***

February 1921 *Coming Due*

Pulling their chairs near the coal stove and keeping their voices low Hyrum and Isabella laid their situation out in words and tears. The promissory note on their Heber house was due' plus the interest for the year. The interest on the ranch mortgage was due, the loans for feed were due, taxes were due, and the irrigation shares were delinquent. Their resources and savings were used up and winter continued to hang on like cockleburs in pant legs.

"I don't see any other way Tressa, we have to sell something, and the Heber house must be it if we intend on following through here. How do we do that? Isn't it part of the promissory note for the ranch?" Isabella asked him. "Can we do that?"

Throughout the following weeks Hyrum worked with his creditors for extensions on his loan's interest payments; sold the house his parents had given him as part of their estate in Heber City. They were given a reprieve by another interim loan from the Bank of Duchesne. The Nicol clan was going to hold on, even if it was only by their fingernails.

Hyrum's reputation and standing in the community were the last resources they could count on in their battle to beat back bankruptcy. The future was a shaky house of cards, mortgaged to the breaking point, their faith in a better future was all that kept them going. Then their house of cards collapsed overnight.

Returning from Heber with sixteen hundred dollars cash in hand from the sale of the house to Nephi and America Jacobson and a mortgage note for the remaining six hundred and fifty dollars, Hyrum rode into town with a glimmer of hope for restoring the equilibrium of their lives. His countenance was brighter than it had been all winter when he walked in the door and said, "We might have a chance to make it one more year until we can rebuild our herd."

"We aren't the only ones struggling to cope with the ravages of this winter; it seems like most everyone's story is the same as ours. Resources all gone, cattle dead or dying, and everyone has drawn most of their savings and are surviving like us, by hook and crook. I'll deposit the proceeds from the sale, write drafts for the loan and interest payments and we will have some breathing room."

March 1921 *Bank Collapse*

"The bank closed." [lxi] Hyrum stepped into the kitchen and his statement seemed to echo on and on and on. "The bank closed. Our money is gone. The drafts will not be honored."

Isabella looked on in shock, her heart fell and she could only watch as Hyrum made his way to the table, and dropped into a chair as his hands grasped his head.

Shocked, Isabella moved slowly to his side, placed her hands on his shaking shoulders and began to cry with him, the tears springing from her heart. She knew what he was feeling, what he was thinking, because it was what she was feeling and what she was thinking. This was it. It was the end of their hopes and their dreams.

He said, "We're done. There is no more room, no other ways to turn. We're caught in the trap and we can't break free."

Alva and Alma came running, laughing at a game, then stopped, laughter dying on their faces. Seeing the faces of their parents they knew something wasn't right. "Mother what's wrong?"

"Not now Alva," Isabella replied, not harshly but also not looking at them. "Go take care of Brigham when he wakes. Let us be for a while."

Like startled deer they swiftly turned and left their parents sitting in the despairing darkness that seemed to surround them. All the while, the thin spring sun was brightly falling through the windows and dappling the table and walls.

Sinking to her knees, her heart overwhelmed, Isabella bowed her head in supplication for support during this time of tragedy. Arising from her solemn prayer she slid back into her chair beside Hyrum. She took his hand and said, "Nothing is impossible Hyrum, remember that. Nothing is impossible, especially with God."

With those words she felt a small ray of hope glowing in the despair and darkness of spirit surrounding them. She said, "We aren't licked yet." Hyrum's head lifted, his red eyes searching her face as if to reach out and hold on to her fire of faith. She was his foundation, as long as Tressa was by his side, together they would survive.

***

BANK OF DUCHESNE CLOSES

Heavy withdrawals, coming at the same time forces suspending of operations.

After a long period of continued falling off of deposits, the Bank of Duchesne was closed, by order of the state banking department, when the required reserve was not sufficient to pay the unusually large cash letters. Three weeks ago, in order to prevent the closing of the bank, the directors devoted all their efforts and time in raising the necessary money to keep the bank open. They were successful and conditions looked better than they had for sometime. However, since that time, there has been a steady decrease in deposits and then several of the larger depositors decided that they wanted their money and drawing at the same time made the paying of their checks impossible. The bank was closed last Friday afternoon, much to the surprise and consternation of the county.

The state banking department did not send anyone to look into conditions, but appointed E. C. Robbins as receiver with instructions to work out the situation as best he could. It is not considered likely that the depositors will suffer the loss of any of their money but the appointing of a receiver has disappointed many as they had hoped that an effort would be made to have the bank reorganized and reopened within a short time.

Directors and stockholders of the bank expect that they will have to take a heavy loss but they are confident that depositors will be paid in full. Hopes are maintained that parties with sufficient capital can be interested in the taking over of the bank so that the long and hard process associated with a receivership can be avoided. As the closing the air so that, up to this time, no particular effort has been made, or concerted action taken, toward getting a new organization to take control.

Depositors in general are inclined to view the situation philosophically and are anxious to help all they can. On the other hand, although the deposits were very low, they represented about all the ready cash of this section of the county and in many cases living expenses until the harvesting of crops in the fall. It is not expected that borrowers will be unduly forced as pressure, under the present condition, would force a great many into bankruptcy. Federal Reserve Bank officials expressed a desire to be as lenient as is in any way possible should the collection of notes, that they now hold as rediscounts and security, be left to them for collection. A gloom has spread about the locality but there

69 *Duchesne Record March 10, 1921 – Bank Closure*

The family pulled together more tightly than ever. The town's hope that the bank would be reorganized and reopen wasn't realized. Although the bank was insured as a member of the Federal Reserve, the savings depositors had not seen any of their funds.

After the war prices of everything had gone up and continued to rise. Hyrum and Isabell were grateful that the Federal Reserve, which had taken over the assets of the bank, weren't pressing those whose mortgages and loans they held as collateral, knowing that by doing so they would push many people into bankruptcy.

***

July 1921 *Another Calling*

"Hyrum," Isabella said as they met up after they had each been visiting with friends, and they gathered their family together to go inside the chapel. "Stake President Billings has asked us to stay after Sacrament Meeting, he wants to talk with us."

"Thank you for staying. Hyrum, Sister Nicol," he said shaking their hands. "Please have a seat."

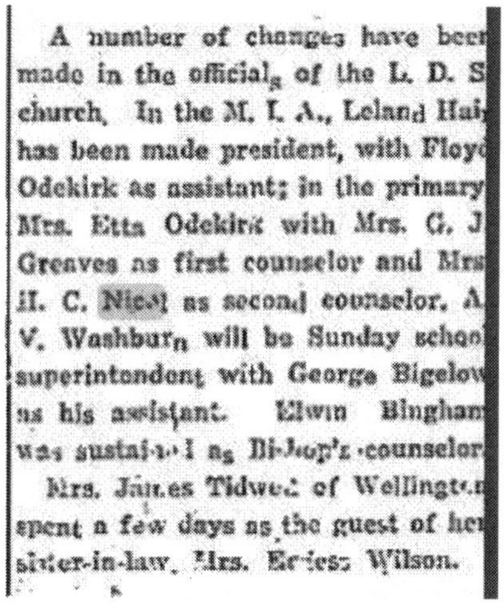
A number of changes have been made in the officials of the L. D. S church. In the M. I. A., Leland Hai has been made president, with Floyd Odekirk as assistant; in the primary Mrs. Etta Odekirk with Mrs. G. J Greaves as first counselor and Mrs H. C. Nicol as second counselor. A V. Washburn will be Sunday school superintendent with George Bigelow as his assistant. Elwin Bingham was sustained as Bishop's counselor.

Mrs. James Tidwell of Wellington spent a few days as the guest of her sister-in-law, Mrs. Ernest Wilson.

70 Duchesne Record July 21 1921– Mrs H. C. Nicol 2nd Counselor Primary

It didn't take long for him to come to the reason he asked to see them. "Sister Nicol, we are reorganizing the Stake Relief Society presidency and the Lord has called you to be the second councilor to the new president Sister Odekirk. Will you accept this call?"

"Yes I will President," Isabella said immediately.

"Hyrum, will you support her in this calling?"

"Yes President, I certainly will."

"That's wonderful, President Billings said, "I never doubted you would accept. You both are such faithful church workers, you have been as long as I've known you. We will ask for sustaining of the church members next Sunday, and we will set you apart next week after Sacrament Meeting." Rising from his chair, he again shook their hands, and walked them to the door.

***

Fall 1921 *Going Hunting*

"Mother, here let me help you with that," Tom said as he came into the kitchen.

Isabella had a large pot on the stove and she was beginning to add coal for additional heat.

"Thank you Tom," she said smiling at her long, lanky son.

Once the door was shut on the stove Tom said, "I'm going hunting with some friends, my chores are done, and Father is with Chase in the upper fields."

"Go on then," she said, "I can handle the hooligans by myself for a while."

"Thank you Mother," he called over his shoulder. She watched his tall, strong-boned figure stride across the room and out the door; he already had his gun belt buckled around his hips and slid the pistol into its holster with practice. She knew he was in a hurry in case she changed her mind.

Stepping outside into the shade of the house Isabella called to the younger of her brood, "fresh bread and honey if anyone wants some."

Where the yard was empty a moment before four sets of feet and legs exploded from behind the barn; new flippers held in Alma and Alva's hands. John Murray smiling, and Brigham running behind dragging a stick. John Murray had been showing the twins how to make their own flippers.

While they were holding thick slices of warm bread dripping with honey, John started to say, or tried to say as the twins broke in, "John is going to take us to practice with our flippers." "

They're already pretty good Mother," he said.

In the midst of the laughing hubbub they heard horses galloping up the road. Jumping from their chairs they all raced to the window to see who was in such a hurry.

Isabella, didn't want to know what was happening. Galloping horses generally were bad news in the life of a mother with seven boys.

Three young men slid out of their saddles, quickly tying the horses to the hitching rail in front of the house and ran over to help Tom off of his horse. Tom was dragging his leg as two of his friends each took one of his arms, pulled them over their shoulders and helped him into the house. Alva and Alma began to swarm around them as they walked sideways through the door, Tom yelping as his foot hit the door seal; apparently he couldn't lift his leg high enough to miss it.

Raising her voice loud enough to lift above the din a roomful of young men and boys can make, Isabella said, "quiet please." In response everyone stopped; they stopped moving, they stopped talking, and they all turned toward her.

"That's better," she said, looking at Tom's bloody pant leg. "Did you shoot yourself Tom?" [lxii] She asked.

Ducking his head he said, "Yes, I did."

"Trying to quick draw again?" "Yes, ma'am."

"Are you boys alright?" she looked over at them, their faces white and anxious.

They said," yes ma'am." "Well that's good." Smiling at them she said, "thank you for helping him home. Are you hungry? There is fresh bread and honey on the cupboard, you can help yourselves while I check Tom's leg."

"I'm not going to cut your pants off Tom, will you stand up and pull them down for me to look at your leg?"

Tom's face turned bright red.

"John Murray go get Tom a sheet to cover up with," then she said, "I'll turn my head while you get the sheet wrapped around you." She often forgot how grown Tom was, and of course he would be embarrassed by his mother seeing him in his underwear.

She pulled from the shelf her medicine and bandage box. "Alma will you bring me my shears, they are in my sewing basket."

"Are you ready now Tom?" "Yes ma'am." "Alright, let's look at that wound. I can see that the bullet went in and out of the front of your leg, through the muscle. It doesn't look like it hit the bone or you wouldn't have been able to ride back without fainting."

"This will hurt Tom, be prepared. I'm going to wash it with carbolic soap and rinse it out as best as I can. Then I'll swab it with methylate and wrap it up."

Tom's red face blanched white as his mother began her ministrations. He was breathing deeply through his nose; he wasn't going to faint in front of his friends.

"I'm glad you only shot yourself this time," Isabella said, remembering when Tom had handed his pistol to his friend Len Neilson and it had gone off accidently shooting Len in the neck.

Isabella looked up when she finished the last wrap of bandaging around Tom's leg, and said, "you boys better head on home, Tom isn't going to be doing much moving around for a few days."

"Thanks again for bringing him home," she said as they trooped out the door.

"John Murray, Twins, go take care of Tom's horse. Give him a good rub down and a handful of oats before turning him out into the corral." Turning back to Tom she said, "You look a bit peaky. Here, I'll help you into your room for a rest." Then her heads-taller son leaned gratefully onto the shoulder of his diminutive mother as she wrapped her arm around his waist and held him as he limped his way out of the room.

***

DUCHESNE WARD RE-UNION

In spite of the very disagreeable weather a large crowd responded to the invitation of Bishop Francis M. Shelton. The gathering was in honor of the retiring Bishopric, consisting of Bihop G. V. Billings and his counselers, H. C. Nicol and Lester Stott.

After a general mingling and visiting among the people present, the program started with a vocal duet by Miss Thelma Billings and Miss Susie Twitchell. These artists were roundly applauded for their number entitled "When the Frost is on the Pumpkin." Mr. A. V. Washburn then sang "I Hear You Calling," and in answer to the continued request for another song, favored his audience with "A Perfect Day." Mrs. Francis M. Shelton officiating at the piano.

Bishop Shelton in a short talk welcomed all those present and expressed the very great appreciation of the people for the services rendered by the retiring Bishop and his

Bishop Shelton in a short talk welcomed all those present and expressed the very great appreciation of the people for the services rendered by the retiring Bishop and his
Counselors. Bishop Billings was then called upon and although not prepared to make a speech, expressed his pleasure at the large turnout which included so many non-members of the Mormon Church. He also thanked all those who had cooperated with him in his work and hoped that the town people would all pull together in the future as they had done in the past.

Mr. Nicol and Mr. Stott assured the people that they had always enjoyed their work with Bishop Billingqs and also so expressed their desire to be of service to any that might call upon them in the future.

John Fortie, who was one of the organizers of this ward, but left here some time ago for Heber City, happened to be in town and at the reunion. He recalled some of the times when he was here and told how much he had enjoyed those days and the work as Counselor to Bishop Billings. He also spoke in very high terms of the present Bishop, Francis M. Shelton, and assured all they would find him a very loyal friend and a father to the entire

and the work as Counselor to Bishop Billings. He also spoke in very high terms of the present Bishop, Francis M. Shelton, and assured all they would find him a very loyal friend and a father to the entire
community.

Bishop Shelton then expressed his desire to be of service to the entire community and hoped that there would be no division on religious or other lines whereby the unity and progress of the town would be endangered. He then introduced the ladies who had been in the background and the feast was on. And what a repast was served. Sandwitches, salad, chicken, baked beans, pickles. Plates would not hold all at one time and the second trip had to be made for the pie and cake. We refrain from telling how some of us indulged a bit too heavily.

The floor was then cleared and the dance, the final to the evening, started but was interupted long enough to allow John P. Madsen to present Messrs Billings, Stott and Nicol with gifts which could show only in a measure the esteem of their fellow associates and the appreciation of their faithfuul efforts toward the building of this locality.

71 Duchesne Record Nov 11 1920 – Honor Bishopric Billings, Nicol, Stott

Hyrum Nicol of the Duchesne Stake Genealogy society and J. P. Madson of Duchesne were present at the afternoon meeting of the Utahn ward conference. They gave some very interesting talks.

72 Duchesne Record November 4, 1920 – Hyrum Nicol talks genealogy

February 1921

Mrs. Hyrum Nicols prěsided at a prettily appointed dinner, Sunday. Covers were laid for Mr. and Mrs. Wm. Baker and Mr. and Mrs. Mickelson.

73 Duchesne Record February 17 1921 - Mrs. Hyrum Nicols hosts dinner party

June 1921

We had with us in attendance at Relief society meeting Tuesday afternoon Sister Maggie Billings and Sister Isabell Nicol of Duchesne who spoke, giving some very choice advise and instructions. There were 28 sisters in attendance with two members of the bishopric who also spoke advising the Relief society sisters to press on in the great work they were doing. After meeting light refreshments were served. President Billings accompanied the sisters.

74 Myton Free Press June 2 1921 Isabell Nicol speaks at Relief Society meeting

PROGRAM FOR 4th OF JULY AT DUCHESNE, UTAH.

Firing of Guns at Sunrise — W. H. Clark.

Marshal of the Day — Sheriff Charles R. Barton

Music—Boy Scout Band— 9 A. M. to 10 A. M.

Flag Ceremony—10 A. M. By Boy Scout Band, Leader Workman.

Public Meeting at Town Hall 10:10.

Selection	Boy Scout Band
Invocation	Pres G. V. Billings
Reading	Maud Wall
Piano Selection	Mrs. F. M. Shelton
Address	Rev. W. H. Pond
Vocal Solo "Flag Without a Stain"	Thelma Billings
Reading	Mrs. Olga Pope
Piano Duet	Pupils of Mrs. Shelton
Selection	Boy Scout Band
Benediction	H. C. Nicol

75 Duchesne Record 1921 June 26 – Planning program for 4th of July H.C. Nicol

July 1921 *Old Burt's Flying Kick*

"Your mother and I are going into town for a meeting. Mind yourselves and get your chores done before we come back." Hyrum saw Tom's face cloud and could almost read his mind; he was eighteen and should have been asked to attend the meeting with them.

He watched as Tom quieted his features, swallowed and said, "Yes Father," before turning and walking toward the barn.

The heat of the afternoon hung heavy, while dust from the straw, scooped and shoveled from the horse stalls, floated in clouds and puffs of air as the manure and refuse was tossed into the wheel barrow. Sweat poured from the faces of the young men moving through the chores they'd done almost every day of their lives. Tom, Chase, and Kenneth sauntered toward the house, lifting their hats, pulling handkerchiefs from their pockets, and mopping their faces. Inside the coolness of the closed house, where they were pumping water ,when Alma ran inside screaming.

While the older boys were working, and John Murray was watching Brigham; Alva and Alma went outside to amuse themselves. They walked to the river and cut willow sticks, thinking they might make poles and go fishing. On their way to the house for string and hooks they saw that old Burt their work horse was grazing around the haystack.

Alva looked at Alma and that invisible twin connection kicked in; they climbed the pasture fence. Burt, taking bites of hay, looked up, disinterested in the boys that ran toward him. Taking their cut willow sticks they started chasing him around and around the haystack hitting him on the heels as he ran. After the third time around Old Burt decided he was done with those pests and let fly a high kick toward them connecting solidly with Alma's forehead. Down he went and Old Burt ran to the far side of the pasture. With the pests disposed of he went back to grazing along the fence line.

Alva screamed, and kept screaming for his brothers to come and help Alma. Alma was dead! Old Burt kicked him in the head.

Ken left the house in two strides, jumped bareback onto his horse and rode toward town in a flurry of hoofs, leaving behind the screams of Alva echoing behind him.

Tom and Chase followed Ken out the door and headed to the pasture their long legs flying to reach Alma, praying that he wasn't dead. A kick in the head by a horse or a mule could outright kill a person or they would die later from their injuries. Alma was laying where he had collapsed in the trampled dirt, blood covered his face and was pooling beneath his head. Tom, lifting his small body ran to the house. Alma didn't move.

Kenneth rode hard to town, bursting through the door to the meeting his parents were at and yelled, 'Alma's been kicked in the head by Old Burt.'[lxiii] Jumping from their seats, Hyrum and Isabella apologized as they stepped over people and quick-stepped to the door.

The wagon bucked and rattled as Hyrum whipped the horse into a trot. Isabella was praying for help and guidance; she also knew that being kicked in the head by a horse could kill a man, and could crush skulls and faces. The three miles from town seemed to pass very slowly. The horse, startled that he was woahed to a stop far from his normal resting place near the barn, jerked his head uneasily before stomping his feet and settling into the traces.

Lifting her skirt and running toward the house, Isabella was almost at the door when Chase held open the door hearing the wagon flying up the road. His mother swept past him into the kitchen.

Tom had laid Alma on the table and had carefully wiped the blood from around the wound and from off his face. Alma lay very still. Gently Isabella reached her hands out and stopped when she saw bone shining out from the gash. She breathed a sigh of relief that his head didn't appear crushed and that he was still breathing.

Her fervent prayers each day always included pleas for protection physically and spiritually for each of her sons, and she knew God answers prayers.

Hyrum turned toward the older boys, "Chase go get the doctor, I don't want to move him while he is unconscious," but as he started for the door the doctor walked in the room. He had been in the meeting when Kenneth sounded his alarm.

John Murray asked, "Father will you give him a blessing?" His voice quavered with the effort to hold back tears.

"We will John after the doctor has taken care of him." The sound of hoof steps and wagon wheels filled the yard again. Bishop Shelton and several other neighbors arrived to give aid and comfort.

The doctor said, "You did a good thing bringing him inside and keeping him quiet. Other than needing stitches, his skull appears to be undamaged though blood clots may develop. He will have at least a mild concussion." He continued, "Keep him down and quiet for a few days and I'll be out to check on him. If he has seizures, or vomits then come get me immediately."

Relief flooded through Isabella as she thanked the doctor and walked him to the door. Her family still encircled Alma on his tabletop bed. Bishop Shelton and Hyrum were preparing to give him a healing blessing.[lxiv] First they washed their hands and said a prayer asking the Holy Spirit to be with them. Hyrum anointed Alma's head with consecrated oil[lxv]. After the anointing the Bishop and Hyrum gently placed the tips of their fingers on Alma's head far back from his wound. Then Bishop Shelton sealed the anointing and pronounced the blessing that Alva would be healed through the power of the Holy Priesthood. He asked the Lord's blessing for a strong and healthy recovery. They also expressed gratitude for the nearness of the doctor, the quick actions of Tom and Kenneth, and the care and support of their neighbors.

***

Several days later, sitting in his bed listening to his brothers outside, Alma was itching to get up and join them. His head still hurt, though not as bad as it had, and the stitches were sore, but he felt better. Getting up the nerve to ask his mother if he could get up and go out, she came into his bedroom and looked him in the eye.

"Are you getting tired of being in bed?" He nodded his head. "Did you learn anything from this experience?"

Isabella used every moment she could to teach her boys lessons that would last more than a few days. "Remember son that God expects us to care for the gifts he has given us, and our animals are his creation and his gift. In Proverbs he teaches us that one sign of a righteous man is that he cares for his animals. Do you want to be a good boy?"

"Yes Mother I do," Alma nodded again.

"Then you must be kind to the animals."

She continued, "Old Burt taught you a hard lesson, didn't he?"

"Yes," Alma whispered.

"Will you remember his lesson?"

"Oh yes Mother!" Alma exclaimed.

"Good. You may get out of bed and go outside, but no running around yet."

Alma almost bounced out of his bed, then he stopped and sat down. "My head still hurts. I think I will just stay in bed and rest." "

Good idea son," Isabella said and left him lying under the light blanket.

***

June 1922 *Kenneth the Sheep Herder*

Spring was gone, the heat of summer already wilting early blooming gardens. Isabella was standing in the shade of the open barn door scattering chicken feed to the flock of hens scratching for bugs and grit around her feet. Kenneth rode in from the field and stopped, "hello Mother," he grinned at her as he lightly dropped to the ground. "May I help you?"

"No thank you Kenneth, I'm done here. You might help me with a quick weeding of the garden; I can start supper sooner," she bargained.

Of course," he said, narrowing his stride to match hers. He was tall for thirteen, his face darkened by the years working the ranch. He was a good rider, and an excellent shot with his rifle, but he was quieter than his brothers.

"Mother?" Kenneth said as he used the spade to loosen the soil around the small weeds in between the rows of vegetables.

"Yes? Do you need something?" She asked bending over to tug at the weeds Kenneth's spade had lifted above the soil.

"I heard a couple of ranchers are looking for summer sheep herders, I thought I'd see if I could get picked up for a job."

"Your father will need you here Kenneth," Isabella replied matter-of-factly.

Countering her argument he said, "Tom and Chase are here and John Murray."

"Well, ask your father when he gets in for supper," she replied. "Looks like we're finished here; many hands make light work," Isabella quoted then said, "I'll go start supper. You'd better get your horse taken care of before your father comes home."

Looking up he said, "I will, right now" and left her standing in the garden while he disappeared around the barn.

"That was a fine dinner Tressa," Hyrum said standing up from the table.

Isabella lifted her eyebrow at Kenneth and nodded her head. "Father? May I ask you something?"

"Sure son, what it is." Hyrum sat back down at the head of the table. "Today I heard some of the sheep ranchers are looking for summer camp help, I'd like to take a job."

Hyrum's face became thoughtful and he said, "I was going to say no because having your help here lightens the load. Herding sheep is a lonely job son."

"I know Father, but I like the quiet like when I'm riding the cattle herd or turning in the irrigation of a night. I think it will suit me." He looked over at his wife who nodded her head and then he said, "Give it a try son."

Two days later as the sun topped the eastern hills Tom and Chase helped Kenneth tie down the extra-large tooled leather saddlebags their father pulled out of the barn for him to use, laying them over the flanks of his horse. They were packed tight with clothing, books, and extra food; the rancher would provide the sheep camp trailer, food, and additional horses.

His bedroll, wrapped in a heavy coat and tarp, was lashed atop the saddle bags. Watching her boys through the window she said to Hyrum, "I'm worried about him."

Hyrum standing behind her nodded and said, "He will do alright Tressa. He's got what it takes and he's a good ranch hand, we've taught him well. He will do a good job."

When the three boys walked into the house it seemed smaller. They were tall and rangy, with dark hair long over their ears, and their foreheads stood out white where their hat brims rode low over their eyes.

"Well, I'm ready to ride Mother," Kenneth said as he leaned into the doorway to the kitchen. Guess I'll be heading out." His hands were planted on either side of the doorframe. He'd let his brothers move ahead when they entered the house.

"Kenneth, you come here and give me a hug before you go. You aren't leaving here without your Father giving you a blessing, and for family prayer." Isabella called to the younger boys, "Kenneth's leaving. Come here, we're going to have family prayer before he leaves."

The month since Kenneth left rode heavy on Isabella's mind. She always had a prayer in her heart for him and longed to know that he was well. Later that afternoon a horseman rode up to the ranch and handed her a message from Kenneth. Quickly unfolding a note written on the back of a faded coffee can label she smiled. He'd written with a lead bullet that he was well. [lxvi] Isabella was so glad to receive his cheerful note that tears filled her eyes. For it was such a tender mercy from a loving Heavenly Father that prompted an almost 14-year-old boy to write a note home.

***

July 1922 *Final Summer*

Tom and Chase left the house laughing and fully anticipating an evening away from the family and the ranch. There were going to be some pretty girls at Elva's party and they were looking forward to seeing them.

Miss Elva, Billings entertained at a swimming party Sunday evening After swimming weinnies and marsh-mellows were roasted over a camp fire. Those participating in the fun were, Nellie Odekirk, Nanna Axelgard, Harriet Bird, Belle Hair, Pearl White, Elva Moulton and Elton Billings, Alton Larsen, Owen Abplanalp, Joe Davis, Tom and Chase Nicols and Stewart and Alger Stott.

76 Duchesne Courier July 21, 1922 – Tom & Chase Nicol attend party

After supper, Hyrum asked the younger boys if they would like to help make ice cream. Isabella prepared the cream and sugar, adding in some vanilla flavoring. After the boys cranked the ice cream maker for a while, just before it set, she would add in chopped peaches. They could all use a treat.

Sitting in the shade of the porch, watching the boys taking turns spinning the crank on the wooden bucket packed with ice and salt, Hyrum reached over and took Isabella's hand, gently massaging her fingers. Then he turned it over, looking at the calluses, hard and tough from the years of hard work homesteading here on the reservation.

Gently stroking her palm he said, "It's over dear Tressa. We have done all we can do here. There is no more money, no more to be done. The mortgages are due." Taking in a deep breath hoping to relieve the tenseness in his throat he shared, "I feel a failure, and I feel I've cheated the good people who supported us through loans and tough times. I can't see any way to regain our footing. We are bankrupt. I think we must leave, but where we go or what we'll do I don't know, but I think it must be soon that we leave."

She replied steady and firm, "we've done our best, haven't we? You have worked as hard as any man around and there is no fault we can lay at our feet. We've done our best and we have been blessed. Haven't we a fine family? She asked and then went on, "our sons are strong and have learned to be honest, hardworking men. They have seen the hand of God in their lives for their protection and the protection of others. They have seen the ups and downs of family and finances. Leaving now may give them an opportunity for more education and to know a world that is more than this dry valley."

From the other side of the porch they heard running feet and a voice said, "Father we can't turn the crank any more, even John says it's too hard. Will you finish up the ice cream?"

Smiling down at his son's upturned face, he said, "well of course." As he walked down toward the circle of anxious boys he turned to Tressa, "better pull out the bowls and spoons we're going to have some ice cream soon."

Lifting the ice cream bucket out of the way, Hyrum sat down on the porch step and finished the final turns to the frozen treat. Four eager faces watched him pull the crank off of the top of the ice cream container. Before Isabella could start scooping the ice cream, the boys gathered around their father who held out the crank the paddle ,coated with the sweet treat said, "Let's eat this first, shall we?"

While they were leaning over one another to lick the paddle, Isabella on the other side of the bucket scooped and piled the cold treat into bowls. Once the paddle was licked clean, she passed a bowl to each excited child, to Hyrum, and then took one for herself. The held the first spoonful in her mouth and let the cold sweetness melt around her tongue and she smiled.

"John Murray, Twins, come get our bowls and take them inside please."

"Yes ma'am," they chimed with sticky lips and chins. "Is there any more left?"

"No there isn't, we cleaned up the whole of it, every drop." Dire financial decisions couldn't dampen her enthusiasm for watching her sons.

***

Resolution

Once the younger boys were washed up and put to bed, and only John Murray remained awake reading in the remaining evening light. Hyrum pulled Isabella to her feet and said, "John we're going for a walk along the river if you need us. Watch the children please."

"Yes sir," he said, not lifting his head from the pages before him.

"It's time to make this decision final, isn't it?" She asked it calmly, much more calmly than she thought she would. She had been expecting it these past two years after that hideously long and cold winter when Brigham was born. They never really were able to recover from those losses. "What are you thinking Hyrum?" she asked, taking his hand as they made their way along the worn path that followed the fence line toward the river.

"I feel a failure Tressa. I feel like I could have done more. Why couldn't I have done more Tressa?" His voice was quiet, almost solemn, and filled with such pain as she had heard only a few times in their nineteen years together.

She tightened her fingers around his hand and said, "I love you Hyrum. I've loved you since we were children. I thought I loved you when we married but I realize that I love you more now than I thought a heart could hold. I expect to love you forever."

She paused, searching for the words to share her feelings. "This is only a change my dear. This chapter of our story may be ending here, but what will the next chapter hold for us? "

"Let's not lose faith now. What more can we do?" She asked, although she continued with certainty and love. "We hold onto each other. We stand firm in our love of God and in our testimonies of Him and of his son Jesus. We trust in Him and in his providence. We stand tall for our sons and move forward knowing we've done our best." Then she stopped, there was no more she could say.

They stood together and watched the sun dip beyond the horizon, and in the rose gold twilight, he wrapped his arms around her and said, "You're a gift I never deserved. I love you too. I love you for now, and for eternity Tressa."

Later that night, kneeling together for prayer, they gave thanks for the love and guidance they had received. They prayed to have faith and courage as they moved forward into their future.

The future may be unknown, but it wasn't dark.

***

September 1922 *Preparation*

During the months after what she had come to call 'the decision', Isabella cleaned, and sorted through all of their belongings; determining what they needed to take, what they might sell, and what they might give away. She dearly wanted to find a way to bring her piano.

They may have been 'broke', but they were not broken. 'Pride still existed in them and they still held hope that through faith and prayer they would be able to see that somehow their children would have the opportunity to achieve the goals they had previously set for themselves after they were married'. [lxvii] She and Hyrum continued to do their church work. Kenneth came home from the herd, and with his father and brothers made the ranch fall and winter ready.

Hyrum sold some cattle, and most of the proceeds of the sale went to pay debts. Isabella harvested the last of her garden, and prepared the soil for spring. She wasn't going to let the next woman who lived here think she was slovenly and didn't know how to care for her garden. After the harvest she continued to bottle the bounty of vegetables to add to the jars she and her sisters had canned during their visit to Heber in August.

Large Attendance at Stake Conference

Saints from every part of Duchesne county attended the quarterly conference at Duchesne last Saturday and Sunday. The largest crowd was on Sunday afternoon when nearly 350 people, Mormons and non-Mormons, heard the eloquet Apostle Lyman deliver his address, the greater portion of which was on the evils which result from the use of tea, coffee, tobacco and booze. He reached the climax when he appealed to the voters to send a man to the state legislature who will refuse to vote for the repeal of the anti-cigarette law.

President Owen Bennion presided at the conference and made most impressive talks. Other speakers were Homer Riser, Sunday school board; Mrs. Julia Brixen, Y. L. M. I. A. board; Mrs. Eliza Bennion, primary association; Mrs. Robinson, general Relief society. At the Mutual meeting on Sunday night splendid talks were made by all, but we desire to especially commend the talk by Mrs. Bennion on modesty. Every young man ane young woman who heard that talk went away benefited.

But few changes were made. Owing to the fact that so many members have left Utahn so as to send their children to school the Utahn ward was disorganized, and all living this side of the mouth of Rock creek will join Duchesne ward and all above the mouth of Rock creek will join Tabiona ward.

sellor Y. L. M. I. A.; Lavina Murdock released, Verna Bennion sustained; second counsellor, Cecelia Olsen sustained.

77 Duchesne Record September 1922 Lg Attendance at Stake Conf. HC Nicol released

When the bishopric was released, Bishop Billings was called to preside as the President of the Duchesne Stake. "We should talk with President Billings, it's time to ask to be released from our callings. It's only a few more weeks before we leave."

"Oh Hyrum, this makes me sad. But I am calm in the midst of the storm, if you know what I'm saying?"

I am sad to have to leave. I'd hoped for something else, but I think God's hand is in this. It's time to change our course and focus ahead."

Hyrum said, "I couldn't have said it better Tressa. Let's stop by his home after Sunday School."

"President Billings, may we speak with you for a minute?"

"Of course Hyrum, come in."

Isabella and Hyrum knew this was the beginning of the process of closing out their lives in Duchesne. Sitting in the Billings' parlor, Hyrum explained their decision and they asked to be released from their callings.

President Billings sat quietly for a few moments before he said, "I know how difficult this decision must be for you. So many families have left the Basin as a result of the ravages of the bank collapse and then the killing winter. I know that combined punch hit you hard Hyrum."

Afterward they talked for a few minutes more, of the town, and the changes their almost twenty years on the reservation had added to the community, Isabella stood and held out her hand and said, "We love you. You have been a faithful leader and the best of friends and we thank you for all you have done for us."

Walking them to the door President Billings said, "You and your family will be missed. You have been stalwart in your support and leadership in the growth of this valley and town. You should be proud of your services to God and to your fellowmen. May God's blessings see you on your way."

"When are you leaving?" He asked as they turned to leave.

Turning back around Hyrum replied, "The first part of October. We've sold some land to Brother Moulton and we will close the deal on the second." Sharing sad smiles, they had another round of shaking hands and left President Billings standing watchfully in the doorway.

***

October 1922 *Departure*

Their wagon stood in front of the house, almost loaded with what seemed like meager possessions that they would be taking with them. The house was strange and echoing now it was empty of almost all of their belongings. The chair legs scraped loudly as the family gathered at the table and knelt for their final prayer in their home.

The boys tilted their heads to look at their father as he cleared his throat, twice, before he spoke. His voice broke with emotion and he prayed, "Thank thee Lord for the lives we have been privileged to live these years in this valley. We are grateful Lord for being able to serve thee. Thank thee for the opportunity to be parents to these seven fine young men. Wilt though please bless us with thy protection, guidance, help and success as we move into the unknown before us. We thank thee for thy gifts and blessings and will thou please see us safely on our way. Again Father, wilt thou please help us to follow thee, and to find our way forward into this time of uncertainty. In Jesus' name. Amen"

Sitting down at their places at the table, oldest next to their father, youngest by their mother, and rather than eat quickly as they usually did with their minds turned toward their next tasks, there was silence. Today, at this breakfast they all took their time not quite wanting the meal to end, each sober within their own thoughts.

Then Alva started to laugh and pointed up toward the patched hole in the corner of the ceiling. He laughed, and Alma laughed, and John Murray joined in. Chase and Kenneth were slapping the table trying to hold in their laughs, their faces soon as red as Tom's. Soon they were all laughing while Tom's face got redder and redder before he too started laughing.

Tom had been cleaning his shotgun at the kitchen table with all the kids sitting around him when the gun went off over Alva's head and shot a basketball sized hole in the corner of the kitchen. After that Alva claimed that his nose holes were put there because of the blast over his head. [lxviii]

With the tension lightened Hyrum said, "I'll ride into town and take care of the property paper work then I'll come back to help if there is any loading left wh-en I get home." He looked over the table at his sons and they got the message, the wagon would be loaded and ready when he returned.

Isabella stood alone in the kitchen after moving slowly from room to room, checking, remembering, laughing, crying, and now she stood considering the windows that she had polished to a gleam. Turning around all she saw was her remaining kitchen things waiting in a box for one of the boys to carry out.

These were the last things left inside the once full-of-life and noisy house. Outside she could hear Alva, Alma, and John Murray capturing the last of the chickens; the hens' squawks of protest loud in the calm morning air, as they were stuck into their crate.

Hyrum rode into the yard as Chase carried the kitchen box out. He waved as he noticed Isabella at the window and swung out of his saddle. Tapping John Murray on the shoulder, then motioning him aside he bent over to pick up the crate of chickens. Tom and Chase quickly came, one to each side, and grabbed an end of the crate while their father tied it to the back of the wagon.

Isabella stood watching and wondered why that scene was so familiar. Then her eyes overflowed with tears and she was a young mother again; sitting on a single chair in the middle of her kitchen with the spring sunlight dappling the bare floors and walls as it filtered through the naked windows of their empty house.

She was feeding baby Chase, and watching Tom wander around the room on sturdy toddler legs trying to catch the sun dust as it floated through the early morning air.

She glanced out the window watching Hyrum tie their crate of chickens to the back of their wagon. She saw him tightening rope, inventorying all their belongings. This morning they would start east to begin their new lives on the reservation. Today they would became pioneers.

Shaking her head and wiping her cheeks she stepped briskly across her scrubbed floors and slid her arms into her coat, buttoned it up, put her scarf around her neck and stepped out the door. She pulled it shut with finality.

"Boys," she called, "time to get into the wagon. Get comfortable, use the extra blankets if you get cold."

Kenneth helped her into the wagon seat before climbing onto his own horse and joined Tom and Chase at the back of the wagon. Three-year-old Brigham sat between his parents on the bench.

Hyrum's familiar, "hi-ya," echoed in their ears as he flicked the reins over the patiently waiting horses' backs. The wagon jerked and rattled to a start. Out from their ranch onto the River Road the Nicol clan slowly crossed the Duchesne River Bridge where Chase had gotten stuck up on the girders. Then they headed west toward Heber City, and a new life somewhere else.

Rattling along on the seat of their old wagon Isabella reached around Brigham and laid her hand on Hyrum's shoulder. He turned toward her searching her eyes. She smiled; softly, kindly, and her face was calm. It was then that Hyrum knew everything would be alright. No matter what the future might hold Isabella was by his side.

Yes this chapter of their lives was closing. They had worked as hard as they could, and they had sacrificed much in the service of their family, their community, and the Lord's church. The foundation they had built their lives on and the precepts they had lived by was that the Lord knew who they were, and what they needed. They also knew deep in their hearts that it was time to change. The Lord had another place in his vineyard for them to work. With unbending faith they turned west toward a different future knowing they had tried everything, and did the best they could through each struggle, trial and triumph.

There was silence and mixed emotions rising and subsiding within each of their hearts and in their thoughts as they passed by the homes of friends and neighbors. They remembered their lives as they rode passed the church they had helped build, and passed by the businesses where they had worked and shopped. Telegraph, telephone, and electric wires now lined the roads. The once frontier town had grown into a city of substance thanks to the tough minded men and women who braved blizzards, starving times, freezing times, drought, and man-made disasters like bank collapses.

Onward they drove and passing by swathes of harvested fields where there was once only dry ground and scrub sagebrush. They moved west into the unknown praying for healing of their broken hearts and help to dry tears. 'It was a sad trip back to their families in Heber City.' [lxix]

***

Epilog

Hyrum and Isabella left the reservation without any financial reserves; having sold most of what they owned attempting to pay debts. They were left with little materially to help sustain them. Once they arrived in Heber to the support and love of their extended families, they determined they would move to Provo hoping their children would have opportunities to gain an education and enrich their lives.

Tom was 19, Chase was17, Kenneth was almost 14, John Murray was 11, Alva and Alma were 7, and Brigham was only 3.

1922 – 1929 *Lean times*

'Life was much different in Provo, after having so much in material things in Duchesne.'[lxx] Hyrum took whatever job, here and there, he could for many years.

Less than a year after they moved to Provo, Isabella at the age of 47, gave birth, to a daughter, whom they named I. Donnavieve[lxxi], on July 12, 1923. That little girl became the light and joy of the family. Her brothers doted upon her and Isabella was thankful that 'things seemed to calm down'[lxxii].

"No boys, we don't work on Sunday, no matter how much we might be paid," Isabella stoutly exclaimed, "you know that." Tom and Chase though heads taller than their diminutive mother, felt small under the strength of her convictions and faith. "We will pay out tithing. We will work hard every other day, but Sunday is the Lord's Day. We keep his commandments, keep the Sabbath day holy, and He provides what we need. He has never, not ever, let us starve nor have a roof over our heads."

"Yes, Mother", they replied, marveling at the strength of will and faith in the Lord that she had. It's one thing to have a watering turn on the Sabbath, she continued, but another thing to deliberately choose to work on Sunday. Sure as the sun rises each morning no good will come of it. We' will be poorer in the end."

***

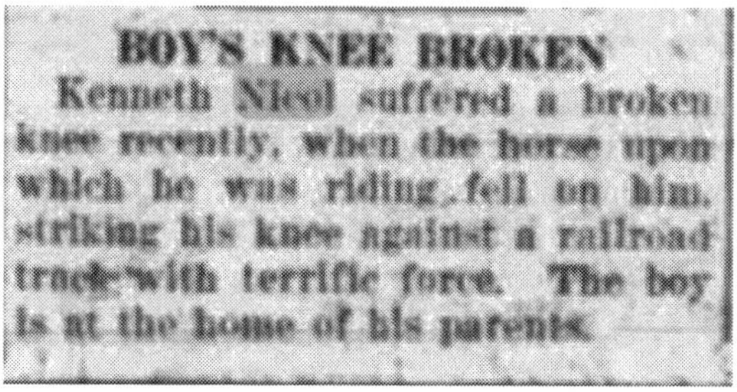

BOY'S KNEE BROKEN

Kenneth Nicol suffered a broken knee recently, when the horse upon which he was riding fell on him, striking his knee against a railroad track with terrific force. The boy is at the home of his parents.

78 Evening Herald May 11 1927 Kenneth Nicol

Trouble with the boys didn't always stop when they moved to Provo. "I'll be fine Mother, thank you." Kenneth said, his full-leg length cast stretch out before him on his bed. "Don't worry about me," he told her.

Late in 2917, Kenneth healed from his broken knee was slowly walking around. Four year old Donnavieve continued to be the bright center of the family's eye. But, the Indian Ranch wore on Hyrum and Isabella's minds. They wore the debt like a millstone, knowing that they could not save their dream, nor pay the debts they had accumulated those last years in Duchesne.

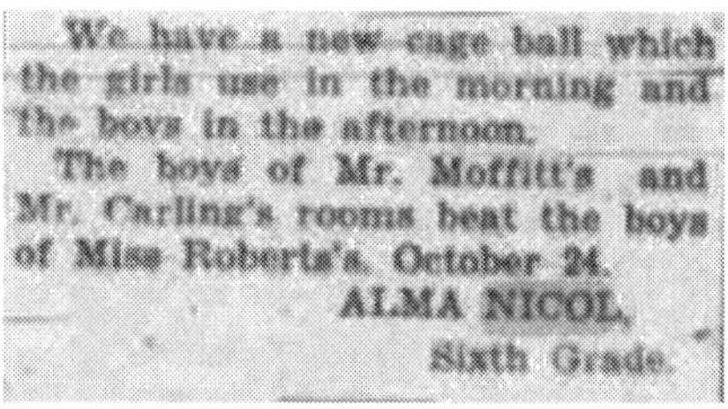

We have a new cage ball which the girls use in the morning and the boys in the afternoon.

The boys of Mr. Moffitt's and Mr. Carling's rooms beat the boys of Miss Roberts's, October 24.

ALMA NICOL,
Sixth Grade.

79 Evening Herald November 5, 1928
Alma Nicol via Timpanogos School News

Hyrum spread the letter from the Clerk of Duchesne City on the kitchen table. Their property was to be sold at a sheriff's sale. Hyrum and Isabella had struggled to maintain a presence in the basin, leasing the ranch in an effort to save their property. Their hope to earn enough to pay off the mortgages before the property went into foreclosure.

On the steps of the Duchesne County Courthouse, the gavel sounded in the early morning air. Sold, for twenty-five dollars, to W. L. Dean, the original homesteader of most of the property in 1927.

"Hyrum", Isabella whispered as they walked into the land office to sign the Quit Claim deeds, "we tried so hard." Her voice full of unshed tears and sadness.

Hyrum, clearing his throat, said to her, "yes we did Tressa. Let's try to put the shame and the heart break behind us because we have done the best we could."

***

"I'm not sure about that girl Tom is seeing. She's divorced!" Isabella said judgmentally. "She's not a Mormon and she smokes too," she continued with a shake of her head. "I don't think he should keep seeing her wistfulness entered her voice.

"She is a nice girl." Hyrum said, and prayed for his oldest son.

Life for Hyrum and Isabella settled into a steady, hardworking rhythm, some stability was returning to their lives. That rhythm came to an abrupt halt October 1929, when the stock market crashed.

Their family, already living on the edge, was washed into the abyss of the great depression.

It was in the beginning of that season of national despair that Tom married Delours Ellis Bethers, the 4th of November 1929, in Evanston Wyoming. They had met when he was playing the piano in the window of a music store located around the corner from the beauty school De was attending[lxxiii].

***

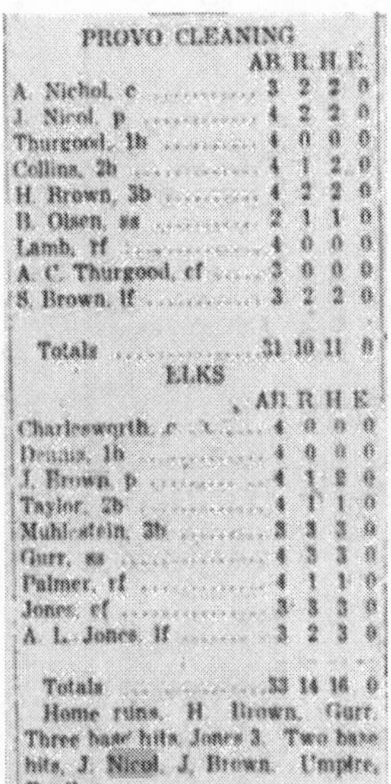

PROVO CLEANING

	AB.	R.	H.	E.
A. Nichol, c	3	2	2	0
J. Nicol, p	4	2	2	0
Thurgood, 1b	4	0	0	0
Collins, 2b	4	1	2	0
H. Brown, 3b	4	2	2	0
B. Olsen, ss	2	1	1	0
Lamb, rf	4	0	0	0
A. C. Thurgood, cf	3	0	0	0
S. Brown, lf	3	2	2	0
Totals	31	10	11	0

ELKS

	AB.	R.	H.	E.
Charlesworth, c	4	0	0	0
Dennis, 1b	4	0	0	0
J. Brown, p	4	1	2	0
Taylor, 2b	4	1	1	0
Muhlestein, 3b	3	3	3	0
Gurr, ss	4	3	3	0
Palmer, rf	4	1	1	0
Jones, cf	3	3	3	0
A. L. Jones, lf	3	2	3	0
Totals	33	14	16	0

Home runs, H. Brown, Gurr. Three base hits, Jones 3. Two base hits, J. Nicol, J. Brown. Umpire, Bradley.

79 Evening Herald June 10, 1929 John Nicol Baseball

Hyrum found it harder and harder to find work and 'money to pay for work performed was very scarce.' They didn't know where their next meals would come from or were they would live the next month. 'It was then 'root hog or die''[lxxiv].

From month to month Hyrum and Isabella gathered together what they could, and the family 'moved ten times' within a year. At one time they 'lived in their tents salvaged from their lives in Duchesne'.

'It was during these times the family ate oatmeal and flour mush daily. Potatoes and gravy with lots of bread and pink-eye beans were the main source of meals'.

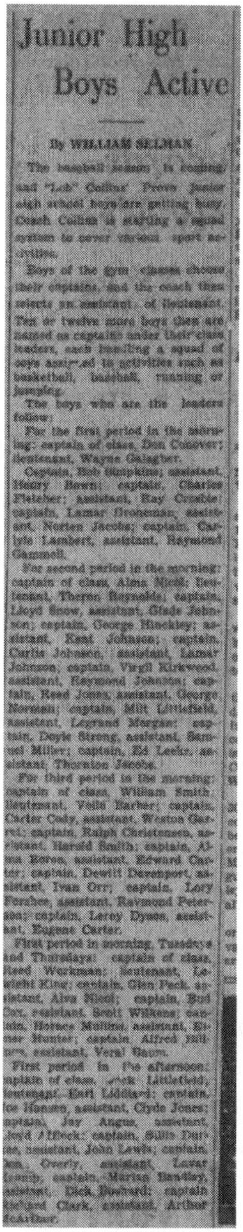

Junior High Boys Active

By WILLIAM SELMAN

The baseball season is [illegible] and "Lob" Collins' Provo junior high school boys are getting busy. Coach Collins is starting a squad system to cover various sport activities.

Boys of the gym classes choose their captains, and the coach then selects an assistant or lieutenant. Ten or twelve more boys then are named as captains under their class leaders, each handling a squad of boys assigned to activities such as basketball, baseball, running or jumping.

The boys who are the leaders follow:

For the first period in the morning: captain of class, Don Conover; lieutenant, Wayne Galagher.

Captain, Bob Simpkins; assistant, Henry Brown; captain, Charles Fletcher; assistant, Ray Crabble; captain, Lamar Droneman, assistant, Norten Jacobs; captain, Carlyle Lambert, assistant, Raymond Gammell.

For second period in the morning: captain of class, Alma Nicol; lieutenant, Theron Reynolds; captain, Lloyd Snow, assistant, Glade Johnson; captain, George Hinckley; assistant, Reed Johnson; captain, Curtis Johnson, assistant, Lamar Johnson; captain, Virgil Kirkwood, assistant, Raymond Johnston; captain, Reed Jones, assistant, George Norman; captain, Milt Littlefield, assistant, Legrand Morgan; captain, Doyle Strong, assistant, Samuel Miller; captain, Ed Leeks, assistant, Thornton Jacobs.

For third period in the morning: captain of class, William Smith; lieutenant, Voils Barber; captain, Carter Cody, assistant, Weston Garrel; captain, Ralph Christensen, assistant, Harold Smith; captain, Alma Boren, assistant, Edward Carter; captain, Dewitt Davenport, assistant, Ivan Orr; captain, Lory Forshee, assistant, Raymond Peterson; captain, Leroy Dyson, assistant, Eugene Carter.

First period in morning, Tuesdays and Thursdays: captain of class, Reed Workman; lieutenant, Lewight King; captain, Glen Peck, assistant, Alva Nicol; captain, Bud Orr, assistant, Scott Wilkens; captain, Horace Mullins, assistant, Elmer Hunter; captain, Alfred [illegible], assistant, Veral Baum.

First period in the afternoon: captain of class, [illegible] Littlefield, lieutenant, Earl Liddiard; captain, Joe Hansen, assistant, Clyde Jones; captain, Jay Angus, assistant, Lloyd Affleck; captain, Billie Durfee, assistant, John Lewis; captain, [illegible] Overly, assistant, Lavar [illegible]; captain, Marion Handley, assistant, Dick Bushard; captain, Richard Clark, assistant, Arthur McArthur.

80 Sunday Herald April 6, 1930 Alva & Alma

In the midst of their trials, they finally 'mortgaged their piano which in the end they would never recover'. 'They felt very bad because it deprived their children of the musical opportunities' they had known.

Isabella continued to work as hard as she had during their first years homesteading on the reservation. 'She put up fruit for the winter cooking over a hot coal-burning stove. Under her direction the boys helped to peel and bottle, scrub floors, scrub clothes on a washing board, and did the ironing. 'Father's little income paid the rent and utilities'.[lxxv]

The 1930 United States Census[lxxvi] workers found them renting a house mid-block between 100 and 200 South on 700 West in Provo. Their rent was $15.00. Hyrum was working as a floor manager at the steel plant, Chase was a brick mason, and Kenneth was working at the pipe plant.

Throughout the tumultuous years of the depression Hyrum and Isabella kept their family together and their faith in God never wavered. Once they had a steadier income they found a rental house in the Grandview area, or the west Provo bench. It would be their home for the rest of their lives. They never owned property again.

In the midst of near homelessness and starvation their faith never wavered. They continued to call upon God in thanksgiving and implored his strength to help them overcome their trials. 'They walked to church and took part. The family was 'always so proud when Hyrum would speak in sacrament meeting or Isabella would sing or take part in drama activities'[lxxvii]

April 1931 *Posterity*

A knock on the front door proceeded the call, “we’re here Mother.” Tom stood aside, holding the door open, as De walked into the room’s warm light holding the small blanket wrapped bundle gently in her arms.

M. I. A. FINALISTS ARE SELECTED

(Continued From Page One)

ing. Mr. and Mrs. Morris Christensen. Costumes—E. H. Eastmond and Mrs. Gladys Corbett. Electrician—Newell Talbot. Cast: Dorotha Reid, Orpha Nelson, Mary Prows, Lorna Moffitt, Edna Lyon, Ann Whiting, Ethe B. Christensen, Hannah Reynolds, Rennon Wilson, Nork Prows, Dean Rishet, Melvin Swapp, George Brown, Dean Thirot, Herbert Smart, Duane Anderson, Ben M. Doty, Leo Andrew, Morris Christensen, Merlin Vance.

Pioneer ward—"The Reward"; Written and directed by Florence Christiansen. Music director — Grover Miller. Accompanist—Millie Nelson. Characters: Miss M. I. A., Mariam Flygare; L. D. S. ideals — Chastity, Emily Norman; Faith, Belva Batty; Word of Wisdom, Helen Brown; Truth, Afton Lewis; Loyalty, Elva Peterson; Obedience, Florence Durrant; Fields—Music, Leah Fisher; dancing, Corlea Byland; Public Speaking, Dagmar Lyland; Drama, Helen Christiansen; Retold Story, Elma Smith; Worldliness, John Pullen; His fields: Lethoure, Bill Howe; Cigaret, Chester Perry; Intoxicating Drink, Max Cox; Gambling, Kenneth Nicol; Immorality, Bill Wilkens; Gamblers: Horace Peay, Darrell Servoss; Worldly Sweethearts, Vivian Christensen, Mary Christiansen; Margie, Evelyn Oren; Paul, Martin Rigby; Father Time, Marion Hinckley. Worldly rewards—Crime, Woodrow Washburn; Imprisonment, Alva Nicol; Disease, Sterling Durrant; Divorce, Kay Hinckley; Regret, George Norman; Poverty, Floyd Affleck; Unhappy Homes, Bill Norman. M. I. A. rewards—Contentment, Josephine Norman; Peace, Rae Shipp; Liberty, Phyllis Snyder; Health, June Servoss; Fidelity, Keith Williams; Prosperity, Margaret Woods; Happy Homes, Lenore Wall. M. I. A. members—Genece Wilkins, Eleanor Williams, Ruby Durrant.

TEN-MINUTE CLASS

Second ward—"Southern Melodies"; Director—C. W. Robbins. Accompanist—Mrs. George B. Carter. Cast: Carl Johnson, Ivan Madsen, Woodrow Eggertsen, Elmer Millet, Archie Millet, Dean Knudsen, Rodger Farrer.

Fourth ward—"The Witching Hour"; Director—Mrs. Celestia J. Taylor. Accompanist—Mrs. Agnes Blackham. Cast: Frances Benedict, Zule Garfield, Lola Hawe, Lottie Payne, Ethel Hunter, Argene Vance, Genevieve Cook, Afton Coleman, Fawn Jacobsen, Peggy Evans.

First ward—"Universal Gathering"; Directors—Mabel W. Jones, Yeoma J. Done, Edith W. Bush. Accompanist—Melba Fletcher. Cast: Helen Farley, Marvelle Willis, Hazel Fletcher, Mary Whitehead, Nora Ellis, Afton Johnson, Ethel Fletcher, Cyril Johnson, Joseph Ahlander, Anita Smoot, Beth Done.

81 Evening Herald Nov. 13 1930 Ken & Alva Nicol Finalists

“Our first grandchild”, Isabella whispered, as she walked out of the kitchen and stood next to De, while pulling back the blanket revealing the face of the newest member of their family.

Donnavieve flew out of her room calling to Tom, “can I hold him? Let me see, let me see!” her voice rose shrilly as she tried unsuccessfully to get nearer to the new baby.

“What’s his name? What’s his name Tom?” Donnavieve asked. Tom started to lift his voice above the melee when De quietly said, his name is Thomas Keith. We are going to call him Keith”.

After everyone had held the little brown eyed boy and said he was the image of his parents, Isabella said, “It’s time for dinner. If we wait much longer it will be cold.”

***

DIXON SCHOOL SETS EXERCISES

(Continued from Page One)

Boardman Andrew Boswell, Elaine Bott, Ruth Bourne, Lester Brown, Lynn Brown, Mary Brown, Ida Burrows, Gordon Byland.

Bessie Carter, Ethelyn Clark, Fae Clark, Walter Clark, Afton Coleman, John Cook, Lester Corbett, Theresa Courture, Jack Craighead, Elma Croft, Viola Cuddeford.

George Davis, Fae Davis, Ivie Davis, Victor Davis, Anna Dixon, Evelyn Dixon, Madge Durrell, LeRoy Dyson.

Harold Field, Ashton Fielding, Eleanor Forsythe.

Raymond Gammell Lois Gardner, John Gould, Ruth Graams, Ray Green.

Hope Halladay, Robert Halladay, Max Halverson, Louis Hansen, Weston Hardy, Eugene Harris, Dan Harrison, Clyde Hauser, Annie Hawks, Naomi Henrickson, Marion Hiatt, Albert Hickman, Vern Hindmarsh, Vick Hindmarsh, Naomi Hoover, Floyd Horton, Orvil Howe, Lillian Hunt, LaRue Hunter.

Raymond Jacobson, Maurice Jenkins, Ernest Jeppson Clarence Johnson, Curtis Johnson, Fern Johnson, Gilda Johnson, Lou Johnson, Margaret Johnson, Fawn Jones, Fay Jones.

DeVon Kelson, Wilford Kemp, Merlin Killpack, Glenn Kirkwood, Leslie Knudsen, Wesley Knudsen.

Dee Larsen Norma Larsen, Retta Lee, Doris Leeks, LeGrand Lewis.

Agnes Madsen, Coleman Madsen, Clyde Madsen, Dick Madsen, Ray Marrett, LeRoy Marrett, Ben Marshall, Marvin McPhie, Ruth Mentore, Ardith Mitchell Brigham Mitchell, Katherine Mitchell, Joy Millett, Gwen Moir, Vivian Montgomery, Vern Moon, Emmitt Murdock.

Lynn Nelson, Billie Nelson, Alma Nicol, Alva Nicol, George Norman, Josephine Norman.

Ardith Olsen, Pearl Ostler.

Glenn Peck, Pearl Pearod, Fay Perry, Alfred Phillips.

Kay Reese, Theron Reynolds, Eldon Rowley, Easton Russell.

Veri Scott, Dawson Sellers, June Servoss, George Sheya, Rae Shippe, William Simpson, Wanda Singleton Elmer Skinner, Rex Small, Vaughn Spendlove, Jimmie Strong.

Myrtle Tanner, Dee Taylor, Ruth Taylor, Vesta Taylor, Robert Thomas, George Thompson.

Donald Van Wagenen, Donna Van Wagenen, Byrnece Vincent, Dean Vincent, Geniel Vincent, Howard Vincent.

Jack Walton, Woodrow Washburn, Keith Wright, Venice Wignal, Scott Wilkins, Fawn Williams, Milton Woods.

Glen Young, Grant Young, Lois Young, Marjorie Eggertson, Peggy Evans.

85 Evening Herald May 18, 1932 Alva & Alma Graduate Jr High

The box score:

ELKS

	AB	H	R	E
Olsen, 2b	4	1	1	0
H. Reves, 3b	4	0	0	0
K. Baum, ss	4	1	2	0
Perry, cf	4	2	3	0
Davis, c	4	0	0	0
Jolley, f	4	2	2	0
Durkee, 1b	2	2	0	0
Mitchell, rf	3	1	2	0
Denhalter, lf	3	1	0	0
Totals	32	10	8	0

DENTISTS

	AB	H	R	E
V. Baum, c	3	0	0	0
Taylor, p	3	0	0	1
Alma Nicol, ss	3	0	1	0
Manson, 1b	2	0	0	0
Alva Nicol, 2b	2	0	0	0
Daniels, 3b	2	0	0	0
Craighead, rf	2	0	1	0
Horton, lf	2	0	0	0
Miller, cf	2	0	0	0
Totals	21	0	2	1

Summary: Home runs — Jolley 2; two base hits, Mitchell, Alma Nicol. Struck out by Jolley 8, by Taylor, 15. Umpire, Castleberry.

84 Sunday Herald June 3, 1932Alma & Alva Play Baseball

Entertains For Son

In honor of her son Max, who came from San Francisco to spend the holidays in Provo, Mr. and Mrs. M. B. Pope entertained at a card and dinner party Thursday evening. The guests included Miss Eliza Nelson, Miss Mildred Dixon, Miss Gwen Nelson, Chase Nicol and Sam Whetton.

86 Provo Evening Herald January 3, 1933Chase Nicol

Mr. and Mrs. Thomas Nicol have a 12 pound girl, born Monday at the family home. Mrs. Nicol was formerly Dee Bethers. Mother and baby are doing fine.

83 Evening Herald June 14 1933 Mary Jean Nicol Birth Announcement

Provo High Boys Installing Walks

New cement walks for the main building at the Provo high school are being built by the shop boys of the school under the direction of at angles to the main steps so that the students will not walk on the lawn to be planted later. The boys who helped with the project are Bill McCausland, Jack Palmer, Max Williams, Melvin Hoover, John Nicol and Herman Rowley.

Today the boys organization are beginning final preparations of the

82 Evening Herald March 29, 1933 John Nicol

PIONEER

	Ab.	R.	H.	E.
A. Nicol, c	3	2	1	0
Tanner, 3b	3	2	2	0
Morgan, ss	3	1	1	0
Carter 2b	3	0	0	0
Peay, p	1	1	1	0
Fisher, lf	3	1	0	0
K. Nicol, cf	3	1	0	0
Olsen, 2b	3	1	1	0
Skinner, rf	3	0	0	0
Totals	25	9	6	0

DeMOLAY

	Ab.	R.	H.	E.
Gillis, 2b	3	0	1	0
Bray, 3b	3	0	0	1
J. McCausland, p	1	0	0	0
Boshard, ss	2	0	0	1
Shipman, rf	2	0	0	0
De Moisy, cf	2	0	0	2
Street, 1b	2	0	0	0
Jacobs, lf	2	0	0	0
B. McCausland, c	2	0	0	0
Totals	9	0	1	4

Summary: Two base hits—A. Nicol, Tanner, Morgan, Peay; struck out by—Peal 12, McCausland 6; umpire—Leeds.

92 Evening Herald August 1, 1933Ken & A. Nicol

Choir Members Enjoy Social

A delightful time was enjoyed by members of the Pioneer ward choir Monday evening at the home of Mr. and Mrs. Grover Miller.

Several games were played, William Norman and Le Grande Lewis winning the favors. A delicious luncheon was served to the following:

Mr. and Mrs. L. L. Woods, Mrs. Myrtle Hanseen, Mrs. Hazel Hundley, Mr. and Mrs. Grover Miller, Mr. and Mrs. William D. Norman, Mr. and Mrs. Rodney Duffin, Miss Ruby Durrant, Miss Lucile Hundley, Samuel Hannt, Dutton Miller, Le Grande Lewis, Bud Johnson, Horace Peay, Mrs. C. J. Anderson, Mrs. Louise Snow, A. W. Gren, Miss Lenore Wall, Miss Nelda Newren, Miss Anneliese Buggert, Lloyd Affleck, George Norman, Kay Reese, Miss Elvira Jenkins, Grant Young, Clarence Johnson, Alma Nicol, Fred Washburn, Merlin Killpack, Margaret Woods, Don H. Checketts, the latter being a guest from Ogden.

* * *

89 Evening Herald January 16, 1934 Alma Nicol Choir

PAGE THREE

SERVICES FOR PROVO WOMAN

Funeral services for Mrs. Bertha Anderson Rasmussen, widow of Nels C. F. Rasmussen, who died Friday, were held Tuesday afternoon at the Pioneer ward chapel.

Bishop Louis Newren presided and remarks were made by Freeman Tanner, Andrew Knudsen and William D. Norman. The opening prayer was offered by J. H. Keeler and the benediction by Edward S. Meservy. Hyrum C. Nicol dedicated the grave at the Provo city cemetery.

The ward chorus, under the direction of Dutton Miller, sang "The Lord Is My Shepherd," "I Need Thee Every Hour," and "Abide With Me." William Knudsen rendered the vocal solo "Perfect Day," and a cello solo was played by Gustav Buggert. Mrs. Sophie Beck was the accompanist.

The services were well attended and there were many beautiful floral offerings.

91 Evening Herald February 2, 1934 H C Nicol

GRAND VIEW

MRS. CLARK CARTER, Reporter

Mrs. Luella Hills entertained the members of her sewing club Thursday afternoon. The afternoon was spent in sewing after which a delicious luncheon was served. Mrs. Belva Wentz, Mrs. Fern Hills and Mrs. Monk were special guests and the club members present were: Mrs. Margaret Johnson, Mrs. Ruby Stratton, Mrs. Dot Davis, Mrs. Tillie Dixon and Mrs. Clark Carter.

Mrs. Laurel Gibson entertained the Grand View camp of the Daughters of the Pioneers at a quilting party, Friday afternoon at her home. Mrs. Gibson and Mrs. Isobel Nicol served a hot dinner assisted by the rest of the ladies who brought the dessert. The following ladies were served: Mrs. Lucy Clyde, Mrs. Melissa Brown, Mrs. Grace Nuttal, Mrs. May Tanner, Mrs. Eva Hortt, Mrs. Ada Carter, Mrs. Clara Smith, Mrs. Kate Carter, Mrs. Emma Stratton, Mrs. Sarah Strassburg, Mrs. Lottie Davies and Mrs. Dezzie Lamb.

90 Evening Herald March 23, 1935 Isabella Nicol

77 SEMINARY STUDENTS TO GET DIPLOMAS

Commencement Exercises To Be Held May 26 In Tabernacle

Seventy students of the Provo L. D. S. Seminary will receive graduating diplomas at the commencement exercises to be held in the Utah stake tabernacle, Saturday, May 26, according to an announcement by J. A. Washburn, principal, today.

The musical program will be furnished by the music department of the Provo high school, directed by Ernest Paxman, and short talks will be given by members of the graduating class on seminary topics. One of the graduates will take charge of the exercises and President T. N. Taylor will present the diplomas.

The graduates are as follows: Lynn Brown, Mary Brown, Thornton Booth, Thiel Buttler, Cleo Long, Kenneth Laws, Robert Halladay, John Cook, Thomas Barrett, Dorothy Barrett, Glenna Hatch, Myrtle Bennett, Beatrice Edwards, Vere Hales, Albert Clark, Faye Perry, Norma Jackson, Glen Hardy, Robert Thomas, Dawson Sellers, Curtis Johnson, Lynn Nelson, Lester Corbett, Raymond Green, Vurell Jones, Keith Hansen, Allen Draper, Woodrow Thompson, Max Ferre, Ned Morgan, Alma Nicol, Alva Nicol, Naoma Peterson, Woodrow Washburn, LeGrand Lewis, Gordon Miner, Dean Olsen, Cornell Peters, Wilford Kemp, Vida Fanaldson, Don Larsen, Vera Marrett, Leon Steadman, Jay Stevens, Wesley Knudsen, Ida Lewis, Gordon Ryland, Orvald Howe, Theresa Anderson, Katharine Mitchell, Gwynn Moser, Margaret Johnson, Roy Boyer, Genial Stevens, Anna Hooks, George Norman, Geraldine Elliott, Rae Shipp, Mary Thompson, Myrna Thorson, Lucy Larsen, Luella Cummings, LaPriel Winterton, Raymond Gammell, Ruth Bourne, Don Taylor, Herald Field, Lydia Allred, Donna Van Wagenen, Ruth Taylor, John Walton, Ardith Olsen, Ethelyn Clark, Grant Young, Leona Pearce, Hal Taylor, Evelyn Dixon.

87 Evening Herald May 11, 1934 Alva & Alma Nicol

GRAND VIEW

MRS. CLARK CARTER, Reporter

The "M" Men and Gleaners enjoyed a bonfire party and weiner roast down by the river Monday evening. Those attending were: Alta Buckner, Margaret Nuttal, Afton Davies, Raisa Weeter, Earl Buckner, Glen Davis, Brigham Nicol, Alva Nicol, Harold Kartchner, Mr. and Mrs. M. E. Kartchner

88 Evening Herald May 1, 1936 Brigham & Alva Nicol

Former Provo Man Wed In California

Announcement is made of the marriage of Chase Nicol, son of Mr. and Mrs. H. C. Nicol of Provo, and Miss Bonnie Anne Bussio of Pittsburgh, Cal., which took place Nov. 24 at Berkeley.

Max Pope of Provo attended the groom, and his brothers, Kenneth and Alma Nicol were in attendance, also, Lucian Beelar, former Provoan.

The bride is employed at the high school at Pittsburgh and Mr. Nicol is assistant superintendent of the wire and nail department at the steel mills of that city.

94 Evening Herald December 2, 1935 Chase Nicol & Anne Bussio Marry

Progressive Party Enjoyable Affair

A delightful progressive party was enjoyed by the "M" Men and Gleaners of the Grand View ward M. I. A. Monday evening at the following homes: Miss Afton Davies, Mrs. Reed Nuttall and Earl Buckner.

Each home was arranged to represent a different country, Mexico, Germany and America being featured. Games were followed by a course of the delicious luncheon.

Participating in the affair were Mr. and Mrs. Dean Nuttall, Mr. and Mrs. Jesse Nuttall, Raisa Weeter, Earl Buckner, Margaret Nuttall, John Nicol, Alta Buckner, Oscar Peck, Afton Davies, Glen Davis, Donna Carter, and Mr. and Mrs. Reed Nuttall.

93 Evening Herald January 15, 1936 John Nicol

VINEYARD

Reporter—Phone 01-R-4
MRS. GEORGE F. WELLS

Camp Tamarack of the D. U. P. met Friday afternoon at the home of Mrs. Nora Harding. The entertaining rooms were decorated with flowering tamarack and lilacs. Vice Captain Sarah B. Shaw presided. Prayer by Chaplain Pricilla Madsen. Mrs. Ellen Bunnell was chosen camp custodian of relics and Pioneer Bertha Madsen was chosen assistant chaplain. Mrs. Malicent Wells and Mrs. Sarah Shaw were voted to act as a clipping committee to make a camp scrap book. An original poem, "To the Tamarack" was read by Mrs. Clara Taylor. The life histories of the late Patriarch John M. Murdoch and his wives, Ann Steel and Isabella Crawford, were given by a granddaughter, Miss Joan Murdoch. A song composed by John M. Murdoch on leaving Scotland was sung by Mrs. Maybell Moulton, Mrs. Nora Harding, Mrs. Tressa Nicol and Mrs. Malicent Wells. Organist Lizzebelle Davis was at the piano. Mrs. Nettie McMullin of Heber City 80-year-old daughter of Mr. Murdoch was present and spoke. County Captain Mrs. T. Dahlquist and Vice Captain Sarah B. Cummings also spoke. The closing song a duet "Do They Think of Me At Home," was sung by Mrs. Maybell Moulton and Mrs. Malicent Wells. Closing prayer by Pioneer Bertha Madsen.

95 Evening Herald May 11, 1936 Mrs. Tressa Nicol

Nuttall - Nicol Reception Colorful Social Function

MR. AND MRS. W. A. NUTTALL were hosts to 250 relatives and friends at a wedding reception in honor of their daughter, Margaret Alice, and John M. Nicol, who were married in the Salt Lake temple Friday.

The attractive social function was held Monday evening in the Grand View ward amusement hall. Mr. Nicol is a son of Mr. and Mrs. Hyrum Nicol, also of Grand View.

The bride presented a lovely picture in her gown of white satin and her long white tulle veil, caught with pink roses. She carried pink brides roses and white sweet peas. Mrs. Juliet Bigler, her sister, was matron of honor, and she wore white net. Another sister, Miss Dianna Nuttall, maid of honor, was in orange organdie, green trimmed, and the following young women served as bridesmaids: Miss Merl Davis, who was in orange organdie; Ellen Pulsipher, in green net; Mrs. Darrell Moulton, orange net, and Anna Dixon, green organdie. They wore dainty pink rose corsages. Darrell Moulton stood up with the groom.

In receiving the guests, the bridal party was joined by the parents, Mr. and Mrs. Nuttall and Mr. and Mrs. Nicol.

Interspersed with the dances, the following program numbers were furnished, with Dean D. Nuttall, a brother, as master of ceremonies: vocal solo, Ervin Terry, accompanied by Norma Hampshire; duet, Mrs. Olea Shumak and Miss Ellen Pulsipher, accompanied by Melba Pyne; acrobatic dance, Ora Thompson; military tap dance, Miss Geraldine Hair and the Misses Ora Thompson and Ida Boyd.

Tasty refreshments were enjoyed. The hall was a mass of beautiful roses and summer garden flowers. Handsome wedding gifts were received.

Mr. and Mrs. Nicol will reside in Provo.

* * *

97 Sunday Herald John Murray & Margaret Nuttall Marry June 26, 1936

GRAND ViEW

MRS. CLARK CARTER
Reporter

Mr. and Mrs. H. C. Nicol have returned from Duchesne where they attended a birthday party for a brother A. M. Murdoch.

96 Evening Herald May 6, 1937

Dinner Given

Mrs. Chase Nicol is returning to her home in Pittsburg, Cal., after spending two weeks here with relatives and friends.

Mr. and Mrs. M. B. Pope entertained at a dinner in her honor, also for Mr. and Mrs. H. C. Nicol and daughter Donna V. of Provo.

99 Evening Herald June 6, 1937

Alma Nicol, son of Mr. and Mrs. H. C. Nicol of Provo, is spending a week's vacation with his parents. He has spent the past year as an apprecntice in the shops of the Columbia Steel company at Pittsburgh, California.

98 Evening Herald July 28, 1936 Alma Nicol

Vacationists Entertained

Mr. and Mrs. John M. Nicol entertained at a delightful weiner roast Monday at Nuttall's grove, honoring Miss Betty Birely and Kenneth Nicol of Pittsburgh, Cal., who are vacationing here with relatives and friends.

In attendance were: Mr. and Mrs. W. A. Nuttall, Mr. and Mrs. Hyrum C. Nicol, Miss Diana Nuttall, Miss Donna V. Nicol, Lynn Brown, George Palmer, Alva Nicol, Albert Nuttall and Irwin Harward.

* * *

104 *Evening Herald* August 17, 1937

Missionary Is Feted at Party

Honoring Lynn Brown, who is leaving soon for an L. D. S. mission to the Netherlands, Mr. and Mrs. H. C. Nicol entertained a group of his friends at their home Wednesday evening.

Games were played, prizes being won by Marvin Peterson and Alva Nicol. A short program was enjoyed and many fine gifts were presented to the guest of honor, after which a delicious luncheon was served by the host and hostess.

In attendance were: Donna V. Nicol, Mr. and Mrs. Cleve Brown, Mr. and Mrs. John M. Nicol, Lynn Brown, Verna Day, Marvin Peterson, Fay Brown, Brigham Nicol, Donna Day, Alva Nicol, Elvira Pyne, George Thompson, and Virtue Fisher of Sandy.

* * *

106 *Evening Herald* October 17, 1937

GRAND VIEW

MRS. CLARK CARTER
Reporter

Primary conference was held Sunday evening with LeRoy Taylor of the bishopric presiding and Mrs. Spencer Young conducting. The program was as follows: song, "The Lord is My Shepherd," prayer, Fay Haws; welcome speech, Mrs. Young; Mrs. Lettie Hatch, president, was released and the following officers were sustained: Mrs. Hyrum Nicol, president, Mrs. Spencer Young and Mrs. Varnal Williams as counselors; sustaining of the officers by the secretary, Mrs. Loretta Carroll; beginners and

105 *Evening Herald* December 21, 1937

GRAND VIEW

MRS. CLARK CARTER
Reporter

Ashted Taylor, adult class leader of the M. I. A. had charge of conjoint meeting Sunday evening. A New Year's reading was given by M. E. Kartchner. Short talks were given by Hettie Carter, C. L. Riding, Mrs. Hyrum Nicol, John Stratton and Dee Brown; the Allred sisters sang a duet and John Kuhni a solo.

Mrs. Thora Haws gave the teachers topic at Relief society Monday afternoon and the theology lesson was given by Mrs. Annie Tanner.

A short skit "Work and Play" was presented during the assembly program Monday evening at Mutual. The following persons took part. Ilene Harward, Inez Jones, Nelda Carter, John Stratton, Irwin Harward, Glen Buckner, Dean Buckner, Margaret Nicol, Diana Nuttall, Alta Buckner and Mr. and Mrs. LeRoy Davis.

Mr. and Mrs. Carl Taylor and Reed Taylor of Wendel, Idaho visited the first part of the week at the home of Mrs. Ida Taylor. Mrs. Taylor and small son Gene accompanied them home and will visit there for a week.

Mr. and Mrs. Arthur Clyde left Wednesday morning for a trip through California. They will visit many points of interest while away.

A vaudeville show was presented in the ward amusement hall Wednesday evening as follows: A short skit by the Primary under the direction of Mrs. Ora Griffith; an act from the Sunday school with Dean Nuttall taking part; the M Men and Gleaner Girls presented a short skit with Margaret Nicol in charge; a xylophone number by Miss Fran-

100 *Evening Herald* January 6, 1938

Hyrum Nicol was the speake
at sacrament meeting Sunday eve
ning.

102 *Evening Herald* January 6, 1938

GRAND VIEW

MRS. CLARK CARTER
Reporter

An enjoyable time was had by all those attending the ward outing Saturday and Sunday at Giles ranch in South Fork, Provo canyon. A bonfire program was given under the direction of the Mutual with John Nicol, president of the Young Men in charge. The program was as follows: Community singing under the direction of Mrs. Ora Griffith; prayer, Leo Taylor; reading, Mrs. Christine Jolley; remarks, Bishop Jolley; duet, Garn and La Von Harward; duet, Mr. and Mrs. Dean Nuttal; song by Irwin Harward, accompanied by Rex Griffith; duet, Mr. and Mrs. Heber Harward; song, Nadeline Harward; song by congregation and prayer by B. H. Jolley.

Sunday school was held Sunday morning in the form of a pageant depicting Joseph Smith's first prayer. The pageant was written by Mrs. Lucy Clyde and she was the reader. The singing was furnished by Mrs. Afton Atkinson and Vivia Davies, accompanied by Mrs. Anna Jolley at the organ. Explanations were made by Bishop Jolley and the main character parts were taken by William Nuttal as Christ the Father; La Von Harward, Jesus, and Blair Williams, representing Joseph Smith. Following the program, which was under the direction of Hyrum Nicol, Mr. and Mrs. Sharland Harward and Mr. and Mrs. Ralph Carter had babies blessed. During the afternoon, games and races were enjoyed. A large crowd was in attendance, many staying over Saturday night.

Mr. and Mrs. Tom Nicol and children of Pittsburg, California, have returned to their home after spending the past week visiting at the home of Mr. Nicol's parents, Mr. and Mrs. Hyrum Nicol.

101 *Evening Herald* August 8, 1938

VINEYARD

MRS. GEORGE F. WELLS
Reporter—Phone 61-R-4

Mrs. Cumorah Eldredge and daughters Mae and Jean, Miss Jane Stewart, Quis Larsen and Louis Stewart, of Salt Lake and Mrs. Elizabeth Larsen of Long Beach, California, visited here Monday with Mr. and Mrs. C. M. Mrs. Thomas Wells, Delbert Mills, accompanied them home where he will attend the Mills family Reunion and visit for several weeks.

Bishop T. C. Hebertson and son Leon accompanied Joseph Beveridge to Hiawatha Saturday and spent the day. Mr. and Mrs. Beveridge and children are moving from Hiawatha to Vineyard for the summer.

Mr. and Mrs. Hyrum Nicol of Grand View visited here Saturday with relatives.

103 *Evening Herald* May 1, 1938

"We had lived in the Provo-Orem area for some time when Mother became very ill from the many trials and struggles and emotional concerns engendered by the process of life's adventures. A serious health problem occurred, and Mother needed attention all the time.

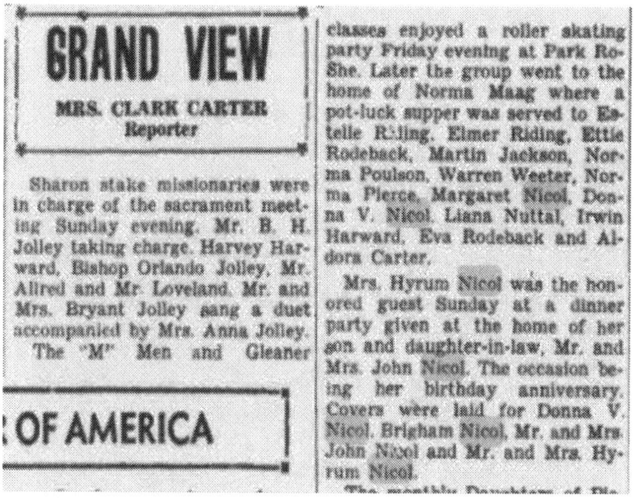

GRAND VIEW

MRS. CLARK CARTER
Reporter

Sharon stake missionaries were in charge of the sacrament meeting Sunday evening. Mr. B. H. Jolley taking charge. Harvey Harward, Bishop Orlando Jolley, Mr. Allred and Mr. Loveland. Mr. and Mrs. Bryant Jolley sang a duet accompanied by Mrs. Anna Jolley.

The "M" Men and Gleaner classes enjoyed a roller skating party Friday evening at Park Ro-She. Later the group went to the home of Norma Maag where a pot-luck supper was served to Estelle Riding, Elmer Riding, Ettie Rodeback, Martin Jackson, Norma Poulson, Warren Weeter, Norma Pierce, Margaret Nicol, Donna V. Nicol, Liana Nuttal, Irwin Harward, Eva Rodeback and Aldora Carter.

Mrs. Hyrum Nicol was the honored guest Sunday at a dinner party given at the home of her son and daughter-in-law, Mr. and Mrs. John Nicol. The occasion being her birthday anniversary. Covers were laid for Donna V. Nicol, Brigham Nicol, Mr. and Mrs. John Nicol and Mr. and Mrs. Hyrum Nicol.

... OF AMERICA

107 Provo Evening Herald January 11, 1939 Isabella's Birthday

The older boys had left and found work away from home. The younger boys and Donnavieve were at home. John remained out of school for one year to help care for Mother's needs.

Mother never fully recovered from this illness, and later in the twilight years. Father went to work while the three children remained at home with Mother."

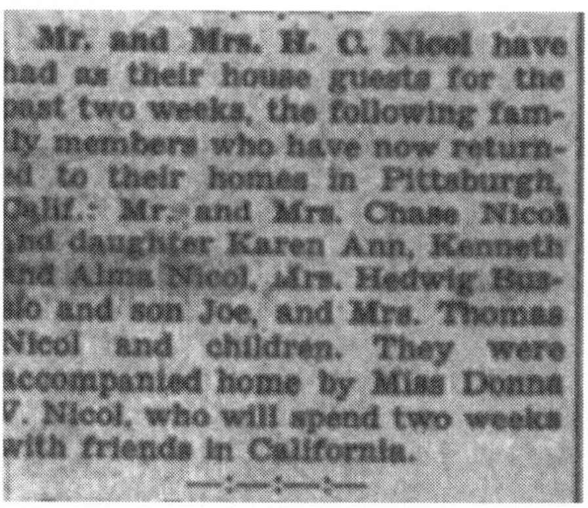

Mr. and Mrs. H. C. Nicol have had as their house guests for the past two weeks, the following family members who have now returned to their homes in Pittsburgh, Calif.: Mr. and Mrs. Chase Nicol and daughter Karen Ann, Kenneth and Alma Nicol, Mrs. Hedwig Busalo and son Joe, and Mrs. Thomas Nicol and children. They were accompanied home by Miss Donna V. Nicol, who will spend two weeks with friends in California.

108 Provo Daily Herald July 9 1940

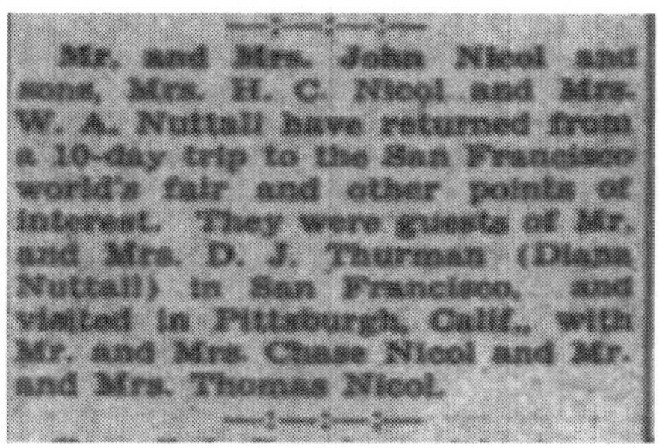

Mr. and Mrs. John Nicol and sons, Mrs. H. C. Nicol and Mrs. W. A. Nuttall have returned from a 10-day trip to the San Francisco world's fair and other points of interest. They were guests of Mr. and Mrs. D. J. Thurman (Diana Nuttall) in San Francisco, and visited in Pittsburgh, Calif., with Mr. and Mrs. Chase Nicol and Mr. and Mrs. Thomas Nicol.

109 Evening Herald July 22, 1940

Hyrum Chase & Isabella Crawford Murdoch Nicol Family

July 1940

110 Hyrum and Isabell Nicol with Family 1940
Brigham, Alma, Alva
Kenneth, Donnavieve, John
Chase, Hyrum, Isabella, Tom

In her closing hours she would sit or lie on the bed and guide her family in preparation of things around the house.

When she would get terribly ill she would always ask for the elders to come and give her a blessing.

Because of her severe pain and the burden she felt she was putting on the family, Mother desired to die.

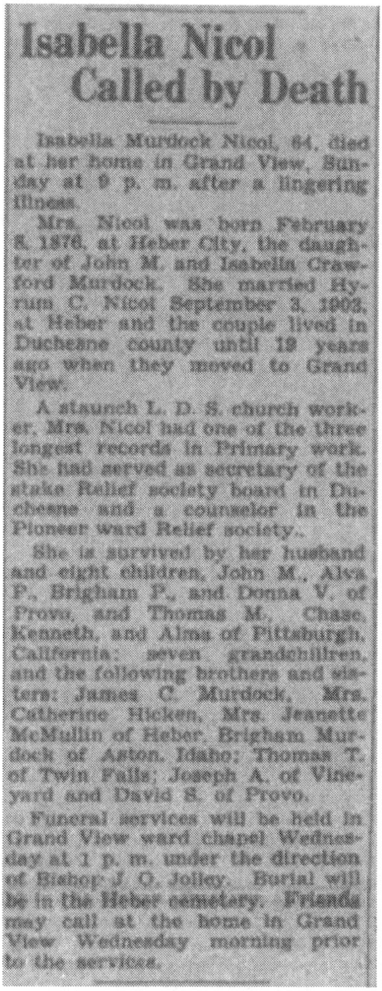

Isabella Nicol Called by Death

Isabella Murdock Nicol, 64, died at her home in Grand View, Sunday at 9 p. m. after a lingering illness.

Mrs. Nicol was born February 8, 1876, at Heber City, the daughter of John M. and Isabella Crawford Murdock. She married Hyrum C. Nicol September 3, 1903, at Heber and the couple lived in Duchesne county until 19 years ago when they moved to Grand View.

A staunch L. D. S. church worker, Mrs. Nicol had one of the three longest records in Primary work. She had served as secretary of the stake Relief society board in Duchesne and a counselor in the Pioneer ward Relief society.

She is survived by her husband and eight children, John M., Alva P., Brigham P., and Donna V. of Provo, and Thomas M., Chase, Kenneth, and Alma of Pittsburgh, California; seven grandchildren, and the following brothers and sisters: James C. Murdock, Mrs. Catherine Hicken, Mrs. Jeanette McMullin of Heber, Brigham Murdock of Aston, Idaho; Thomas T. of Twin Falls; Joseph A. of Vineyard and David S. of Provo.

Funeral services will be held in Grand View ward chapel Wednesday at 1 p. m. under the direction of Bishop J. O. Jolley. Burial will be in the Heber cemetery. Friends may call at the home in Grand View Wednesday morning prior to the services.

111 Evening Herald December 2, 1940
Isabella Crawford Nicol Obituary

On more than one occasion she asked, "Hyrum, please, ask Father to take me home. Please let me go. Please my darling." With sorrow and sadness, Hyrum, and John Murray tenderly laid their hands upon Isabella's head, and Hyrum with his throat tighten and tears streaming down his face he said, through the holy Melchizedek Priesthood which we hold, dear Father take this faithful daughter home into your arms that she may be relieved of the suffering and pain she has endured these many years. 'I give her unto you, Lord, and your care and keeping until we shall meet again.'"[lxxviii]

Isabella, lying peacefully upon her bed motioned for the three children watching nearby; Donnavieve, Brigham, and Alva, to come near. She smiled at each of them as they dropped to their knees in prayer around her as they had done all the days of their lives.

That night Mother passed away. She was faithful to her family and the gospel of Jesus Christ unto the very end."[lxxix]

Later that night, consoling their father and talking with one another, Donnavieve said, "Just before Mother's death she motioned for us – Alva, Brigham, and I – toward her. We could tell she was passing on. On our knees at her bedside we prayed to the Lord for help. But Mother had passed away. As I looked up for moment from praying, I saw the spiritual image of Mother, rise from her body, hover there shortly, and leave."[lxxx]

"Even to the day of her death Mother was always cheerful. Though she suffered intolerable pain, and had for many years, she would never complain.

Mother passed from this life to the next on December 1, 1940, at her home in Grandview Ward, Provo, Utah.

After the lovely service in the chapel, Mother was escorted for the last time up Provo Canyon to the Heber City cemetery, where her own mother and father were laid to rest.

Mother's seven sons were her pallbearers. AT the gravesite the casket was opened for the last time, and Father and the children placed their rose boutonnieres around Mother's neck in necklace form as a last loving tribute to a wonderful angel Mother." [lxxxi]

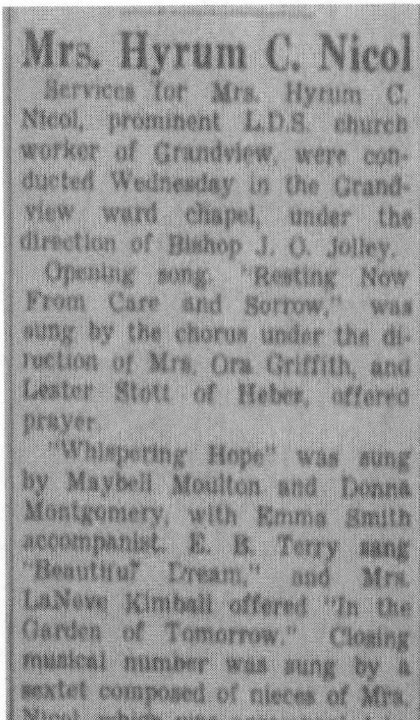

Mrs. Hyrum C. Nicol

Services for Mrs. Hyrum C. Nicol, prominent L.D.S. church worker of Grandview, were conducted Wednesday in the Grandview ward chapel, under the direction of Bishop J. O. Jolley.

Opening song, "Resting Now From Care and Sorrow," was sung by the chorus under the direction of Mrs. Ora Griffith, and Lester Stott of Heber, offered prayer.

"Whispering Hope" was sung by Maybell Moulton and Donna Montgomery, with Emma Smith accompanist. E. B. Terry sang "Beautiful Dream," and Mrs. LaNeve Kimball offered "In the Garden of Tomorrow." Closing musical number was sung by a sextet composed of nieces of Mrs. Nicol, which was accompanied by another niece.

Remarks were made by George Victor Billings of Salt Lake City; Jesse A. Washburn and Leon Newren of Provo, and J. O. Jolley of Grandview. David H. Hicken offered the benediction.

Following services at Grandview, the body was taken to Heber where the casket was opened for a brief period at the home of H. G. Cook.

Burial was in the Heber cemetery, and the grave was dedicated by J. A. Fortie.

112 Evening Herald December 6, 1940
Isabella Crawford Nicol Funeral

The boys being inducted from the north district were listed at the local selective service office as follows:

Alva Nicol, Kimm Peterson Rex D. Bray, Arthur A. Nielson, Lloyd Powell, Victor Ray Baker, Marion Hiatt, Philip Dewitt Trotter, Glen R. Hardy and Don Ostler of Provo; Kenneth McDaniel and Lyman Terry of Alpine; Richard Dudley, Leonard Allen, Harold Marion Paxman, Wilson H. Hayward, Carl Richan and Rulon Carlson of American Fork; Reed B. Newman, Ivan Jacob, Garth Heber Roundy, Richard Snyder, and Lavar R. Hooley, of Pleasant Grove.

117 Sunday Herald Jan 19, 1941 Alva Inducted

M. I. A. president with two new counselors, Mrs. Ruby Larsen and Alta Buckner, replaced Mrs. Verl Johnson and Mrs. Rita Jolley. Mr. Hyrum Nicol was named chairman of the adult aaronic priesthood committee. The Primary organization remains the same with Mrs. Mary Camenish president.

116 Evening Herald June 11, 1941

Alva M. Nicol, son of H. C. Nicol of Provo, recently advanced to technical sergeant in the U. S. army radio division, is home from Alaska for a brief visit. Upon expiration of his furlough he will enter officers training school in Virginia.

115 Daily Herald April 1, 1943

Mr. and Mrs. John Nicol are rejoicing over the safe arrival of a baby son.

114 Provo Daily Herald March 12, 1941

Mr. and Mrs. John Nicol, Mr. Hyrum Nicol, Donna V. and Alma Nicol of California, left Tuesday for a vacation trip to Yellowstone park. They expect to be gone a week.

113 Daily Herald July 31, 1941

Sharon Seminary To Graduate 172; Exercises Sunday

[illegible]

119 Provo Daily Herald May 8, 1941

After spending a month on the coast, Hyrum Nicol has returned to his home here. He has been visiting his sons, Tom, Chase, Kenneth and Alma Nicol, all of Pittsburgh, Calif.

118 Provo Daily Herald October 8, 1942

115 to Graduate From Lincoln

A total of 115 students will graduate from the Lincoln high school of Orem at commencement exercises May 15, according to A. P. Warnick, principal.

This the largest graduating class in the history of the school.

Members of the senior class with John Watts, Vonna Vernon and Donna Stubbs representing the graduating class with addresses, will give the commencement program.

Applicants for graduation are Ella May Adams, Garth Earl Adams, Mary Allen, Dee Anderson, Lois Baker, Xavier Beffort, Steve Bunnell, Mary Beth Berry, Duane Blair, Nolan Brown, Norma Burr, LaMar Bylund, Thelma Carter, Arlya Chatwin, Melba Christensen, LaVern Clinger, Gair Corbett, Weston Cordner, Cammie Crandall, Winnie Davis, Virginia Dickey, Kathleen Downs, Sydney Duffin, Max Edwards, Melba Edwards, Minnie Ekins, Stanford Ekins, Carl Lloyd Evans, Richard Farnworth, Leo Farnworth, Lucy Ferris.

Mary Firth, Bert Wesley Fox, Virginia Fronk, Margaret Gammon, Atland Garrick, Thelma Gillies, Jean Gillispie, Genevieve Gordon, Wanda Gurr, Donald Guyman, Fay Hansen, Barbara Hansen, Elden Harding, Rhea Hatfield, Wallace Ivers, Nile Johnson, Robert Lewis Johnson, Sylphia Johnson, Dorothy Jones, Edith Jones, Jay Kallis, Marie Kerby, Viola Kerby, June Kitchen, Iris Lamb, Austin Larson, Orpha Laudie, Dean Loveless, Dee Loveless, Donald Lunceford, Virginia Lunceford, Marelly Lustrup, Carlos Madsen, Verl Madsen, Emelia Mauris, Bryce McBride, Norma McEwan, Fred Mecham, Joseph Meyers, Naomi Miller, Mavis Moore, Kirk Nielsen, Ruth Nielson, Bernice Nowell, Daniel Eugene Nowell, Donnavieve Nicol, Edward Nimer, Dean Olsen, Dorothy Park, Velma Ruth Park, Coward Penrod, Letty Pomeroy, Joel Powell.

Wallace Prestwich, Willis Prest-

121 Provo Daily Herald April 28. 1941Donnavieve Graduates

Marriage Of Popular Couple

The marriage of Miss Ruby Phillips, daughter of Mr. and Mrs. J. A. Phillips of Provo to Brigham R. Nicol, son of Hyrum Nicol of Grandview is an event of interest to their many friends.

President David A. Broadbent performed the ceremony in the Salt Lake temple, Friday, Dec. 12, in th presence of Mr. and Mrs. Phillips, Mr. Nicol, Mr. and Mrs. John Nicol, Mrs. Grace Nuttall, Mrs. Lois Shaffer, Mrs. Jesse Nuttall and the groom's uncle, Joseph A. Murdock.

The bride wore a lovely white satin and chiffon gown and wore a gardenia and pink carnation corsage.

Following the marriage, a wedding dinner was served at a Salt Lake cafe for the entire party and Miss Donna V. Nicol, sister of the groom and Miss Sylpha Johnson.

A reception was given last night by the bride's parents, second north and fourth east, when many friends called.

The entertaining rooms were lovely with a pink and white color scheme, in the receiving line were the parents of the young couple, the best man, Carlos Phillips, a brother of the bride, of the U. S. army air corps, stationed at Pocatello, Idaho, Mr. and Mrs. John Nicol and the bridesmaids, Miss Donna V. Nicol and Miss Marie Phillips, the bride and groom's sisters. The bride wore her white wedding gown, with long chiffon veil caught with cornet head dress and carried a bouquet of pink Ophelia rose buds and the bridesmaids wore dainty pastel formals with corresponding corsages.

During the evening an interesting program was given, with Bishop Rodney C. Kimball acting as master of ceremonies. Lovely gifts were received by the popular young couple and refreshments served.

Mr. and Mrs. Nicol plan to make their home in Provo.

122 Sunday Daily Herald December 13, 1942 Brig & Ruby Phillips Marry

Sgt. Alva Nicol, who has been in the army for 27 months, visited relatives here Sunday. His father, Hyrum Nicol, and his brother, Brigham, accompanied him. Sgt. Nicol is enroute to Virginia to attend a technician radio school, having been stationed in Alaska the past two years.

123 Provo Daily Herald April 7, 1943

Alma and Pfc. Alva Nicol, twin sons of Hyrum Nicol, Edgemont, have both been in Provo for the past few days while Pfc. Nicol is home on furlough from Camp Gruber, Oklahoma. Alma is now employed at the Geneva Steel plant, having been transferred from Pitsburgh, California. Pfc. Alva will leave Saturday to return to his base.

120 Sunday Daily Herald October 10 1944

Deaths

Nicol Funeral Set for Thursday

Hyrum C. Nicol, 69, died of a heart attack at his home in Provo Sunday at 8 p. m.

He was born Feb. 9, 1876, in Heber, a son of Thomas and Christine Handberg Nicol. He married Isabelle Crawford Murdock Sept. 23, 1903, in the Salt Lake LDS temple. She died Dec. 1, 1940.

Mr. Nicol

Always an active L. D. S. church worker, he was a high priest at the time of death and had filled an LDS mission to New Zealand from 1900 to 1903. He was reared in Heber, but when a young man, went to Duchesne as one of the early settlers. He was the owner and operator of the Indian ranch at Duchesne. He moved to Provo in 1921, where he had lived since.

He is survived by eight children, Thomas M., John M., Rue and Donna V. Nicol, Provo; Hyrum Chase and Kenneth Crawford Nicol, Pittsburg, Calif., and Alva and Alma Nicol, twins, in the armed services; 16 grandchildren and one sister, Mrs. Matilda Crook, Heber City.

Funeral services will be conducted in the Grand View LDS ward chapel Thursday at 1:30 p. m. by Rodney Kimball, bishop. Friends may call at the home of John Nicol, on the state highway in Grand View, from 11:30 a. m. until 1 p. m. Thursday, and at 4 p. m. for half an hour at the home of Mrs. Matilda Crook at Heber. Burial will be in the Heber City cemetery.

124 Provo Daily Herald Wed. May 23 1945 Hyrum C Nicol Obituary

Deaths

Hyrum C. Nicol

Funeral services for Hyrum C. Nicol, 69, who died at his Grand View home, were conducted Thursday afternoon in the Grand View LDS ward chapel by Rodney C. Kimball, bishop.

G. Victor Billings, J. Orlando Jolley and J. A. Washburn were speakers at the impressive services, while Bishop Kimball offered closing remarks. Invocation was by O. Harvey Harward, benediction by B. H. Jolley, patriarch, and graveside dedicatory prayer by John R. Forti, patriarch.

Musical selections included a duet by Maybelle Moulton and Janet Clegg, vocal solo by Leno Martin, duet by Mrs. LeNeive Kimball and Mr. Martin, and vocal solo by Elvis B. Terry. Mrs. Orrilla Groneman gave an appropriate reading.

Interment took place in the Heber City cemetery.

Short Biography of Hyrum Chase Nicol[lxxxii]

Pioneers and Prominent Men of Utah

NICOL, HYRUM CHASE (son of Thomas Nicol and Johanna Christina Handberg). Born Feb. 9, 1876, Heber City, Utah.

Married Isabella Crawford Murdock Sept. 22, 1903, Salt Lake City (daughter of John Murray Murdock and Isabella Crawford of Heber City), who was born Jan. 10, 1876.

Member 20th quorum seventies; missionary to New Zealand Jan. 1, 1900 to June 8, 1903; high priest; counselor to Bishop George Victor Billings, Theodore ward, Duchesne stake; Sunday school teacher Heber City and Theodore wards; ward teacher at Theodore. Helped in every possible way the first settlers who came to Uinta reservation May 1906, and has assisted in all improvements incident to a new country.

Rancher. Vice president of Duchesne Irrigation Company; now associated with Pioneer Supply Company; and also engaged in farming.

"There is a beauty among the senses that expresses the feelings of love and devotion that defy description, our parents had this very special way about them."

"Mother was one of those choice spirits who came to this earth to bear her testimony to the divinity and truthfulness of the gospel. Our home was a home of faith and prayer, and she always knew that God was near to give aid when it was needed."

"Through the faith and prayers of Mother, several of her children [were] saved from serious accidents or severe health problems. She knew man had to do the work for the Lord, but that the Lord gave the directions."

"Mother was always good to [us] and supported us in all the things we wanted to do, as long as they were in harmony with the teaching of the Church [of Jesus Christ of Latter-day Saints]."

"She and Father together were a good team. Their thoughts and actions were always commendable and they always set a good example for rest of us to follow. They always made a special time to give council and to teach [us] a better way of life."

"[It is our] deep and abiding testimony of Jesus Christ and his gospel. It [is our] testimony that we know that we have a living Mother and Father in Heaven, and that the truth has once more been restored to the earth. [We are] sure that Joseph Smith was a true prophet and that through him the gospel has been restored. [We] are also sure and have taught that since the time of the Restoration of the Gospel, that every President of the Church was and is a true prophet of the living God. "[lxxxiii]

Posterity

Children and Grandchildren of Hyrum Chase Nicol and Isabella Crawford Murdoch Nicol

Thomas Murdoch Nicol b. 26 August 1904 married Ellis Delours Bethers 24 November 1929 in Evanston, Wyoming

Thomas Keith Nicol b. 1931
Mary Jean Nicol b. 1933
Carol De Nicol b. 1935
Paul Lavar Nicol b. 1936
Betty Gay Nicol b. 1938

Hyrum Chase Nicol, Jr. b. 19 March 1906 married Anne Bonnie Bussio 24 November 1935 at Berkeley, California

Karen Anne Nicol b 1939
Alan Chase b 1943

Kenneth Crawford Nicol b. 11 July 1908 married Charlotte Lampman 12 December 1941 Pittsburg, California

Cheryl Nicol b. 1940
Donna Key Nicol b 1942
Kenneth Crawford Nicol, Jr. b. 1943

John Murray Nicol b. 20 June 1912 married Margaret Alice Nuttall 26 June 1936 Salt Lake City, Utah

John Murray Nicol, Jr. b. 1937
Robert Rue Nicol b. 1941
Grant Chase Nicol b. 1943
William Wayne Nicol b. 1944
David Lee Nicol b. 1948
Lynn James Nicol b. 1956

Alva Moroni Nicol b. 6 March 1916 married Mary Martha Gaylor 19 January 1946 in Provo Utah

Richard Allen Nicol b. 1946
Janet Nicol b. 1949
Steven Ted Nicol b. 1950
Tressa Nicol b. 1952
Shauna Nicol b. 1954
Gayle Nicol b. 1959
Scott Brady Nicol b. 1963

Alma Victor Nicol b. 6 March 1916 married Olga Allred 18 August 1950 Manti, Utah

Sandra Kay Nicol b. 1955
Lynda Gayle Nicol b. 1956
Tanya Marie Nicol b. 1957
Diana Nicol b. 1960

Brigham Rue Nicol b. 27 June 1919 married Ruby Phillips 11 December 1942 Salt Lake City, Utah d. 19 November 1963

Michael Rue Nicol b. 1943
Phillip Kent Nicol b. 1947
Hyrum Dale Nicol b. 1949
Kevin Rex Nicol b. 1953
Kathryne Nicol b. 1957

I. Donnavieve Nicol b. 12 July 1923 married Roy Blackburn Smith 29 September 1949 Provo, Utah

Carol Lynn Smith b. 1943
Garyl Duane Smith b. 1946
Tressa Colleen Smith b. 1952
Travis B. Smith b. 1956

Bibliography

James and Mary Murray Murdoch Family History, by James and Mary Murray Murdoch Family Organization 1982

Daughters of the Utah Pioneers, History of the Uintah Basin

Pioneers and Prominent Men of Utah, by Frank Esshom, 1913 eBook Google.com

A History of Duchesne County, Utah Centennial County History Series, John D. Barton, 1998

A History of Wasatch County, 1859 – 1899, Leslie Shupe Raty, 1954 BYU Scholars Archive

Indian Affairs, Laws and Treaties, by United States, eBook Google.com

Builders of Uintah, Daughters of the Utah Pioneers Uintah Chapter, 1947

Utah Digital Newspapers, 1850 -1985 https://newspapers.lib.utah.edu

Brigham Young University Digital Archives: The Encyclopedic History of the Church of Jesus Christ of Latter-day Saints, Andrew Jensen

U. S. Department of the Interior, Bureau of Land Management General Land Office Records; https://glorecords.blm.gov/default.aspx

Library of Congress; Sanborn Fire Map Duchesne February 1917 & 1931

Book of Mormon; Intellectual Reserve, Church of Jesus Christ of Latter-day Saints

Holy Bible, KJV

Church of Jesus Christ of Latter-day Saints; Familysearch.org

Ancestry.com

Fold3.com

National Archives and Records Administration, https://www.archives.gov/

Google.com Digital Book Repository

Duchesne Fire Map 1917 Sanborn Fire Insurance Map from Duchesne, Duchesne County, Utah. Sanborn Map Company, Apr, 1917. Map. Retrieved from the Library of Congress, <www.loc.gov/item/sanborn08840_001/>.

Table of Figures

Endnotes

---

i Holy Bible Isaiah 35:1

ii The Indian & Settler Conflicts in the Utah Territories 1847 – 1910

iii Opening Indian Lands for Use and Settlement 1880 – 1910 Utah Centennial County History Series - Uintah County 1996, Utah Digital Newspapers, Utah State Archives, The Uintah Valley Reservation – Principal Meridian Project pmproject.org, Duchesne County History www.duchesen.utah.gov

iv John Murray & Isabella Crawford Murdoch – married into polygamy 8 August 1862 Salt Lake City, Utah. Isabella is the youngest of their 7 children.

v John Murray & Ann Steel Murdoch – married 1848 Kirkconnel, Scotland

vi Uinta Basin Information; http://www.uintabasin.info/history.html

vii Ogden Examiner, Utah Digital Newspapers Wasatch Letter & Controversy over Mormon v Gentile Settlement

viii History of Sanpete and Emery counties, Utah : with sketches of cities, towns and villages, chronology of important events, records of Indian wars, portraits of prominent persons, and biographies of representative citizens" San Pete Indian Wars 1850

ix Murdock Honored in Duchesne Footsteps Celebration, July 4th (Alva Moroni Murdock) https://www.familysearch.org/

x Joseph Stacey Murdock was the Author of "Come Listen to a Prophet's Voice", Church of Jesus Christ of Latter-day Saints Sacred Music, P. 21

xi Vernacular of the day dinner is equal to lunch, supper is the evening meal.

xii Department of the Interior General Land Office at Vernal, original documentation undiscovered; information extracted from Notice of Intention to make final commutation proof, to establish claim published in Duchesne Record.

xiii James and Mary Murray Murdoch Family History: The James and Mary Murray Murdoch Family Organization, p. 581

xiv Ibid, p. 207-208

xv Ibid, p. 207

xvi Author's Note There is no documentation that this was the reason Hanne purchased land in Duchesne.

xvii Department of the Interior General Land Office Records (online) Glorecords.blm.gov Hanne Nicol, Patent Details Hanne Nicol Homestead Entry Serial Number 02956

xviii Vernal Express, February 02, 1911 "Some Correspondence and New County"; Utah Digital Newspapers https://newspapers.lib.utah.edu

xix Church of Jesus Christ of Latter-day Saints Book of Mormon, Another Testament of Jesus Christ; Mosiah 4:21

xx Duchesne Record, Utah Digital Newspapers; newspapers.lib.utah.edu George Victory Billings called as Bishop of the Duchesne Ward December 1910. Available records do not identify counselors called at that time. Reunion honoring released bishopric Duchesne Record Nov 11, 1920 identifies counselors including H.C. Nicol.

xxi Church of Jesus Christ of Latter-day Saints; History of Primary

xxii Church of Jesus Christ of Latter-day Saints; History of Primary;

xxiii Church of Jesus Christ of Latter-day Saints; Handbook2:Administration of the Church - Priesthood Ordinances and Blessings

xxiv James & Mary Murray Murdoch Family History: The James and Mary Murray Murdoch Family Organization; p. 574

xxv Ibid; p. 573-574

xxvi Ibid; p. 569

xxvii Utah State Archives Indexes; SLC Obituary Duchesne Record 2 Feb 1913 Death Certificate

xxviii Church of Jesus Christ of Latter-day Saints Doctrine & Covenants 30:1-2

xxix Church of Jesus Christ of Latter-day Saints – Church Historians Press (Churchhistorianspress.org) "The Collum Bill was the third attempt since the end of the Civil War to pass federal legislation to punish polygamists and curtail the economic and political power of The Church of Jesus Christ of Latter-day Saints. The Wade Bill (1866), the Cragin Bill (1869), and the Cullum Bill all proposed legal means for enforcing the 1862 Morrill Anti-Bigamy Act, which banned bigamy and restricted the church's ownership of property but did not designate officers or funds for enforcement."

xxx Minutes of "Ladies Mass Meeting" January 6, 1870 "Minutes of a Ladies Mass Meeting," Jan. 6, 1870; Fifteenth Ward, Salt Lake Stake, Relief Society Minutes and Records, 1868 1968, vol. 1, 1868 1873, pp. 139 142, CHL (LR 2848 14). See images of the original document at dcms.lds.org. The First Fifty Years of Relief Society, published Church Historian Press

xxxi James and Mary Murray Murdoch Family History: The James and Mary Murray Murdoch Family Organization, p. 6

xxxii James and Mary Murray Murdoch Family History: The James and Mary Murray Murdoch Family Organization, p. 576

xxxiii Ibid, p. 576

Xxx Catherine Campbell Murdoch Hicken second child of John and Isabella Crawford Murdoch. Isabella Murdoch lived with Catherine's family after John Murray Murdoch died.

xxxv The descriptions of the trip are fictional although the cabin, frozen Tom, and the blizzard are not. Family story of Thomas Murdoch Nicol was related independently by Thomas Keith Nicol (son) and Jean Nicol Robison (daughter) to Keri Vest (Tom's oldest grand-daughter).

xxxvi John and Mary Murray Murdoch Family History: The James and Mary Murray Murdoch Family Organization, p.575

xxxvii Ibid; p. 578

xxxviii Ibid; p. 576

xxxix Wasatch Wave; Isabella Crawford Murdoch Obituary / Funeral Article titled "Another Pioneer Called"

xl James & Mary Murray Murdoch Family History: The James and Mary Murray Murdoch Family Organization; p. 577

xli Maritime Archaeology Trust https://forgottenwrecks.maritimearchaeologytrust.org/wrecks-and-sites/explore-the-wrecks/articles/ss-housatonic

xlii World War I Draft Registration Card for Hyrum Chase Nicol located at National Archives and Records Administration (NARA) downloaded from Ancestry.com

xliii US Department of the Interior; General Land Office Records

xliv Pearl of Great Price, Church of Jesus Christ of Latter-day Saints

xlv John and Mary Murray Murdoch Family History: The James and Mary Murray Murdoch Family Organization, p. 581

xlvi Ibid, p. 579

xlvii Department of the Interior, General Land Office Hyrum C. Nichol N2 NW4 Section 13 Township 5S Range 5W 80 AC 0.75 per acre for total of $60.00

xlvii Hyrum C. Nichol S2 Section 14 Township 5S Range 5W Uinta Special Meridian Containing 320 acres at $0.50 per acre for $160.00 Patent Number 630989

xlviii John and Mary Murray Murdoch Family History: The James and Mary Murray Murdoch Family Organization, p. 570

xlix Author's Note: This fictionalized story of the shooting of Len Nielson is based upon the true experiences of Thomas M. Nicol (age about 14) and H. Chase Nicol (age about 12) as told to Tom's son Keith Nicol and recounted in the James and Mary Murray Murdoch Family History: The James and Mary Murray Murdoch Family Organization. Additional facts of the prayer given by John Murray Murdoch (age 85) to author Keri Nicol Vest-Vergari (Tom's oldest granddaughter). Author's License: As to who actually went to Len's aid is unknown from family lore. As a mother I could not imagine that Isabella would stay at home waiting, but rather go as quickly as possible to offer aid to what may have become a tragedy.

l Church of Jesus Christ of Latter-day Saints; Doctrine & Covenants, Section 9 Verse 6

li John and Mary Murray Murdoch Family History: The James and Mary Murray Murdoch Family Organization, p. 570

lii Duchesne County Land Records; 734 N Center St. Duchesne Utah NE4SW4:E2SE4NW4 Section 25 Township 3 South Range 5 West 8/31/1918 Entry No: 10753 Book 7 P. 192 Lewis Cherveny & Wife (Grantors) to Hyrum Nichol (Grantee) Warranty Deed $100. 60 Acres

liii http://www.in2018dollars.com $5,000 in 1919 is equivalent in purchasing power to $72,574.23 in 2018, a difference of $67,574.23 over 99 years. The 1919 inflation rate was 14.57%. The inflation rate in 2018 was 2.44%.

liv Duchesne County Land Records;

lv Now Thank We All Our God: Words-Martin Rinkhart, 1586-1649; trans. by Catherine Winkworth, 1829-1878 Music-Johann Crüger, 1598-1662 lvi James and Mary Murray Murdoch Family History: The James and Mary Murray Murdoch Family Organization, p. 582

lvii Ibid, p. 582

lviii Ibid, p. 580

lix Ibid, p. 570

lx Ibid, p. 578

lxi Duchesne Record March 10 1021; Utah Digital Newspapers. State of Utah Banking Records 1921-22

lxii James and Mary Murray Murdoch Family History: The James and Mary Murray Murdoch Family Organization, p. 570

lxiii Ibid, p. 580

lxiv Church of Jesus Christ of Latter-day Saints, Handbook 2: Administering the Church – Priesthood Ordinances and Blessings Administering to the Sick

lxv Church of Jesus Christ of Latter-day Saints Handbook 2: Administering the Church – Priesthood Ordinances and Blessings

lxvi James and Mary Murray Murdoch Family History: The James and Mary Murray Murdoch Family Organization, p. 579

lxvii Ibid, p. 570

lxviii Ibid, p. 580

lxix Ibid, p. 571

lxix Biography of Hyrum Chase Nicol, Pioneers and Prominent Men of Utah, by Frank Ellwood Esshom

lxx James and Mary Murray Murdoch Family History: The James and Mary Murray Murdoch Family Organization, p. 571

lxxi I. Donnavieve: The "I" is a single initial. She was named for two of Isabella's close friends; p. 580

lxxii Ibid, p. 580

lxxiii Detail provided by Thomas M. Murdoch to granddaughter Keri Vergari 1988.

lxxiv James and Mary Murray Murdoch Family History: The James and Mary Murray Murdoch Family Organization, p. 571. "Root hog or die" means provide for yourself or do without and die.

lxxv Ibid, p. 571

lxxvi US Census Utah, Utah County, Provo City, Ward 13 April 4, 1930 Enumeration District 25-43 Sheet 5A P. 60 (Ancestry.com)

lxxvii James and Mary Murray Murdoch Family History: The James and Mary Murray Murdoch Family Organization, p. 571

lxxviii Ibid, p. 578

lxxix Ibid, p. 578

lxxx Ibid, p. 572

lxxxi Ibid, p. 573

lxxxi James and Mary Murray Murdoch Family History: The James and Mary Murray Murdoch Family Organization, p. 582

Made in the USA
San Bernardino, CA
18 December 2019

61818465R00151